Contents

5

To the memory of
Alfréd Rényi

THE TEACHING OF
PROBABILITY & STATISTICS

THE TEACHING OF PROBABILITY & STATISTICS

Proceedings of
the first CSMP International Conference
co-sponsored by
Southern Illinois University and
Central Midwestern Regional Educational Laboratory

Edited by
LENNART RÅDE

WILEY INTERSCIENCE DIVISION
JOHN WILEY & SONS, INC. NEW YORK, LONDON, SYDNEY

ALMQVIST & WIKSELL

© Almqvist & Wiksell Förlag AB
Stockholm 1970

Illustrations by John Jonsson

Library of Congress Card Number 77-129972

Printed in Sweden by
Almqvist & Wiksells Boktryckeri AB
Uppsala 1970

Editor's preface

Under the sponsorship of the Central Midwestern Regional Educational Laboratory (CEMREL) and Southern Illinois University, the first international CSMP (Comprehensive School Mathematics Program) conference was held in Carbondale, Illinois, USA, from March 18 to 27, 1969. The subject of the conference was the teaching of probability and statistics at the pre-college level. In this volume are contained all the papers presented at the conference, background information about CEMREL and CSMP, the recommendations of the conference and a bibliography on the teaching of probability and statistics.

As organizer of the conference and editor of this book, I want to express my deep gratitude to Dr. R. W. MacVicar, Chancellor of the Carbondale campus of Southern Illinois University, and to Dr. W. M. Robinson, Executive Director of CEMREL. Their personal interest and support helped to make this conference possible. I also want to thank Burt Kaufman, Director of CSMP, who from the very beginning gave this conference his wholehearted support. My thanks are also due to all staff members of CEMREL and CSMP and to A. Marcec of Southern Illinois University for their help in the planning and organization of the conference. Finally, I want to express my sincere gratitude to the editorial committee, A. Engel, B. Kaufman, J. Gani, S. Holm and A. Mark, for their great help in preparing this book.

Mathematics teaching on all levels is in a state of change all over the world. It is my hope that the information given and the ideas presented in this book will be a help and stimulus in educational programs in different parts of the world.

January 1970   *Lennart Råde*

1. Background

Burt Kaufman, Director, CSMP

CEMREL-CSMP
Carbondale, Illinois, USA

Mathematics teaching is in a state of transition in all parts of the world. Numerous experiments aimed at modernizing the mathematics curriculum have been undertaken.

The Comprehensive School Mathematics Program (CSMP) was envisioned in 1963 as a response to a research impetus in mathematics education manifested in the reports of several prominent committees of mathematicians and mathematics educators from the United States and abroad.

CSMP, located in Carbondale, Illinois, U.S.A., is a major effort to modernize both the content of the pre-college mathematics curriculum and the methods of teaching.

In 1966, CSMP was established and became affiliated with Southern Illinois University. A proposal for a long range curriculum development project was written during this year. The proposal was presented to the Central Midwestern Regional Educational Laboratory (CEMREL), and CSMP was incorporated as one of its major programs in the spring of 1967.

The Central Midwestern Regional Educational Laboratory was established under Title IV of the Elementary and Secondary Education Act of 1965 and began operation in June, 1966. One of 15 educational laboratories in the United States, whose purpose is to improve education for the children of the nation, CEMREL, has set as its mission the development of individualized curricula in mathematics and the arts and humanities for all students in kindergarten through twelfth grade; it is also concerned with the development of effective instructional techniques and materials for children who have learning disabilities. Foremost authorities from across the nation compose the advisory committees to these programs. CEMREL is also concerned with developing instructional management systems, making use of the latest technology, to be used in conjunction with the curriculum development programs. Various related projects, as well, are a part of CEMREL's activities.

CEMREL is governed by a Board of Directors made up of outstanding educators, civic leaders, businessmen and labor officials from Illinois, Kentucky, Missouri and Tennessee. Headquarters for the laboratory are located in St. Ann, Missouri at 10646 St. Charles Rock Road, and program offices are maintained in Carbondale, Illinois; Bowling Green, Kentucky, and in Memphis and Nashville, Tennessee. Wade M. Robinson is executive director.

CEMREL works cooperatively with the State Departments of Education in the four states as well as with colleges, universities and, of course, the elementary and secondary schools.

The primary goal of CSMP is the development of individualized mathematics curricula for students of ages 5–18 which provide for each student a program sound in content, enjoyable and most appropriate for his needs and abilities. Each activity package will provide a teaching program which may involve individual study, teacher instruction, small group interaction, reading a text, watching a demonstration film, listening to a tape, playing mathematical games, or a combination of these and other procedures.

In considering strategies to achieve this ultimate goal, namely the development of mathematics curricula that are sound in content and appropriate for the needs of future adults in a changing society, the developers of CSMP decided the program must be discipline-oriented. By this is meant that, while all pedagogical aspects of mathematics education are of deep concern, priority is given to the selection of *mathematical content* that is sound, relevant and enjoyable. The implications of this decision are that the mathematical community must be deeply involved in the program, that there be mathematicians physically in residence, and that mathematicians must guide the program. To date this has been the case and it is a principle of CSMP procedure that every phase of future development of the program will continue to enjoy the strong involvement of mathematicians.

The major role of mathematicians in CSMP is the selection and analysis of content. The CSMP attitude is that content selection should, as far as is possible, be unfettered by traditional notions of "what children can do" or "what teachers can teach", it should instead be guided by what is important in mathematics, by what the outcomes of mathematics instruction should be and by what students actually demonstrate they can do. For these reasons content selection within CSMP is based on empirical data gathered from probes made with students in the trying out of ideas generated by mathematicians. Serious content suggestions are accepted or rejected only after adequate trials in the classroom.

To have a truly individualized curriculum, one must take into account the different views of mathematics held by various people. The creative research mathematicians view it in various ways, depending on their fields of research. There are various users of mathematics (scientists, engineers, social scientists, businessmen, etc.) who view mathematics in other ways; mathematics educators are concerned with curriculum and methods, while school administrators, parents, students and the man in the street view it in terms of the exigencies of their situations and in terms consistent with their backgrounds. Each has needs that some form of mathematics can fulfill. Each can enhance his services to society by bringing to his vocation an "appropriate" background in mathematics.

An assumption accepted by CSMP is that all these views of mathematics are viable and valid. One goal for the content of CSMP is a curriculum so designed that none of these views is excluded; students at each stage of their schooling have, therefore, a maximum number of avenues open for their adult uses of mathematics.

In order to obtain such a curriculum several alternative approaches to one and the same topic will need to be developed. It is, therefore, essential that a detailed analysis of the content selected for the CSMP curriculum be made by the mathematicians involved. CSMP has to be open to any suggestions which might affect its goals, its choices of content and techniques of presentations. This means that the program should have channels of information about trends in mathematics as a developing science as well as research in mathematics education throughout the world.

Such a fruitful channel is expected to be opened by a series of five CSMP international conferences on the teaching of specific mathematical subjects. This book is a report on the proceedings of the first of these conferences held in Carbondale in March 1969 to investigate the teaching of probability and statistics in the schools. The second conference will be held in Carbondale in March 1970 on the teaching of geometry. Future conferences will examine the teaching of algebra, analysis and logic and foundations.[1]

On many occasions during the last ten years when educators, mathematicians and teachers have met for international and national conferences to discuss the teaching of mathematics, they have strongly recommended that probability and statistics be included in school mathematics curricula. Such recommendations were made, for instance, by the Commission on Mathematics in 1959, the Royaumont Seminar in 1959, the OECD-Conference in Athens in 1963 and the Cambridge Conference in 1963. Extracts from these recommendations read as follows:

Just as mathematics deals with situations in which the facts can be determined, it also provides ways to study, understand, and control uncertainty. Many of the newer applications of mathematics use the theories of probability and statistical reasoning.

[1] For a fuller description of CSMP philosophy and activities, see the CSMP-Basic Program Plan and Supplement—available from CSMP, 103 South Washington Street, Carbondale, Illinois, U.S.A. 62901.

Increasingly, modern science—physics, biology, social science—makes use of probabilistic descriptions of phenomena.

The Commission believes that it is desirable that material in these areas be introduced into the high school curriculum. Statistical thinking is playing more and more of a part in the daily lives of educated men and women. An introduction to statistical thinking is an important supplement to an introduction to deductive thinking.

(Program for college preparatory mathematics, Report of the Commission on Mathematics, 1959.)

Elementary probability must be recognized as an appropriate part of mathematics taught in secondary schools.

a) Statistical inference must be recognized as applied mathematics which contributes in an essential way to decision processes in the spirit of the "scientific method" basic to so many fields, both in the physical sciences and in fields of human behavior. Furthermore, it must be recognized that statistical reasoning is of growing importance in the field of public affairs.

b) Suitable elementary instruction in probability and statistics must be introduced into the curricula of secondary schools.

c) Suitable preparatory courses for teachers of these subjects must be introduced in normal schools and teacher-training institutions.

(New Thinking in School Mathematics, Report of The Royaumont Seminar, 1959.)

It is necessary to recognize the importance for science specialists of the following topics: vector space, the calculus, and probability and statistics.

Also, students other than science students should receive a sound mathematical education. Their courses should include the fundamental concepts, together with a knowledge of their applications. Particularly, these courses should include probability and statistics.

(Mathematics Today, Report from the Athens OECD-Conference, 1963.)

We suggest that probability should be taught in four doses through the curriculum.

1. In the elementary school, empirical study of the statistics of repeated chance events, coupled with some arithmetic study of the workings of the law of large numbers.

2. In Junior high school, probability as an additive set function on finite sets. Conditional probability, independence, binomial distribution, expectation, variance, and some simple statistical tests.

3. In Senior high school, after the first work on limits and series, probability as an additive set function on countable sets. Poisson distribution, law of large numbers, etc.

4. In Senior high school, after integral calculus, probability as an additive set function of intervals on the line. Continuous distributions on the line and in several dimensions, normal distribution, limit theorems, etc.

(Goals for School Mathematics, The Report of the Cambridge Conference on School Mathematics, 1963.)

With this professional support, it is remarkable to find that so little has been done to implement these recommendations. Only a few experiments have been undertaken, and only a few countries have included short courses in probability and statistics in their pre-college mathematics curricula. One reason for this rather slight activity might be that since probability and statistics have traditionally been studied only at the university level, nobody knows how to treat them at a lower school level. Another reason is the shortage of qualified teachers.

An early introduction of probability and statistics is important for many reasons. One is the relevance of probability and statistics to almost all activities of modern society. Many of the students will, in their future lives, use notions from probability and statistics as tools in their professions, and almost all will have to take standpoints on arguments based on probabilistic or statistical reasoning. The introduction of probability and statistics in the mathematics curriculum will have a highly stimulating effect by giving the student contact with a dynamic branch of mathematics and by giving numerous opportunities for presenting to the student interesting applications of mathematics.

It will be some time before a full evaluation of the success of this first conference will be known. This will depend largely on how widely this report is diffused and the impact it has on the teaching of probability and statistics in the schools. From the CSMP standpoint, the conference appears to have met and even exceeded its goals; readers will judge for themselves that this report contains a wealth of ideas for content selection and analysis in this field. Much CSMP curriculum material should be motivated from the papers presented herein. If these proceedings have a reasonable influence on other curriculum endeavors, then the ultimate goal of the conference will have been fully realized.

2. Recommendations by the conference

1. We, the participants at the International Conference on the Teaching of Probability and Statistics, Carbondale, having received a brief but thorough introduction to the Comprehensive School Mathematics Program, wish to commend it as a highly interesting experiment in mathematical education. Any program whose aim is to bring school mathematics closer to current directions of mathematical usage and discovery performs a useful social function. The CSMP project, because of its breadth of approach, absence of dogmatism, flexibility and rich content of new didactic ideas (among them the individual package concept) deserves the most serious encouragement. The participants feel that it would be desirable to develop similar coordinated programs in other disciplines.

2. In designing their program, the CSMP staff would do well to bear in mind:

(*a*) the need to stress the various applications of mathematics in the biological, physical and social sciences;

(*b*) the role of logic in mathematics, including the context of computer strategies;

(*c*) the role of the teacher in the implementation of the program;

(*d*) the desirability of handbooks for school mathematics curriculum designers, and teacher manuals as helpful supplements to the text and package material.

3. The participants strongly endorse CSMP's efforts to introduce probability and statistics as subjects for study at elementary and secondary school levels. They believe that these subjects should be taught starting from a wealth of realistic examples. Some emphasis should be placed on their use as tools, both for the development of mathematical structures and in the building of applied models.

4. In teaching probability, full advantage should be taken of practical experiments, and in particular of simulation methods. The knowledge acquired from such experiments should be directly reinforced by a theoretical framework; this should not be too rigid. In view of the different possible approaches to the subject, the formal concepts and theories presented should

be eclectic. Probability courses at the secondary level might include, in addition to the usual topics, the weak law of large numbers, some game theory and elementary stochastic processes.

5. Descriptive statistics of physical, biological and social data are subjects of great importance to every citizen. They can be taught at almost every level. Material of this kind could serve as an introduction to a school course which might include further topics in statistical theory and inference. Such a course should be taught in careful coordination with probability theory and should make use of realistic data wherever possible. Estimation, elementary tests of hypotheses, non-parametric statistics and decision theory might be suitable topics for inclusion in a course in statistics at the secondary level.

6. The participants greatly enjoyed the conference and they would appreciate continued contact with the CSMP Center at Carbondale. The dissemination of the program's results and material abroad, as well as in the U.S.A., would be most useful. Duplication of effort would be avoided, and constructive comments and criticism from teachers and research workers all over the world would be encouraged.

The participants feel that there is a strong need for further CSMP Conferences in different fields of mathematics, to discuss content and curricula and to exchange teaching experiences and ideas. Part of the content of lectures and discussions in such conferences should be closely related to the work done at the Carbondale Center. The interest in the present conference was such that several of the participants expressed their willingness to act as advisors to CSMP at the discretion of its staff.

3. Combinatorics for school mathematics curricula

Edwin F. Beckenbach

University of California
Los Angeles, California, U.S.A.

INTRODUCTION

3.1. *Problems of Organized Complexity*

Warren Weaver [14] has contrasted three different types of analytical problems:

Problems of Simplicity
Problems of Disorganized Complexity
Problems of Organized Complexity

Modern business, industry, and science are very concerned with problems of the last of these types: analyzing social trends; investigating models of subsystems of human physiology; operating a petroleum-processing plant or a military organization; or planning, constructing, launching, guiding, and recovering space craft.

These problems contrast strongly with the problems of relative *simplicity* of the seventeenth, eighteenth, and nineteenth centuries, which dealt mostly with continuous systems and were largely two-variable or few-variable problems: the relation between distance and gravitational force, between voltage and electric current, between pressure and the volume of a gas, and so on.

They contrast also with problems of *disorganized complexity*, on which much progress was made at the start of the present century through the application of statistical techniques. Thus, although the exact solution of a ten-body problem, such as the motion of ten pool balls on a pool table, can be quite complicated, statistical mechanics can give good answers for average behavior when we are dealing with huge numbers of molecules or of subatomic particles [1, pp. xi–xii].

In the 1950's, professional mathematicians were employing new *finite* techniques, such as linear programming and the theory of games, and were using the new electronic digital computing machines to obtain numerical solutions for complicated boundary-value problems by treating differential equations as huge, but *finite*, systems. Even problems in the social and life sciences were being treated successfully with the new mathematical techniques. It came to be realized, slowly at first and then with dramatic explosiveness, that mathematics programs in the schools had virtually stood still for more than a century and no longer suited present needs or reflected current developments. Thus the "new math" was born.

In attempting to characterize the new math, some say it is just the old math in new garb, which of course it largely is. Others speak of (1) sets, (2) structure, and (3) understanding. I rather think, however, that in truth much of what is novel in the material and methods of the new math is subsumed under the broad and diffuse blanket of combinatorial theory.

3.2. *What is Combinatorial Mathematics?*

Generally speaking, combinatorial analysis is concerned with *problems associated with arrangements of objects according to specified rules* [4, p.V].

To see what types of problems might be involved in combinatorial analysis, let us consider a simple example: For a round-robin tennis tournament with a given number of players and a given number of courts, is it possible to arrange the schedule so that each of the courts is used in each succeeding play, yet no participant plays twice consecutively?

The question just asked is one of existence. There is little value, however, in knowing that a solution exists if we do not have a solution in hand; a practical person would prefer a constructive existence proof. Thus *existence* and *construction* problems are closely related in combinatorial theory.

For variety in subsequent tournaments, it might be desirable to list, or enumerate, all the different possible schedules. Sometimes, though, it is sufficient to know only how many solutions there are, not necessarily to list them. Thus we have related *enumeration* and *counting* combinatorial problems.

Different solutions often have different properties, to which values might be ascribed; that is, we might be concerned with *utility functions*. One tournament might be deemed to be more enjoyable than another in that it sustains interest through having the better players meet each other later in the tournament. Thus we evaluate solutions, and evaluation often involves computations; that is, we have *evaluation* and *computation* problems in combinatorics.

The choice of the very most enjoyable of all the possible tournaments is an extremization problem, and directing the solution process toward this choice calls for control (perhaps in the form of tact). Finally, then, we have combinatorial problems of *extremization* and *control*.

To recapitulate, we see that in combinatorics we have the following types of problems:

Existence	Construction
Enumeration	Counting
Evaluation	Computation
Extremization	Control

Most combinatorial problems are of one or another of the types listed above, or can be factored into a succession of problems of these types, although of course the distinction is not always precise. Computation, in particular, is often involved in problems of each of the other types.

To review the foregoing succession of types of combinatorial problems, we might think of the decision problems that faced our space scientists at the start of the 1960 decade in hypothetically fitting together "objects" (men, vehicles of different sorts, and procedures) for a projected round trip to the moon: "Is the project feasible? (Existence.) Show me some particular program that might succeed. (Construction.) List the feasible solutions. (Enumeration.) How many are there? (Counting.) What are their relative significant qualities? (Evaluation.) Let me see the computations that justify your conclusions. (Computation.) Everything considered, which is the program most likely to succeed? (Extremization.) How shall we go about putting this program into effect? (Control.)"

SOME SIMPLE PRELIMINARY EXAMPLES

Combinatorics can be introduced into the curriculum of the earliest school years, and the subject should recur in a spiral development throughout the K-12 (kindergarten through twelfth-grade) program. Let us begin with some simple preliminary examples that involve space visualization, orderly thinking, and the challenge of the mathematical unknown.

3.3. *Paths on a Cube*

The teacher might show the members of an elementary class a cubical wooden block and, after discussing the number of vertices, edges, and faces, ask how many different paths along three consecutive edges (Fig. 3.1) an ant might follow in going from one vertex to the opposite vertex [10, p. 16].

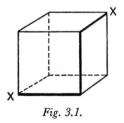

Fig. 3.1.

19

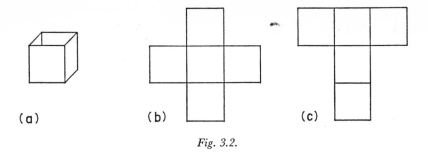

(a) (b) (c)

Fig. 3.2.

The correct answer, of course, turns out to be $3 \cdot 2 \cdot 1$, or 6, and in determining it the children well might be on the way toward discovering an important counting principle.

3.4. *Painting a Cube*

The teacher might next ask in how many different ways the cubical wooden block could be painted, with each face being painted either red or green [3, p. 152]. (Two blocks are considered as being painted differently if they cannot be placed in matching positions with corresponding faces of the same color.) An efficient way of solving this problem—the solution should not be rushed—is to observe that there is just one way of having 0 red faces; one of having 1 red face; two of having 2 red faces, since the 2 red faces are either adjacent or not; and two of having 3 red faces, since there either are or are not two opposite red faces. The numbers for 4, 5, and 6 *red* faces are the same as the numbers for 2, 1, and 0 *green* faces, respectively. Thus the correct answer is $2(1+1+2)+2$, or 10.

3.5. *The Cell-growth Problem*

Finally, the teacher might show the members of the elementary class how to construct topless cubical paper boxes [Fig. 3.2 (a)], say with edges of length 3 inches. When this has been done, the teacher might cut two of the boxes in different ways along edges and spread them out on the table to form different plane figures [Fig. 3.2 (b) and (c)]. Can the children cut along edges to form figures different from these? (Two plane cut-outs are "different" provided that one cannot be placed on the other in such a way that they exactly coincide.) Each figure must be in just one piece!

Actually there is a total of 8 different plane figures of the sort discussed above [2, p. 55]. Perhaps some of the children can make preliminary cuttings in their imagination, so that the supply of paper boxes will not quickly be exhausted. Or perhaps they will proceed in the other direction, to see in how many ways five squares can be fit together along edges to form

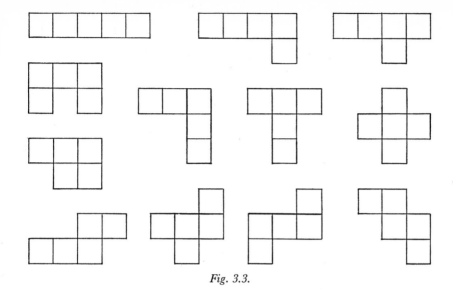

Fig. 3.3.

plane figures (there are twelve ways of doing this; see Fig. 3.3), and will then investigate to see how many of these figures can be folded into topless boxes. (Eight of them can; four cannot.)

Figure 3.3 suggests a similar problem for any number n of congruent square regions: Determine the number N of different ways that n congruent square regions can be joined along edges to form simply connected (no holes) plane regions. This is known as the *cell-growth problem* [6, p. 200]. For $n \leqslant 10$, the number N is as follows:

n	1	2	3	4	5	6	7	8	9	10
N	1	1	2	5	12	35	107	363	1248	4271

As far as the author knows, the value of N has not yet been determined for any $n > 10$, though the problem can easily be understood by a very young child and its solution is not necessarily beyond the reach of a quite talented high-school student. A reasonable computing-machine program for generating each different configuration exactly once would be considered an excellent solution.

3.6. *Other Combinatorial Topics*

There are many mathematical topics having high combinatorial content that either are not regularly included or are only touched on in the K-12 program but that, because of their interest, importance, and pedagogical value, well might be considered for inclusion in any future curriculum revision. These include, among others, the following:

21

groups of rotations, modular systems, permutation groups;
graphs, incidence matrices, transportation networks;
electrical networks, logical networks, Boolean algebra;
Mendelian genetics, Markov chains, stochastic matrices;
linear programming, theory of games, probabilistic solutions;
coding and decoding, error-correcting codes, block design.

A problem of block design might be concerned, for example, with a toothpaste-testing experiment, in which the tubes that each subject receives are distinguished by colors. It might be required that (1) each subject receive the same number of brands of toothpaste, (2) each brand be used by the same number of subjects, (3) each pair of brands be compared by a subject the same number of times, and (4) each brand be given each color the same number of times to help prevent color preferences from unfairly influencing the findings [5, pp. 376–377].

Space permits only passing mention of the topics listed above. In the rest of this paper, we shall restrict our attention mostly to one basic line of combinatorial development.

SETS AND LOGIC

3.7. *Sets and Set Notation*

The new math begins, and is basically concerned, with the consideration of *sets* of objects. Ergo, since combinatorial mathematics is the study of arrangements of the objects in given sets, it is fitting that combinatorics should be introduced in the earliest grades and should recur throughout the K-12 program.

Thus children are introduced quite early to sets A, B, C, etc., of blocks and other objects. They soon understand these set notions:

Element a of set A	$a \in A$
Subset C of set A	$C \subset A$
Universal set	U
Complement of set A	$\bar{A}$
Union of sets A and B	$A \cup B$
Intersection of sets A and B	$A \cap B$
Difference $A \cap \bar{B}$ of sets A and B	$A - B$
The null set	ϕ or $\{\ \}$
Equal sets	$A = B$

The symbols shown at the right above, the slash for negation as in $a \notin A$ and $C \not\subset A$, and such names of sets as $\{1, 2, 3\}$ and

$$\{x : x \text{ is a counting number less than } 4\}$$

should be introduced only gradually, as needed and as the children seem
ready for them.

The notion of the power set

$$\Pi(S) = \{A : A \subset S\}$$

of a given set S is interesting and instructive in studying the binomial coefficients $\binom{n}{r}$, as will be indicated below in Sections 3.16 and 3.17.

The Cartesian product $A \times B$ of sets A and B, defined by

$$A \times B = \{(a, b) : a \in A \text{ and } b \in B\},$$

is most important in applications, as shown for example by our frequent
use of plane coordinates. Besides, Cartesian products furnish a preferred
approach to the notion of multiplication.

Disjoint sets and partitions of sets can be introduced and applied while
the children are quite young. A *partition* of a set S is a collection of subsets
A_i of S such that

$$\bigcup_i A_i = S \quad \text{and} \quad A_i \cap A_j = \phi \quad \text{for } i \neq j.$$

The *cross partition* C of partitions

$$A = \{A_1, A_2, \ldots, A_n\} \quad \text{and} \quad B = \{B_1, B_2, \ldots, B_m\}$$

of set S is the collection of all subsets of S of the form $A_i \cap B_j$. For example,
the children in a class might be partitioned into subsets of blonds, brunettes,
and redheads (if some fine distinctions are made) and also into subsets of
boys and girls (Fig. 3.4).

That the cross partition C of partitions A and B of set S is also a partition of S, and is a refinement of both A and B (each set in C is a subset of a
set in A and is also a subset of a set in B), is an attractive proposition that
rather young children can establish quite satisfactorily for themselves.

3.8. *Laws of Operations on Sets*

The laws governing unions and intersections of sets bear a close resemblance
to the laws pertaining to sums and products of numbers. Thus, for example,
the commutative laws

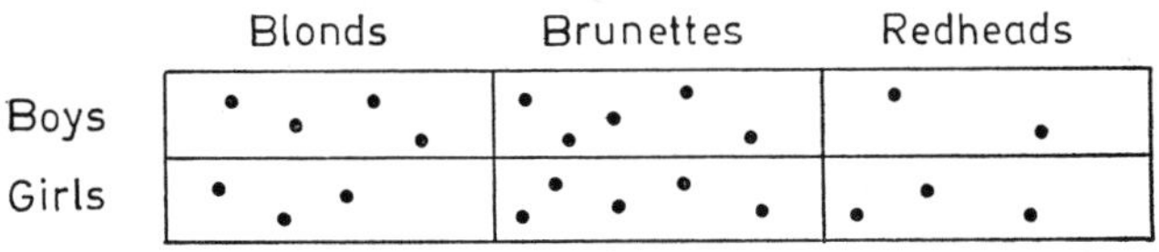

	Blonds	Brunettes	Redheads
Boys	. . . .	. . . .	. .
Girls	. . .	. . . .	. . .

Fig. 3.4.

23

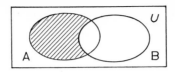

Fig. 3.5.

$$A \cup B = B \cup A \quad \text{and} \quad A \cap B = B \cap A$$

for sets are analogous to the commutative laws

$$a + b = b + a \quad \text{and} \quad a \cdot b = b \cdot a$$

for numbers.

Again, the null set ϕ and the universal set U are the identity elements for the union and intersection of sets, just as 0 and 1 are the identity elements for the sum and product of numbers; that is, we have

$$A \cup \phi = A \quad \text{and} \quad A \cap U = A$$

for all sets A, just as we have

$$a + 0 = a \quad \text{and} \quad a \cdot 1 = a$$

for all numbers a.

It is helpful, accordingly, to point out that the *union* of two sets is sometimes called their logical *sum*, while their *intersection* is called their logical *product*.

The analogy, however, is not complete. For one thing, inverse elements in general do not exist for set union and intersection as they do for numerical addition and multiplication (except that 0 has no multiplicative inverse). For another, there is a striking *duality*, which catches the imagination of many children, between set union and set intersection; thus, for example, not only does intersection distribute over union,

$$A \cap (B \cup C) = (A \cap B) \cup (A \cap C),$$

but also union distributes over intersection,

$$A \cup (B \cap C) = (A \cup B) \cap (A \cup C).$$

The foregoing development should proceed slowly, of course, extending over several years, for there is much for the children to discover and to assimilate. The discussion should be informal at first, so that the formal statements of the laws for unions and intersections of sets will emerge only a brief while before those for sums and products of numbers.

Venn diagrams are most helpful in introducing and understanding notions about sets. Thus the shaded portion of Figure 3.5 schematically rep-

24

p	q	$p \vee q$
T	T	T
T	F	T
F	T	T
F	F	F

Fig. 3.6.

resents the set $A-B$. For results such as those discussed in this section, an illustration using Venn diagrams can be quite as convincing as a formal proof.

3.9. *Logic and Logical Connectives*

The logical connectives "or" and "and" occur naturally in introducing school children to the notions of set union and set intersection, respectively, and similarly "not" appears in introducing them to the notion of the complement of a set. The corresponding logical symbols, "$\vee$", "$\wedge$", and "$\sim$", like set symbols, should be introduced gradually, as needed and as the children seem to be ready for them.

Perhaps logical symbols, compound open sentences, and truth tables (such as the one shown in Figure 3.6) are most advantageously introduced, at whatever school age, in the simple context of sets of blocks, oranges, etc. Thus, for sets A and B,

$$A \cup B = \{x : x \in A \vee x \in B\}$$

introduces the symbol "$\vee$" for "or", contains a compound open sentence in the right-hand member, and exhibits the relationship between "$\cup$" and "$\vee$". Similar comments can be made concerning

$$A \cap B = \{x : x \in A \wedge x \in B\}$$

and

$$\bar{A} = \{x : x \notin A\} = \{x : \sim (x \in A)\}.$$

With the foregoing simple models before the class, it is easy to pass to a discussion of "real-world" compound sentences, truth sets, and truth tables. Whatever method of presentation is used, all this material now belongs in the K-12 program.

It might seem that we are here including a great deal of the mathematics curriculum under the heading of "combinatorics." Actually, Gottfried Wilhelm Leibniz (1646–1716), in introducing the subject in his *Dissertatio de Arte Combinatoria* (1666), claimed much more for the subject, with applications to the whole sphere of science and new germs of the

25

logic of invention, including applications to locks, organs, and syllogisms, to the mixing of colors and to protean verses, to logic, geometry, military art, grammar, law, medicine, and theology. He went on to plan more and more applications to coding and decoding, to games, mortality tables, and combinations of observations, to synthesis, to the same and the different, the similar and the dissimilar, and the absolute and the relative. Eventually he viewed combinatorics as coinciding, or almost coinciding, with his Characteristica Universalis, a sort of generalized mathematics that would deal with everything thinkable and indeed would reduce thinking itself, by the use of appropriate signs and characters, to a sort of calculation [11, pp. 1–2].

THE COUNTING FUNCTION

3.10. *Equivalent Sets*

Of all combinatorial topics, *counting* is by far the most basic.

If there is a one-to-one correspondence between sets A and B, we say that A and B are *equivalent*, and we write $A \sim B$. This relationship has the three equivalence properties:

Reflexive: $A \sim A$.

Symmetric: If $A \sim B$, then $B \sim A$.

Transitive: If $A \sim B$ and $B \sim C$, then $A \sim C$.

At the heart of the new math, the counting function $N(A)$ has finite sets as the elements of its domain and the counting numbers (actually the whole numbers) as the elements of its range. It is defined first for the *standard sets*

$$\{\ \}, \{1\}, \{1, 2\}, \{1, 2, 3\}, \text{etc.,}$$

by

$$N(\{\ \}) = 0,\ N(\{1\}) = 1,\ N(\{1, 2\}) = 2,\ N(\{1, 2, 3\}) = 3,\ \text{etc.,}$$

and then for all finite sets by $N(A) = N(B)$ provided that A and B are equivalent.

The notion of *inequality* can be introduced along with the counting function: We have $N(A) \leqslant N(B)$ if and only if $A \sim C$ for some $C \subset B$, with equality if and only if $A \sim B$.

Children are led to learn the foregoing notions and to increase their most basic counting skills through arranging blocks, playing games, studying figures illustrating equivalent sets in their books, reciting rhymes and singing songs, etc. Incidents in their daily lives, including those that involve monetary allowances and minor purchases, probably help at least as much.

26

3.11. *Disjunctive Counting*

The principle of disjunctive counting is that if the finite sets A and B are disjoint, that is, if $A \cap B = \phi$, then

$$\mathcal{N}(A \cup B) = \mathcal{N}(A) + \mathcal{N}(B).$$

No school child who has worked with sets of apples and sets of oranges would deny the validity of this principle. It is, in fact, essentially the *definition* of addition in the set of whole numbers.

In words, we might say that if one event can occur in p ways, and another, different event can occur in q ways, then one *or* the other of these two events can occur in $p + q$ ways.

This principle is sometimes called the *additive property of alternative choices*.

Thus if Johnny can either play a game or go to a movie, and the available games are baseball, tennis, and golf, while the movies are the Majestic and the Bijou, then he has a total of $3 + 2$, or 5, choices of activity.

The principle can be extended to any number of pairwise disjoint finite sets. Thus if

$$A \cap B = \phi, \ A \cap C = \phi, \ B \cap C = \phi,$$

then

$$\mathcal{N}(A \cup B \cup C) = \mathcal{N}(A) + \mathcal{N}(B) + \mathcal{N}(C).$$

As a corollary, we have the result (which includes the principle of disjunctive counting as a special case) that, whether or not the sets A and B are disjoint,

$$\mathcal{N}(A \cup B) = \mathcal{N}(A) + \mathcal{N}(B) - \mathcal{N}(A \cap B).$$

For example, to determine how many counting numbers $\leqslant 1000$ are divisible by 4 or 5, we might let A and B be the subsets of these numbers that are divisible by 4 and by 5, respectively. Then the numbers in $A \cap B$ are the numbers that are divisible by $4 \cdot 5$, or 20, and we have

$$\mathcal{N}(A \cup B) = \mathcal{N}(A) + \mathcal{N}(B) - \mathcal{N}(A \cap B)$$
$$= 250 + 200 - 50$$
$$= 400.$$

3.12. *Sequential Counting*

The principle of sequential counting is that for any finite sets A and B,

$$\mathcal{N}(A \times B) = \mathcal{N}(A) \cdot \mathcal{N}(B).$$

(See Section 3.7 above for the definition of the Cartesian, or cross, product $A \times B$ of sets A and B.) The principle of sequential counting is so called because the elements (a, b) of $A \times B$ consist of sequences of two elements,

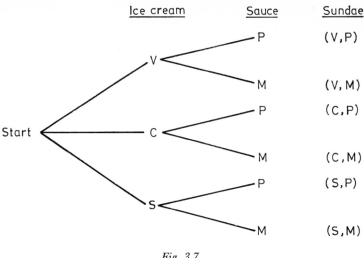

| Ice cream | Sauce | Sundae |

Fig. 3.7.

the first from A and the second from B. The Cartesian-product *definition* of multiplication in the set of whole numbers, expressed in the principle of sequential counting, is equivalent to the successive-additions definition, and to many it is pedagogically preferable.

In words, we might say that if a first event can occur in p ways, and a second event can occur in q ways, then the first *and* the second of these two events can occur in $p \cdot q$ ways.

This principle is sometimes called the *multiplicative property of successive choices.*

Thus in an ice-cream parlor with three flavors (vanilla, chocolate, and strawberry) of ice cream and two flavors (pineapple and marshmallow) of sauce, for a sundae containing exactly one flavor of ice cream and one of sauce there are $3 \cdot 2$, or 6, choices of sundaes.

The actual choices can be exhibited in a *tree diagram*, as shown in Figure 3.7. The choices are read off from the tree diagram, beginning at "start" and proceeding across the diagram from left to right in every possible way.

Ice cream	Sauce	
	P	M
V	(V, P)	(V, M)
C	(C, P)	(C, M)
S	(S, P)	(S, M)

Fig. 3.8.

28

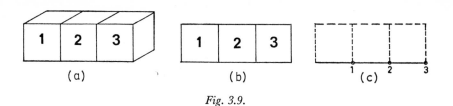

Fig. 3.9.

The choices can also be arranged systematically in a rectangular array, as shown in Figure 3.8.

The principle can be extended to any number of finite sets. Thus we have

$$\mathcal{N}(A \times B \times C) = \mathcal{N}(A) \cdot \mathcal{N}(B) \cdot \mathcal{N}(C).$$

For example, if Mary has 3 skirts, 4 blouses, and 2 scarves, then (ignoring questions of compatibility of colors, etc.) she can arrange $3 \cdot 4 \cdot 2$, or 24, different skirt-blouse-scarf outfits.

GEOMETRIC REPRESENTATION OF NUMBERS

3.13. *The Number Line*

In the combinatorial process of becoming acquainted with the counting numbers, school children might (among many other things) consider in juxtaposition first congruent wooden blocks (Fig. 3.9a), next congruent squares (Fig. 3.9b), and then the line segments at the base of the squares (Fig. 3.9c).

From this, it is only a simple step to the number ray for the whole numbers (Fig. 3.10a), and it seems only natural (although it is not traditional) casually to introduce the negative integers $^-1$, $^-2$, etc., and their representation on the number line (Fig. 3.10b) as you introduce the *vector representation* of subtraction of whole numbers.

3.14. *The Rational Numbers*

The *rational numbers* are introduced combinatorially by considering, for example, that 4 slices of pie make a unit and then taking 3 (Fig. 3.11a) or 7 (Fig. 3.11b) slices. These choices might be represented quantitatively either by (3, 4) and (7, 4) or by $\frac{3}{4}$ and $\frac{7}{4}$, respectively.

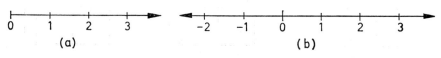

Fig. 3.10.

29

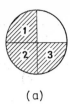

(a)   (b)

Fig. 3.11.

A basketball coach with a squad of 7 players each of whom plays each position equally well has $\frac{7}{5}$ of a team.

The configuration of blocks shown in Figure 3.12 is represented numerically by $\frac{8}{3}$.

For working with the number line, we replace the diagram in Figure 3.12 with squares partioned vertically, as shown in Figure 3.13, and later remove the portion above the number line [7].

The fact that the fractions $\frac{2}{3}$ and $\frac{4}{6}$, for example, correspond to the same point on the number line leads to calling these fractions *names* for the *same rational number*, two-thirds.

The fact that certain rational numbers correspond to the same points on the number line as the integers (rational numbers $\frac{0}{3}, \frac{3}{3}, \frac{6}{3}$ and integers 0, 1, 2, for example) leads, in company with the discussion of equality, addition, and multiplication of rational numbers, to the notion of the *isomorphism* between the set of integers and a subset of the set of rational numbers. It even leads, if one is willing to overlook logical niceties, to the consideration of the set of integers as being a subset of the set of rational numbers.

The addition of rational numbers, like the addition of integers, can be represented combinatorially by geometric vectors, or arrows, on the number line. For fraction names with the same denominator, this is numerically easy; for example (see Fig. 3.13),

$$\frac{2}{3}+\frac{5}{3}=\frac{2+5}{3}=\frac{7}{3}.$$

It remains only to point out that rational numbers can always be given

 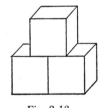 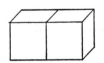

Fig. 3.12.

30

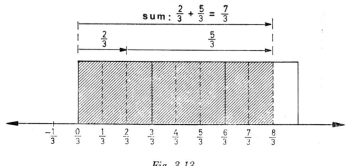

Fig. 3.13.

fraction names with the same denominator, a fact that can be illustrated geometrically by complementary subdivisions of intervals on the number line, so that, for example,

$$\frac{2}{3}+\frac{5}{4}=\frac{2\cdot4}{3\cdot4}+\frac{5\cdot3}{4\cdot3}=\frac{8}{12}+\frac{15}{12}=\frac{8+15}{12}=\frac{23}{12},$$

and, in general,

$$\frac{a}{b}+\frac{c}{d}=\frac{ad}{bd}+\frac{bc}{bd}=\frac{ad+bc}{bd}.$$

We say tha $\frac{a}{b}<\frac{c}{d}$ provided that graph of the $\frac{a}{b}$ lies to the left of the graph of $\frac{c}{d}$ on a number line directed to the right. Using fraction names with a common denominator, we see that, for b and d positive, $\frac{a}{b}<\frac{c}{d}$ if and only if $ad< bc$.

The foregoing test can be applied to show, in particular, that for b and d positive, if

$$\frac{a}{b}<\frac{c}{d} \quad \text{then} \quad \frac{a}{b}<\frac{a+c}{b+d}<\frac{c}{d}.$$

It is *not* true, however, as we shall illustrate in Section 3.20 below, that for positive denominators if

$$\frac{a}{b}<\frac{c}{d} \quad \text{and} \quad \frac{e}{f}<\frac{g}{h},$$

then necessarily

$$\frac{a+e}{b+f}<\frac{c+g}{d+h}.$$

31

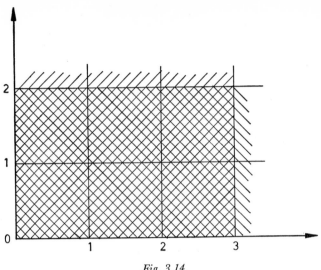

Fig. 3.14.

The product of two counting numbers can be illustrated combinatorially by using perpendicular axes and unit squares. Thus the product 2×3 is illustrated in Figure 3.14. This leads naturally to defining the product of two rational numbers in such a way that, for example (see Fig. 3.15), $\frac{3}{2} \times \frac{8}{3} = \frac{24}{6}$ (notice that unit squares are separated into sixths and that 24 of these are double hatched), and, in general, $\frac{a}{b} \times \frac{c}{d} = \frac{ac}{bd}$.

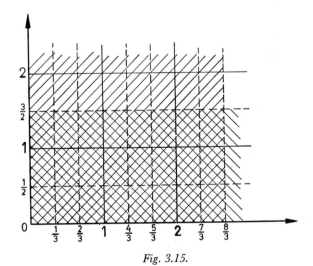

Fig. 3.15.

PARTITIONS

3.15. *Arrangements and Partitions*

For a set A of n objects, $A = \{a_1, a_2, \ldots, a_n\}$, suppose we have n boxes arranged in order, as shown in Figure 3.16. The "1" on each box indicates

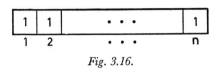

Fig. 3.16.

that exactly 1 of the objects is to be placed in each box. Each of the ways of putting the n objects in the n boxes so that there is exactly one object in each box is called an *arrangement* of the objects.

How many such arrangements are there? Of course, the answer is well known: There are n choices of objects for the first box, with each of these choices there are $n-1$ choices for the second box, and so on. Accordingly, by the multiplicative property of successive choices (Section 3.12 above), the number $_nP_n$ of such arrangements is given by

$$_nP_n = n \cdot (n-1) \cdot \ldots \cdot 1 = n!.$$

The arrangements of A are the partitions (see Section 3.7 above) of A with the greatest possible number of non null subsets.

Suppose, now, that we have k boxes as pictured in Figure 3.17, and we wish to form a partition of A by putting n_j objects in the jth box, $j = 1, 2, \ldots, k$, with $n_1 + n_2 + \ldots + n_k = n$. If we let $\begin{pmatrix} n \\ n_1 \, n_2 \ldots n_k \end{pmatrix}$ denote the number of ways in which this can be done and we *imagine* the cells in Figure 3.17 to be subdivided into unit cells as in Figure 3.16, then we see that with each of the $\begin{pmatrix} n \\ n_1 \, n_2 \ldots n_k \end{pmatrix}$ partitions we can arrange the objects in the first of the k boxes in $n_1!$ ways, and so on. Thus by the multiplicative property of successive choices, we can do all this in $\begin{pmatrix} n \\ n_1 \, n_2 \ldots n_k \end{pmatrix} \cdot n_1! \cdot n_2! \cdot \ldots \cdot n_k!$ ways.

Note, however, that we have just described the total number $_nP_n$ of arrangements of the n objects. Hence we have

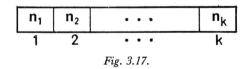

Fig. 3.17.

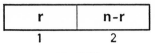

r	n-r
1	2

Fig. 3.18.

$$\binom{n}{n_1\, n_2\, \ldots\, n_k} \cdot n_1! \cdot n_2! \cdot \ldots \cdot n_k! = {}_nP_n = n!,$$

or

$$\binom{n}{n_1\, n_2\, \ldots\, n_k} = \frac{n!}{n_1! \cdot n_2! \cdot \ldots \cdot n_k!}. \tag{*}$$

For example, a laboratory technician who has 9 white mice and wishes to put 2 of them in a first cage, 4 in a second cage, and the remaining 3 in a third cage can do this in $\binom{9}{2\,4\,3} = \dfrac{9!}{2!\,4!\,3!}$, or 1260, ways.

3.16. *Combinations and Permutations*

In this section, we shall discuss two special cases of the formula (*) developed in Section 3.15 above.

(1) If $k=2$ in Figure 3.17, so that there are only 2 boxes, with $n_1 = r$ and therefore $n_2 = n - r$ (Fig. 3.18), then $\binom{n}{r\ n-r}$ is denoted simply by ${}_nC_r$ or $\binom{n}{r}$, and (*) becomes

$$_nC_r = \binom{n}{r} = \frac{n!}{r!(n-r)!}.$$

Any allocation of r objects to the first box is called an r-element *combination* (an obsolescent name for an r-element subset) of the n objects in A. This implicitly allocates the remaining $n-r$ objects to the second box, so that $\binom{n}{r\ n-r}$, or $\binom{n}{r}$, is the number of combinations of n things taken r at a time.

The power set

$$\Pi(S) = \{A : A \subset S\}$$

Set S	$\Pi(S)$
ϕ	$\{\phi\}$
$\{a\}$	$\{\phi, \{a\}\}$
$\{a, b\}$	$\{\phi, \{a\}, \{b\}, \{a, b\}\}$
$\{a, b, c\}$	$\{\phi, \{a\}, \{b\}, \{c\}, \{a, b\}, \{a, c\}, \{b, c\}, \{a, b, c\}\}$

Fig. 3.19.

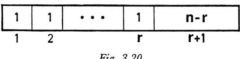

1	1	$\cdots$	1	n-r
1	2		r	r+1

Fig. 3.20.

of a given set S (see Section 3.7 above) is instructive both in the discussion of sets in general and in the discussion of the symbols $\binom{n}{r}$. By definition, $\binom{n}{r}$ is the number of r-element subsets (combinations) of any n-element set S; see Figure 3.19. By counting subsets, from this figure we can see that $\binom{n}{0} = \binom{n}{n} = 1$ for $n = 0, 1, 2, 3$, and also $\binom{2}{1} = 2$ and $\binom{3}{1} = \binom{3}{2} = 3$.

(2) If $k = r + 1$ in Figure 3.17, with $n_1 = n_2 = \ldots = n_r = 1$ and therefore $n_{r+1} = n - r$ (Fig. 3.20), then $\left(\underbrace{1\ 1 \ldots 1}_{r} \ n - r \right)$ is denoted by $_nP_r$

and (*) reduces to

$$_nP_r = \frac{n!}{1! \cdot 1! \cdot \ldots \cdot (n-r)!} = \frac{n!}{(n-r)!}.$$

Any allocation of one object to each of the first r boxes is called an r-element *permutation* of the n objects in A. This implicitly allocates the remaining $n - r$ objects to the $(r+1)$st box, so that $_nP_r$ is the number of permutations of n things taken r at a time.

As an exercise, one might first derive the formula for $_nP_r$ and then derive the formula for $\binom{n}{r}$ directly from the multiplicative property of successive choices. This, indeed, is the order in which these formulas traditionally are derived, with the formula (*) on p. 34 being established last.

3.17. *Generating Functions*

Generating functions, which we shall presently define, furnish a useful means of unifying the treatment of many combinatorial problems. Their study might profitably be given a somewhat more prominent place in the K-12 curriculum.

The bionomial theorem is essentially a statement of the fact that $(x + 1)^n$ is a generating function for the combinatorial expressions $\binom{n}{r}$ of section 3.16. Too often in the K-12 program, however, this theorem apparently is considered virtually as an isolated result. The fact that the coefficients are the expressions $\binom{n}{r}$ is presented as little more than a curious accident, and the proof of the theorem as given is an algebraically complicated, manipulative example of mathematical induction.

Repeated applications of the distributive law to the polynomial

$$P_3(x, A) = (x + a_1)(x + a_2)(x + a_3),$$

where A is the sequence $(a_1, a_2, a_3, \ldots)$, gives

$$P_3(x, A) = x^3 + (a_1 + a_2 + a_3) x^2 + (a_1 a_2 + a_1 a_3 + a_2 a_3) x + a_1 a_2 a_3.$$

More generally, by rather simple mathematical induction, for

$$P_n(x, A) = (x + a_1)(x + a_2) \cdots (x + a_n)$$

we have

$$P_n(x, A) = x^n + (a_1 + a_2 + \ldots + a_n) x^{n-1} + (a_1 a_2 + a_1 a_3 + \ldots + a_{n-1} a_n) x^{n-2} +$$

$$+ \ldots + a_1 a_2 \ldots a_n.$$

Here the coefficient of x^{n-1} exhibits, alternating with "$+$" signs, an enumeration of the elements of all the one-element subsets of $A_n = (a_1, a_2, \ldots, a_n)$; the coefficient of x^{n-2} similarly exhibits an enumeration, as products, of the elements of all the two-element subsets of A_n; and so on. These facts can readily be explained in terms of the application of the distributive law—a useful explanation that must, in effect, be included in any proof of the binomial theorem. We say that $P_n(x, A)$ is a *generating function* for *enumerating* the subsets of A_n.

If in $P_n(x, A)$ we replace A with $C = (1, 1, 1, \ldots)$, then $P_n(x, A)$ becomes $P_n(x, C) = (x + 1)^n$, each summand in the coefficient of x^{n-k} reduces to 1, and the coefficient gives simply the *number* $\binom{n}{k}$ of k-element subsets of A_n.

For this reason, the combinatorial numbers $\binom{n}{k}$ are also called *binomial coefficients*. We say that $P_n(x, C)$ is a generating function for the $\binom{n}{k}$, or for *counting* the subsets of any n-element set.

Much more generally [9; 12; 13], for any sequence of linearly independent *indicator functions* $(f_0(x), f_1(x), f_2(x), \ldots)$, such as $(1, x, x^2, \ldots)$, and for any finite sequence $C_n = (c_0, c_1, \ldots, c_{n-1})$,

$$\varphi_n(x, C_n) = \sum_{j=0}^{n-1} c_j f_j(x)$$

is a *generating function* for C_n. No such general point of view should be assumed, of course, in the K-12 program.

36

Let us close this section with a few additional examples of generating functions:

From the definition of the combinatorial expressions $\binom{n}{n_1\,n_2\,\ldots\,n_k}$, it follows readily that the polynomial $(x_1+x_2+\ldots+x_k)^n$ is a generating function for these expressions. The expressions accordingly are called *multinomial coefficients*.

The polynomial

$$(1+ax+a^2x^2)\,(1+bx)\,(1+cx) = 1+(a+b+c)\,x+(ab+ac+bc+a^2)\,x^2+$$
$$+(abc+a^2b+a^2c)\,x^3+a^2bcx^4$$

is a generating function for the combinations of the objects a, b, and c, where a may be chosen twice.

The polynomial

$$(1+ax)\,(1+a^2x)\,(1+bx)\,(1+cx) = 1+(a+b+c+a^2)\,x+$$
$$+(ab+ac+bc+a^3+a^2b+a^2c)\,x^2+(abc+a^3b+a^3c+a^2bc)\,x^3+a^3bcx^4$$

is a generating function for the result of selecting boxes, one containing a, one containing two a's, one containing b, and one containing c.

THE DENSITY FUNCTION

3.18. *Densities and Weights*

In many applications, the density function D, defined by

$$D(A) = \frac{N(A)}{N(U)},$$

for $N(U)\neq0$, is at least as important as the counting function N itself.

For example, in the universal set U of three-letter "words" formed with the letters H and T:

HHH	*THH*
HHT	*THT*
HTH	*TTH*
HTT	*TTT*

the density of the set A of words containing exactly two T's is given by

$$D(A) = \frac{N(A)}{N(U)} = \frac{3}{8}.$$

Since, as we saw in Section 3.11,

$$\mathcal{N}(A \cup B) = \mathcal{N}(A) + \mathcal{N}(B) - \mathcal{N}(A \cap B),$$

it follows that

$$D(A \cup B) = \frac{\mathcal{N}(A \cup B)}{\mathcal{N}(U)} = \frac{\mathcal{N}(A) + \mathcal{N}(B) - \mathcal{N}(A \cap B)}{\mathcal{N}(U)}$$

$$= \frac{\mathcal{N}(A)}{\mathcal{N}(U)} + \frac{\mathcal{N}(B)}{\mathcal{N}(U)} - \frac{\mathcal{N}(A \cap B)}{\mathcal{N}(U)}$$

$$= D(A) + D(B) - D(A \cap B).$$

This reduces to

$$D(A \cup B) = D(A) + D(B)$$

if and only if $D(A \cap B) = 0$, that is, if and only if $\mathcal{N}(A \cap B) = 0$, or $A \cap B = \phi$.

In many applications, also, the counting function is replaced by a non-negative additive *weight function* $W(A)$, with $W(U) > 0$. In this case, we define the density function D by

$$D(A) = \frac{W(A)}{W(U)}.$$

Basic computations can very well be illustrated in terms of the counting function, however, and applied problems can be arbitrarily closely approximated with counting-function models. Accordingly, except for the brief discussion of weights that follows, we shall henceforth restrict our attention largely to the counting-function definition of the density function.

To introduce weights, we might think of a universal set U composed basically of marbles of equal size and weight, but with various subsets of the marbles permanently enclosed in sacks of negligible weight. The sacks of marbles would then be thought of as the elements of U, and the "weight" of each element would be equal to the number of marbles in the sack. Equivalently, as far as the density function is concerned, the number of ounces that the sack of marbles actually weighs might be used.

In fact, if physical weight alone is to be considered, then there is no need for the marbles to be of equal size or weight, or for the elements to be sacks of marbles at all; the elements might be any physical objects whatever. Their weight might be determined by using scales, or simply estimated by lifting them.

There are many other kinds of "weight," such as volume, dollar value, etc.

A pie might be cut into slices, and the slices given weight equal to the measure of their central angles. These and other weights might theoretically even be irrational numbers. Thus the sectors A, B, C, D in Figure 3.21 would

38

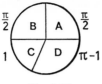

Fig. 3.21.

be given weights $\pi/2$, $\pi/2$, 1, and $\pi - 1$, respectively. One-fourth of a pie (sector A) would be assigned weight $\pi/2$,

$$W(A) = \frac{\pi}{2},$$

but density $\frac{1}{4}$,

$$D(A) = \frac{W(A)}{W(U)} = \frac{\frac{\pi}{2}}{2\pi} = \frac{1}{4}.$$

The two positions of a tack, "point up" and "point over" (Fig. 3.22), might be assigned "weights" by tossing the tack 100 times and recording the results. Corresponding positions for another tack of slightly different shape might then be assigned weights by guessing what the result might be if that tack, too, were to be tossed 100 times, and so on.

All this leads, with ever-increasing sophistication, to considerations of postulational weight, determination of weights by integral calculus, and measure theory.

3.19. *Relative Density*

For two sets A and B in U, with $N(B) \neq 0$, we might be concerned not only with the density of A (in U),

$$D(A) = \frac{N(A)}{N(U)},$$

but also with the *relative density* of A in B, $D(A|B)$, which is defined by

$$D(A|B) = \frac{N(A \cap B)}{N(B)}.$$

Fig. 3.22.

39

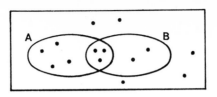

Fig. 3.23.

If also $N(A) \neq 0$, then $D(A) \neq 0$, and therefore there is a unique constant K, $K \geqslant 0$, such that

$$D(A|B) = K \cdot D(A), \tag{1}$$

that is,

$$\frac{N(A \cap B)}{N(B)} = K \cdot \frac{N(A)}{N(U)}. \tag{2}$$

Multiplying both members of (2) by $N(B)/N(A)$, and using the fact that $A \cap B = B \cap A$, we obtain

$$\frac{N(B \cap A)}{N(A)} = K \cdot \frac{N(B)}{N(U)},$$

or

$$D(B|A) = K \cdot D(B). \tag{3}$$

It is interesting to observe, from equations (1) and (3), that $D(B|A)$ is related to $D(B)$, and $D(A|B)$ is related to $D(A)$, by *precisely the same* multiplicative constant K. For example, in Figure 3.23 we have

$$D(A) = \frac{N(A)}{N(U)} = \frac{7}{14},$$

$$D(B) = \frac{N(B)}{N(U)} = \frac{5}{14},$$

$$D(A|B) = \frac{N(A \cap B)}{N(B)} = \frac{3}{5} = \frac{3}{5} \cdot \frac{14}{7} \cdot \frac{7}{14} = \frac{42}{35} \cdot D(A) = K \cdot D(A),$$

$$D(B|A) = \frac{N(B \cap A)}{N(A)} = \frac{3}{7} = \frac{3}{7} \cdot \frac{14}{5} \cdot \frac{5}{14} = \frac{42}{35} \cdot D(B) = K \cdot D(B),$$

with $K = \frac{42}{35} = \frac{6}{5}$.

The foregoing density relationship

$$D(A|B) = K \cdot D(A),$$

or equivalently

$$D(B|A) = K \cdot D(B),$$

can be put in symmetric form. Multiplying both members of equation (2) above by $N(B) \cdot N(U)$, we obtain

$$N(A \cap B) \cdot N(U) = K \cdot N(A) \cdot N(B),$$

whence

$$\frac{N(A \cap B)}{N(U)} = K \cdot \frac{N(A)}{N(U)} \cdot \frac{N(B)}{N(U)},$$

which can be written as the symmetric density relationship

$$D(A \cap B) = K \cdot D(A) \cdot D(B). \tag{4}$$

In this symmetric form (4), the assumptions that $N(B) \neq 0$ and $N(A) \neq 0$ are not needed; but if either or both of $N(A)$ and $N(B)$ vanish then also $N(A \cap B) = 0$, and K might be given any nonnegative value whatsoever.

We might separate the possible values of K into three categories:

$$0 \leqslant K < 1,$$
$$K = 1,$$
$$K > 1.$$

In these three cases we shall say, respectively, that the elements of U are *logically sparse*, *logically normally dense*, and *logically abundant* in the logical product $A \cap B$ of A and B. The factor K itself will be called the *logical density coefficient*.

Let $N(A-B) = p$, $N(B-A) = q$, $N(A \cap B) = r$, and $N(\overline{A \cup B}) = s$, as indicated in Figure 3.24. Then, again with the assumption that $N(A) \neq 0$ and $N(B) \neq 0$ we have

$$K = \frac{N(A \cap B) \cdot N(U)}{N(A) \cdot N(B)} = \frac{r(p+q+r+s)}{(p+r)(q+r)} = 1 + \frac{rs - pq}{(p+r)(q+r)},$$

and we can readily determine the effect on the logical density coefficient K of varying the numbers p, q, r, and s. For example:

1. If r, s, and $p+q$ are fixed, then K is a maximum when $pq = 0$ and is a minimum when $p = q$ ($p+q$ even) or $p = q \pm 1$ ($p+q$ odd).

2. If q, s, and $p+r$ are fixed, then K is a minimum (0) when $r = 0$ and is a maximum when $p = 0$.

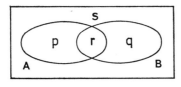

Fig. 3.24.

41

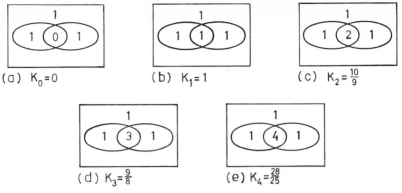

(a) $K_0=0$ (b) $K_1=1$ (c) $K_2=\frac{10}{9}$

(d) $K_3=\frac{9}{8}$ (e) $K_4=\frac{28}{25}$

Fig. 3.25.

3. If q, r, and $p+s$ are fixed, then K is a minimum when $s=0$ and is a maximum when $p=0$.

4. If p, q, and $r+s$ are fixed, then K is a minimum (0) when $r=0$. If $r+s \leqslant \sqrt{pq}$ (the geometric mean of p and q), then K is a maximum at $s=0$; but if $r+s > \sqrt{pq}$ then K is a maximum at $r=\sqrt{pq}$ or at one of the two integers nearest $\sqrt{pq}$.

5. If p, q, and s are fixed, then (curiously enough) the logical density coefficient K does not always increase with r. For the sets indicated in Figure 3.25, for example, in (a) the elements of U are logically sparse in $A \cap B$, in (b) they are logically normally dense in $A \cap B$, and in (c), (d), and (e) they are logically abundant in $A \cap B$. Distinguishing the values of K with subscripts showing the number of elements in $A \cap B$, we have

$$K_0=0,\; K_1=1,\; K_2=\frac{10}{9},\; K_3=\frac{9}{8},\; K_4=\frac{28}{25},$$

so that $K_0<K_1<K_2<K_3$, but $K_3>K_4$.

6. If $K=1$, then (strangely enough) the sets A and B are sometimes said to be "independent." A necessary and sufficient condition for $K=1$ turns out to be simply

$$rs - pq = 0.$$

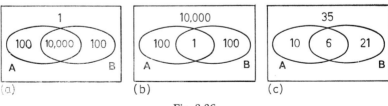

(a)   (b)   (c)

Fig. 3.26.

42

Thus in Figure 3.26 (a), (b), and (c), the sets A and B are "independent." Similarly, you have $K<1$ or $K>1$ if and only if $rs-pq<0$ or $rs-pq>0$, respectively.

3.20. *Some Related Examples*

Simple inequality facts and nonfacts concerning rational numbers should hardly have to await the formal study of probability and statistics before being considered in the K-12 program.

In Section 14 we showed that, for b and d positive, if

$$\frac{a}{b}<\frac{c}{d},$$

then

$$\frac{a}{b}<\frac{a+c}{b+d}<\frac{c}{d};$$

and we indicated that, with positive denominators, for

$$\frac{a}{b}<\frac{c}{d} \quad \text{and} \quad \frac{e}{f}<\frac{g}{h}$$

it is *not* necessarily true that

$$\frac{a+e}{b+f}<\frac{c+g}{d+h}.$$

All this will be illustrated in the three related examples that follow.

Suppose that disjoint sets M and W are each partitioned into subsets A and $\bar{A}$ and also into subsets T and $\bar{T}$, and that the cross partitions (see Section 3.7) of these partitions also are formed, as indicated in Figure 3.27 (a) and (b). [Ignore, for the moment, the small numerals 15 and 16 in the $(\bar{A}, T)$ cell for W.]

Entries in the corresponding cells of the M and W partitions are added to obtain the entries of the partitions of the union $H=M \cup W$ of M and W, as shown in Figure 3.27 (c).

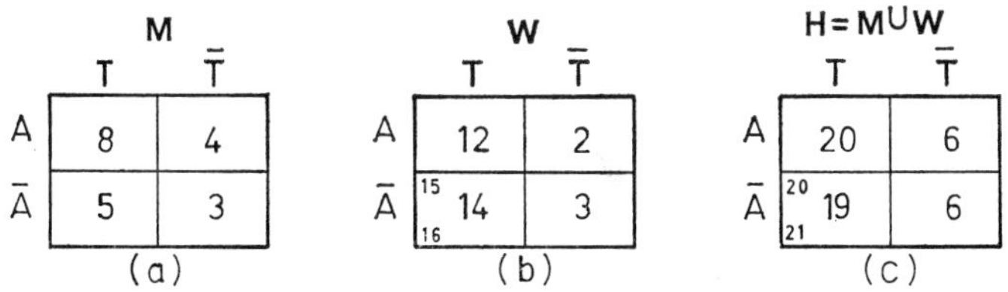

Fig. 3.27.

43

Table 3.1.

	M	W	$M \cup W$
$D(A\|T)$	$\frac{8}{13}$	$\frac{12}{26}$	$\frac{20}{39}$
$D(A\|\bar{T})$	$\frac{4}{7}$	$\frac{2}{5}$	$\frac{6}{12}$
$D(A)$	$\frac{12}{20}$	$\frac{14}{31}$	$\frac{26}{51}$

The density of A, and the relative densities of A in T and $\bar{T}$, for the three sets M, W, and $H = M \cup W$ are shown in Table 3.1.

Notice that $\frac{8}{13} > \frac{4}{7}$, $\frac{12}{26} > \frac{2}{5}$, and $\frac{20}{39} > \frac{6}{12}$, so that in all three cases we have $D(A|T) > D(A|\bar{T})$.

If the entries listed in Figure 3.27 represent the number of men (M) and women (W) who are alive (A) or not alive $(\bar{A})$ after being treated (T) or not treated $(\bar{T})$, in a certain investigation, then the fact that the inequality $D(A|T) > D(A|\bar{T})$ holds in all three cases indicates an advantage in being treated rather than not, both for men and for women, whether viewed separately or together.

Notice also that $\frac{8}{13} > \frac{12}{20} > \frac{4}{7}$, $\frac{12}{26} > \frac{14}{31} > \frac{2}{5}$, and $\frac{20}{39} > \frac{26}{51} > \frac{6}{12}$, so that in each case $D(A)$ is between $D(A|T)$ and $D(A|\bar{T})$. This actually is an instance of the inequality fact mentioned above, that $\frac{a+c}{b+d}$ lies between $\frac{a}{b}$ and $\frac{c}{d}$, since

$$D(A|T) = \frac{N(A \cap T)}{N(T)},$$

$$D(A|\bar{T}) = \frac{N(A \cap \bar{T})}{N(\bar{T})},$$

and
$$D(A) = \frac{N(A)}{N(U)} = \frac{N(A \cap T) + N(A \cap \bar{T})}{N(T) + N(\bar{T})},$$

for $U = M$, W, or $M \cup W$.

Does the fact that $D(A|T) > D(A|\bar{T})$ for $U = M \cup W$ follow in some similar way from the fact that it holds for $U = M$ and $U = W$? To help answer

Table 3.2.

	M	W	$M \cup W$
$D(A\|T)$	$\frac{8}{13}$	$\frac{12}{27}$	$\frac{20}{40}$
$D(A\|\bar{T})$	$\frac{4}{7}$	$\frac{2}{5}$	$\frac{6}{12}$
$D(A)$	$\frac{12}{20}$	$\frac{14}{32}$	$\frac{26}{52}$

Table 3.3.

	M	W	$M \cup W$
$D(A\mid T)$	$\frac{8}{13}$	$\frac{12}{28}$	$\frac{20}{41}$
$D(A\mid \overline{T})$	$\frac{4}{7}$	$\frac{2}{5}$	$\frac{6}{12}$
$D(A)$	$\frac{12}{20}$	$\frac{14}{33}$	$\frac{26}{53}$

this question, let us consider a second example [8, p. 216], differing from the one just discussed only in that the numeral in the $(\overline{A}, T)$ cell for W is replaced with 15, and consequently the 19 in the corresponding cell for $M \cup W$ is replaced with 20 (see Figure 3.27). Densities for this example are shown in Table 3.2. We still have $\frac{8}{13} > \frac{12}{20} > \frac{4}{7}$, and we also have $\frac{12}{27} > \frac{14}{32} > \frac{2}{5}$, so that $D(A\mid T) > D(A) > D(A\mid \overline{T})$ both for M and for W; but now $\frac{20}{40} = \frac{26}{52} = \frac{6}{12}$, so that $D(A\mid T) = D(A) = D(A\mid \overline{T})$ for $M \cup W$. It thus appears that in this investigation it is advantageous to be treated if attention is paid to sex, but otherwise survival is "independent" of treatment.

As a final example, let us advance the entries in the $(\overline{A}, T)$ cell for W and for $M \cup W$ one more, to 16 and 21, respectively (see Figure 3.27). Densities for this example are given in Table 3.3.

Once more we have $\frac{8}{13} > \frac{12}{20} > \frac{4}{7}$, and we also have $\frac{12}{28} > \frac{14}{33} > \frac{2}{5}$, so that $D(A\mid T) > D(A) > D(A\mid \overline{T})$ for both M and W; but now $\frac{6}{12} > \frac{26}{53} > \frac{20}{41}$, so that $D(A\mid \overline{T}) > D(A) > D(A\mid T)$ for $M \cup W$. It thus appears that in this investigation it is statistically advantageous to be *treated* if attention is paid to sex, but otherwise it is statistically advantageous *not* to be treated!

Entries such as those in Figure 3.27 might be considered relative to other situations. Thus, in baseball statistics, A might designate "Hits" and T might designate "First half of season," with $\overline{A}$ and $\overline{T}$ their complements for the season. M and W might then denote "Mike" and "Willie," or, for Mike alone, "First half of game" and "Second half of game."

These examples, in the author's opinion, emphasize the importance of the combinatorial study, in the K-12 program, of one-, two-, and three-dimensional vector spaces, denominate numbers, and inequalities as they relate to rational numbers.

3.21. *Barques' Theorem*

Suppose we have a set U of books, some of them red (R) and the rest green (G), and suppose some of them are contained in a first book bag (B_1), some in a second book bag (B_2), and the rest in a third book bag (B_3).

This suggests two partitions (R and G; and B_1, B_2, and B_3) of the set U of books, as indicated in Figure 3.28.

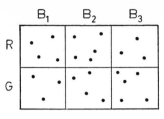

Fig. 3.28.

Suppose, further, that B_1, B_2, B_3, and G are all nonnull sets, and that the densities $D(B_1)$, $D(B_2)$, and $D(B_3)$ are known. It is useful for applications to have a formula giving the relative densities $D(B_1|G)$, $D(B_2|G)$, $D(B_3|G)$ in terms of these known values.

This can readily be established, as follows: For $j = 1$, 2, or 3, we have

$$D(B_j|G) = \frac{N(B_j \cap G)}{N(G)}.$$

Now

$$N(B_j \cap G) = N(G \cap B_j),$$

and

$$N(G) = N(G \cap B_1) + N(G \cap B_2) + N(G \cap B_3),$$

so that

$$D(B_j|G) = \frac{N(G \cap B_j)}{N(G \cap B_1) + N(G \cap B_2) + N(G \cap B_3)}$$

$$= \frac{\dfrac{N(G \cap B_j)}{N(B_j)} \cdot \dfrac{N(B_j)}{N(U)}}{\dfrac{N(G \cap B_1)}{N(B_1)} \cdot \dfrac{N(B_1)}{N(U)} + \dfrac{N(G \cap B_2)}{N(B_2)} \cdot \dfrac{N(B_2)}{N(U)} + \dfrac{N(G \cap B_3)}{N(B_3)} \cdot \dfrac{N(B_3)}{N(U)}}$$

$$= \frac{D(G|B_j) \cdot D(B_j)}{D(G|B_1) \cdot D(B_1) + D(G|B_2) \cdot D(B_2) + D(G|B_3) \cdot D(B_3)}.$$

Thus, for the set U of books indicated in Figure 3.28, we have

$$\frac{D(G|B_1) \cdot D(B_1)}{D(G|B_1) \cdot D(B_1) + D(G|B_2) \cdot D(B_2) + D(G|B_3) \cdot D(B_3)}$$

$$= \frac{\dfrac{3}{7} \cdot \dfrac{7}{21}}{\dfrac{3}{7} \cdot \dfrac{7}{21} + \dfrac{4}{9} \cdot \dfrac{9}{21} + \dfrac{5}{8} \cdot \dfrac{8}{21}}$$

$$= \frac{3}{12} = \frac{1}{4} = D(B_1|G).$$

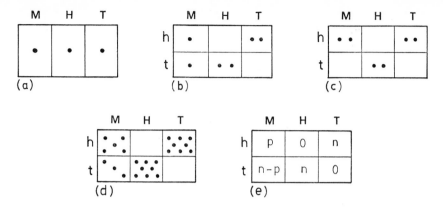

Fig. 3.29.

The foregoing discussion could equally well be given for any number k of book bags, and thus we have the following result.

Barques'[1] Theorem[2]. Let A be a nonnull subset of a universal set U, and let $\{B_1, B_2, ..., B_k\}$ be a partition of U, with each $B_j \neq \phi$, $j = 1, 2, ..., k$. Then for each j, $j = 1, 2, ..., k$,

$$D(B_j | A) = \frac{D(A | B_j) \cdot D(B_j)}{\sum\limits_{i=1}^{k} D(A | B_i) \cdot D(B_i)}.$$

The theorem applies, for example, to the well-known prisoner's paradox. One of three prisoners, Matthew (M), Henry (H), and Timothy (T) is to be executed and the others set free. A simple "chances of being executed" universal set U is shown in Figure 3.29 (a), with $D(M) = D(H) = D(T) = \frac{1}{3}$.

After the decision as to which of the prisoners is to be executed has been made, but before the prisoners have been given this information, Matthew convinces the truthful jailer that since at least one of Henry and Timothy is to go free, the jailer should tell Matthew the name of one of the two, Henry (h) or Timothy (t), who will surely go free.

[1] Not Beckenbarques'!

[2] This combinatorial version of a famous probabilistic theorem is here facetiously yet purposefully attributed to the Afghan pegadogue Kennel Barques, who, when asked at what level of the curriculum it might be introduced, replied, speaking slowly and gesturing as he emphasized his words with his characteristically long pause: "I am glad you pronounced 'curriculum' with two r's. Actually, *the bay is worse than the bark*, and, while I never like to speak categorically, it is my dogmatic opinion that my theorem should fit admirably into the later portion of the K-9 program. I feel confident that Professor Begle would concur— I mean, agree—or at least almost agree, with me in this evaluation."

E.F.B.

Suppose the jailer names Henry. Now, since one of Matthew and Timothy is to be executed, it might appear, paradoxically, that $D(M|h) = D(T|h) = \frac{1}{2}$; but this is not true. We have

$$D(h|M) = \tfrac{1}{2}, \; D(h|H) = 0, \quad \text{and} \quad D(h|T) = 1,$$

so that, by Barques' Theorem,

$$D(M|h) = \frac{\tfrac{1}{2} \cdot \tfrac{1}{3}}{\tfrac{1}{2} \cdot \tfrac{1}{3} + 0 \cdot \tfrac{1}{3} + 1 \cdot \tfrac{1}{3}} = \tfrac{1}{3}$$

[see Figure 3.29 (b)]. Thus $D(M|h) = D(M)$, and the jailer's naming Henry does not alter Matthew's "chances of being executed."

The foregoing analysis implies, however, that there is *no* additional information concerning the executee implied by the jailer in naming Henry. This might be the case, for example, if the jailer agrees simply to send Matthew a coin, five minutes later, showing heads (h) if Timothy is to be executed (for then Henry will go free), tails (t) if Henry is to be executed (for then Timothy will go free), and either heads or tails, determined by one fair toss of the coin, if Matthew is to be executed (for then both Henry and Timothy will go free).

If, however, Matthew somehow knows that the jailer is so eager to name Henry as the one to go free that he will surely do so if he truthfully can, then

$$D(h|M) = 1, \; D(h|H) = 0, \quad \text{and} \quad D(h|T) = 1.$$

Under this hypothesis, we do have $D(M|h) = \frac{1}{2}$, since, by Barques' Theorem,

$$D(M|h) = \frac{1 \cdot \tfrac{1}{3}}{1 \cdot \tfrac{1}{3} + 0 \cdot \tfrac{1}{3} + 1 \cdot \tfrac{1}{3}} = \tfrac{1}{2}$$

[see Figure 3.29 (c)]. This possibility of bad news, however, is balanced by the possibility of good tidings: $D(M|t) = 0$.

Any intermediate case of partial information imputed by Matthew to the jailer's idiosyncrasies can be treated [Figure 3.29 (d)] or arbitrarily closely approximated [Figure 3.29 (e)] with whole numbers. Thus, *by whatever method the chances are assigned*, the situation can be represented as closely as desired by means of a whole-number combinatorial model.

CONCLUSION

3.22. *Probability and Statistics*

Since the other contributions at the present conference have been concerned with the teaching of probability and statistics as such, and since the present author is not an expert in these fields, attention has here been restricted almost exclusively to combinatorial theory.

Perhaps, however, we might be excused for making a few general comments concerning the principal subjects of the present conference. The study of probability and statistics should of course be introduced early and pursued quite extensively in the K-12 program. Both intuitive feelings and sound foundations for these subjects should be stressed, and technical skills should be developed.

In presenting Newtonian mechanics, we traditionally offer some historical information, indicate that the subject has been found to be useful in real-world situations, perhaps perform a few experiments, and then proceed to explore the theory, work problems, and develop skills. The same general procedure, it seems, is appropriate in the teaching of probability and statistics, without too much time being spent at first on deep and difficult philosophical questions.

Probabilities are not innate properties of events. It should be emphasized at the start—and from time to time repeated—that they are subjectively, though consistently, assigned in the light of current knowledge; but this point should hardly be overly belabored.

Statistics and probability complement each other, since in statistics we make inferences concerning an entire population from information regarding suitable samples, whereas in probability we draw likely conclusions concerning samples from information regarding the entire population. Each of the two subjects should reinforce the spiral development of the other.

3.23. Combinatorics

We have indicated the basic role of combinatorics in the school mathematics program, beginning with the early development of notions regarding the systems of integers and of rational numbers and relating to much of the mathematical development of the K-12 curriculum.

Probability and statistics are among the most attractive vehicles for the presentation of combinatorial material, for these subjects catch the attention of children because of their very real applicability in everyday life. Yet probabilistic notions sometimes becloud the simple combinatorial facts that are being developed, and it seems preferable, for clarity, often to present the pure combinatorial models along with or somewhat before the probabilistic applications.

There are other quite attractive and important applications of the same combinatorial models, and this fact should be developed. The impact of the electronic computing machine is forcing an increased attention to combinatorial analysis, which is today helping dramatically to shape much of our scientific, business, and industrial life.

Among other possible future combinatorial developments in the K-12 curriculum, we might mention the introduction of simple matrix facts and applications much earlier in the program, the study of networkflow problems, linear programming, and the theory of games, further emphasis on programming and logic for computing machines, and an increase in attention to generating functions.

The development of the new math is now at a stage where the teachers at all levels are well acquainted with the material, and the children are well oriented regarding it. Accordingly, the developers of programs should now be able without constraints to organize the material precisely as the developers think it should be presented, starting at the very beginning of the K-12 program and working systematically through to the end.

Since combinatorial considerations play such a pervasive role in this program, it would seem to be desirable to organize conferences, such as the present excellent and productive one on probability and statistics, for investigating the most useful content and the most effective presentation of combinatorial mathematics.

REFERENCES

1. Beckenbach, Edwin F. (ed.), Applied Combinatorial Mathematics, John Wiley and Sons, Inc., New York, 1964.
2. Beckenbach, Edwin F., *et al.*, Informal Geometry, Booklet No. 14 in Topics in Mathematics for Elementary School Teachers, National Council of Teachers of Mathematics, Washington, D.C., 1968.
3. de Bruijn, N. G., Pólya's Theory of Counting, Chapter 5 in Reference 1 above.
4. Hall, Marshall, Jr., Combinatorial Analysis, Blaisdell Publishing Company, Waltham, Mass., 1967.
5. Hall, Marshall, Jr., Block Designs, Chapter 13 in Reference 1 above.
6. Harary, Frank, Combinatorial Problems in Graphical Enumeration, Chapter 6 in Reference 1 above.
7. John, Lenore, *et al.*, The Rational Numbers, Booklet No. 6 in Topics in Mathematics for Elementary School Teachers, National Council of Teachers of Mathematics, Washington, D.C., 1964.
8. Lindley, D. V., A Non-Frequentist View of Probability and Statistics, CSMP International Conference on the Teaching of Probability and Statistics at the PreCollege Level, this volume.
9. Liu, C. L., Introduction to Combinatorial Mathematics, McGraw-Hill Book Company, New York, 1968.
10. Niven, Ivan, Mathematics of Choice or How to Count without Counting, Vol. 15 in New Mathematics Library, School Mathematics Study Group, Random House and the L. W. Singer Company, New York, 1965.

11. Pólya, G., Introduction, in Reference 1 above.
12. Riordan, John, An Introduction to Combinatorial Analysis, John Wiley and Sons, Inc., New York, 1958.
13. Riordan, John, Generating Functions, Chapter 3, in Reference 1 above.
14. Weaver, Warren, Science and Complexity, American Scientist, vol. 36, 1948, pp. 536–544.

4. Nonparametric statistics at the pre-college level

C. B. Bell

University of Michigan
Ann Arbor, Michigan, U.S.A.

4.1. INTRODUCTION AND SUMMARY

Statistics can be defined as the science of decision-making (under uncertainty) based on data. The techniques of statistics are based on one or more models of the real world. For some models one is lead to classical or parametric statistics, i.e. techniques related to the normal distribution or one of the common distributions characterized by a usually small number of parameters. For other models of the real world a different methodology is developed. This methodology might be called nonparametric or distribution-free statistics.

Generally one can establish some connection between a parametric procedure and at least one "corresponding" nonparametric procedure. Further, it does not seem desirable to draw a precise line between parametric and nonparametric statistics. One who applies statistics should simply employ those methods which are most closely tied to his model of the real world. An experienced user of statistics soon learns that there is a continuum of models, and, hence, at least a continuum of possible techniques.

However, from the point of view of teaching statistics to pre-college students, one can draw some sharp lines between types of techniques. In the opinion of the author the techniques most easily taught and most easily learned are those based on simple counting and ranking procedures. These counting and ranking procedures fall under the general heading of nonparametric statistics.

It can be proved mathematically (e.g. Bell and Donoghue, 1969, [3]) that for appropriate models of the real world, all nonparametric statistics must have discrete (bounded) distributions, and must be based on permutations. For other models it can be proved the statistics based on counting the number of occurrences of certain events in n trials are all nonparametric. (In this context nonparametric or distribution-free statistics can be defined as those whose distributions do not depend on the form of the underlying distribution.)

Although the ranking and counting procedures are quite elementary, they cannot be presented in a pedagogical vacuum. The derivations and uses of these procedures can only be presented to pre-college students after the basic concepts of descriptive statistics and statistical inference have been introduced.

An "ideal" course in statistics for pre-college students should begin with elementary descriptive statistics—histograms, cumulatives, means, ranges, etc. Work with these at most requires mathematics of the first year high school algebra type. Descriptive statistics should be followed by a treatment of populations, samples and the basic ideas of statistical inference, i.e. making inference about a population on the basis of a sample from it. At this point the nonparametric techniques can be brought in. They should be brought in at this point not because the model with which they are associated is logical preferable at this stage of the development; but rather because they are simple and can be grasped without additional mathematics.

In the author's opinion a statistics book for pre-college students should also include the techniques of classical or parametric statistics if only in an appendix. In view of the history of the development of statistical methods as well as that of their application, some discussion of the normal or Gaussian models and related techniques should always be included. (From the practical point of view, it should also be noted that for large sample sizes the "usual" nonparametric statistics have approximations related to the normal distribution.)

The pedagogical difficulty in presenting the normal distribution to pre-college students is simply that it involves an exponential function and an integral. As of this writing it seems unlikely that the majority of pre-college students will have been exposed to both of these concepts before or during the statistics course. There will, of course, be many pre-college students who will have had sufficient mathematics to be able to handle the normal distribution. For such students a good course in statistics should contain a treatment of normal models and associated methodology. Consequently, the latter sections or the appendix of a pre-college statistics text should be devoted to this area of activity.

In terms of applications of statistics one cannot make the general statement that parametric procedures are better than nonparametric procedures or vice versa. The two types of techniques are simply designed for different types of circumstances. However, in some sense the parametric methods are better when the model concerns a population whose form is determined up to a small finite number of unknown parameters. On the other hand the nonparametric techniques are more widely applicable. They can be used (with corresponding loss of efficiency) in cases for which parametric methods were designed as well as in a large number of other cases. In summary one can say that nonparametric methods

(i) are simpler than parametric methods to present to pre-college students;

(ii) are not a substitute for parametric methods but can be used in a a wider variety of situations; (sometimes with loss of efficiency); and

(iii) can be introduced only after basic statistical concepts are known to the students.

From the point of view of the teacher and the students, (i) above is the overriding reason for emphasizing nonparametric statistics in a pre-college course.

The next section of this paper contains an outline of an "ideal" statistics course for pre-college students. The following sections treat in some detail those parts of the outline dealing specifically with variations of two simple nonparametric statistics.

4.2. OUTLINE OF AN "IDEAL" STATISTICS COURSE FOR PRE-COLLEGE STUDENTS

Chapter I. Introduction

Examples and Problems illustrating the need to make decisions under uncertainty.

Chapter II. Descriptive Statistics

Section 2.1. Histograms and Frequency Polygons, Raw Data, Class Intervals, Class Frequency, Grouped Data, Cumulative Frequency, Cumulative Relative Frequency.

Section 2.2. Central Tendency Statistics, Mode, Median, Mean.

Section 2.3. Dispersion Statistics, Range, Variance, Standard Deviation, Percentiles.

Chapter III. Samples and Population

Section 3.1. Definitions and Examples, Population, Sample, Member, Size.

Section 3.2. Basic Premise of Statistical Inference: Sample parameters tend to corresponding population parameters as the sample size increases.

Section 3.3. Random Samples, Definition, Examples, Approximations.

Section 3.4. Random Number Tables, Construction, Properties, Uses.

Chapter IV. Some Elementary Sampling Distributions

Section 4.1. What is a Sampling Distribution? Definition and Examples.

Section 4.2. Dichotomous Populations. Voting, Coin Tossing.

It should be noted that in the above outline probability is never treated as a separate topic. In the write-up based on such an outline probability would simply be brought in as needed in the development of statistics. However, a large number of people who work in probability and statistics feel that about one third of a first course in statistics should be devoted to probability as a separate topic. This, they say, is because the mathematical foundation of statistics is probability.

The author agrees with this latter statement but feels that for pre-college students the emphasis should be on the ideas of statistics i.e. decision making—rather than on their mathematical foundations. Nevertheless, it seems worthwhile to present an outline of a chapter on probability which is intimately related to statistical inference. In this outline the author adopts the frequentist's view of probability and statistics.

Chapter on Statistical Probability

Section 1. Sample Space, Events, Combinations of Events.

Section 2. Relative Frequency Interpretation of Probability.

Section 3. Elementary Properties of Probabilities, Properties of Relative Frequencies, Addition Law.

Section 4. Conditional Probability, Relative Frequency Approach, Multiplication Law, Statistical Independence.

Section 5. Urn Models, Random Sampling (i.e. with replacement), Destructive Sampling (i.e. without replacement).

Section 6. Likelihood Functions, Binomial and Hypergeometric Distributions.

Section 7. Maximum Likelihood Inference, Multidecision Problems as urn models.

Section 8. Random Variables and Distribution Functions.

Depending on where this chapter on statistical probability is introduced in a statistics course, one could include more or fewer statistical examples.

We now turn to the treatment of ranking and counting which are basic to nonparametric statistics.

4.3 URNS, RANKS, AND ORDER STATISTICS

The basic problem here is to find statistics whose probabilistic properties (i.e., sampling distributions) are the same for a "large" family of populations.

When students are familiar with the concept of continuity, one considers observations (or random variables) $X_1, \ldots, X_n$ such that

$$P(X_1 \leqslant t_1; X_2 \leqslant t_2; \ldots; X_n \leqslant t_n) = \prod_{i=1}^{n} F(t_i),$$

where F is a continuous distribution function. In such a case, the $n!$ possible rankings of $X_1, \ldots, X_n$ are all equally likely whatever be F. That is,

$$P\{X_1 < X_2 < \ldots < X_n\} = \frac{1}{n!};$$

$$P\{X_2 < X_3 < X_1 < \ldots < X_n < X_{n-1}\} = \frac{1}{n!}; \quad \text{etc.}$$

(Continuity is needed here to guarantee that the probability of a tie is zero.)

The majority of pre-college students will not be familiar with continuity. Hence, one seeks other models for which the given results hold.

Consider an urn containing numbered balls with no ties. If one samples *without replacement* from this urn, the observations $X_1, X_2, \ldots, X_n$ will satisfy the probabilistic results above. This is so for arbitrary numbering so long as there are no ties within the urn. This is also true if one combines the contents of several urns if there are no resulting ties.

Before employing these ideas it is necessary to express them in terms of order statistics and rank functions (or vectors).

Example 3.1.—If successive balls drawn from an urn exhibit the numbers: 0.4, -1.9, 6.3, 4.2, then one has

(a) $X_1 = 0.4$, $X_2 = -1.9$, $X_3 = 6.3$, $X_4 = 4.2$;

(b) $X_2 < X_1 < X_4 < X_3$.

Further one says $R(X_1) = 2$, i.e., the rank of the first observation is 2; $R(X_2) = 1$, $R(X_4) = 3$, and $R(X_3) = 4$. (Here the rank of a given observation X_i in a sample is the total number of observations in the sample with values less than or equal to X_i.) Still further, one writes: $X(1) = -1.9$; $X(2) = 0.4$; $X(3) = 4.2$; $X(4) = 6.3$; where $X(i)$ is the ith smallest observation.

Summarizing these ideas one has the following result.

Theorem 3.1

Let $X_1, X_2, \ldots, X_n$ be successive observations obtained by sampling without replacement from an urn with no ties. Then one has

$$P(X_{r_1} < X_{r_2} < \ldots < X_{r_n}) = P(R(X_{r_1}) = 1, \ldots, R(X_{r_n}) = n)$$
$$= P(R(X_1) = r_1, \ldots, R(X_n) = r_n)$$
$$= P(X(r_1) = X_1, \ldots, X(r_n) = X_n)$$
$$= P(X(1) = X_{r_1}, \ldots, X(n) = X_{r_n}) = \frac{1}{n!}$$

for all permutations $r_1, \ldots, r_n$ of $\{1, 2, \ldots, n\}$.

This is simply a precise way of saying that all orderings are equally likely whether they are expressed in terms of rankings, ranks or order statistics.

The result here will be used in several contexts. The first context concerns estimates and tests of percentiles of a population—especially its median. The other contexts concern testing various properties by means of summing certain ranks, appropriately.

Before turning to these applications one should mention that: Sampling *with* replacement gives an approximation to sampling *without* replacement and that the approximation is better for urns containing a large number of balls.

4.4. ORDER STATISTICS, PERCENTILES AND THE BINOMIAL DISTRIBUTION

Consider a population with *continuous* distribution F. The $(100\,p)$th percentile $T_p = T_p(F)$ is a value such that a proportion p of the population values are less than or equal to it and a proportion $(1-p)$ of the population values are above it, i.e.,

$$P(X \leqslant T_p) = F(T_p) = p$$

and

$$P(X > T_p) = 1 - F(T_p) = 1 - p.$$

(For $p = \frac{1}{2}$, T_p is the median of the population. This latter case is considered more often than the others in practice. However, it is not conceptually simpler.)

For any given p, the same probability situation can be obtained with an urn model. So that necessary approximations hold one assumes that the urn contains a relatively large number of balls. Then the probabilities will be calculated in terms of sampling *with* replacement, which is simpler to handle.

Let S_n be the number of the observations $X_1, X_2, \ldots, X_n$ which fall at or below T_p, the $(100\,p)$th percentile of values in the urn. One has then that

(a) $P(X_i \leqslant T_p) = p$ for each i, and hence, that

(b) $P(S_n = k) = \binom{n}{k} p^k (1-p)^{n-k}$ for $k = 0, 1, \ldots, n$.

This means that S_n has a binomial distribution with parameters n and p.

In terms of order statistics "$S_n = k$" is equivalent to "$X(k) \leqslant T_p < X(k+1)$". That is, "exactly k observations less than or equal to T_p" means that "the kth smallest observation does not exceed T_p but that the $(k+1)$st smallest observation does exceed T_p".

More precisely, one has the following theorem.

59

Theorem 4.1

(*a*) For sampling *with* replacement the following two conditions are equivalent for all $r < s$.

i) $X(r) \leqslant T_p < X(s)$
ii) $r \leqslant S_n < s$.

(*b*) In either case the probability is

$$\sum_{k=r}^{s-1} \binom{n}{k} p^k (1-p)^{n-k} = B(r, s-1, p, n) \qquad \text{(Definition)}$$

(The probability in (*b*) is approximately valid for sampling *without* replacement. The approximation improves as the number of balls in the urn increases; and increases relative to the number of observations.)

This result can now be used to construct confidence intervals (and equivalently tests) for percentiles.

4.5. CONFIDENCE INTERVALS AND TESTS FOR PERCENTILES

Pre-college students can with arithmetic calculations evaluate the expressions

$$\sum_{k=r}^{n} \binom{n}{k} p^k (1-p)^{n-k}.$$

Hence, tables of these probabilities can be made perhaps as joint class exercises. (Pedagogically, it might be worthwhile to relate these binomial probabilities to coin tossing, thumbtack tossing and other simple repeated trial experiments while tables are being calculated.)

The interval $[X(r), X(s)]$ is a *confidence interval* for the $(100\,p)$th percentile T_p, with *confidence level*

$$\sum_{k=r}^{s-1} \binom{n}{k} p^k (1-p)^{n-k}.$$

This is another way of saying

$$P(X(r) \leqslant T_p < X(s)) = B(r, s-1, p, n).$$

It seems worthwhile to have the students spend lots of time "juggling" the values r, s, n, and p to get a "feel" for their interrelation.

Further, if time permits, one should have students repeatedly take samples of size n from an urn with *known* T_p, and actually note the relative frequency with which the confidence interval contains T_p.

One can prove that the theory of confidence intervals is equivalent to the theory of hypothesis testing. The usage of this fact here will simply be to give *decision rules* of the following type:

(*) Reject the hypothesis that $T_p = z_0$ iff the confidence interval $[X(r), X(s)]$ does not contain the specified value z_0.

In this case the *size* or *significance level* of the test is $1 - B(r, s-1, p, n)$.

In view of Theorem 4.1 this decision rule can also be stated in terms of S_n, the number of $X_1, \ldots, X_n$ which do not exceed T_p. It becomes

(**) Reject the hypothesis $T_p = z_0$ iff

$$S_n < r \quad \text{or} \quad S_n \geqslant s.$$

(As a class project one might consider repeated tests of various hypotheses whose truth or falsity is known.)

The test and confidence intervals given here are two-sided. However, analogous results hold in the one-sided cases. For example,

$$P(T_p < X(s)) = P(S_n < s) = \sum_{k=0}^{s-1} \binom{n}{k} p^k (1-p)^{n-k}.$$

The tests and confidence intervals of this section can be applied to games of chance where one is interested in testing the hypothesis that the probability of a certain event is a certain fixed constant. For example, in coin tossing, one might wish to test $H_0 : P = \frac{1}{2}$; or in roulette, $H_0 : P(\text{Red}) = \frac{18}{38}$, etc. Similarly, one might wish to set up confidence intervals for probabilities of this sort. For a course in pre-college statistics numerous examples and class projects should be built around these ideas.

It is also important that these students realize that although games of chance illustrate the concepts of statistics quite well, the main applications of statistics lie elsewhere. For example, one might wish to estimate one or more percentiles, e.g., the median of the weights of soap in boxes labelled "one pound" or test hypotheses about them. In fact, the idea should be imparted that statistics is a tool for decision-making in many facets of life.

One can now turn to other uses of ranks and order statistics.

4.6. TWO POPULATIONS: RANK SUM TESTS

Quite often in practice a statistician is called upon to decide whether or not two populations have the same statistical distribution. The hypothesis here is usually written $H_0 : F_1 = F_2$. If the unknown populations are known to be normal, one can use one of several techniques depending on which additional assumptions are used. The derivations of each of these techniques, however, is beyond the scope of the majority of pre-college students.

61

A method easily derived and tabulated is as follows.

Let two populations be statistically equal and the probability of ties be zero. (This situation can be approximated to any desired degree of accuracy by urn models.)

Let $X_1, \ldots, X_m$ and $Y_1, \ldots, Y_n$ be samples from the populations in question.

If $F_1 = F_2$, then $P\{X_1 < \ldots < X_m < Y_1 < \ldots < Y_n\}$

$$= P\{Y_1 < X_1 < Y_2 < X_2 < \ldots < Y_n < X_m\}$$

$$= P\{Y_1 < Y_2 < X_2 < X_1 < \ldots < X_m < Y_n\} = \frac{1}{N!}$$

for each permutation of the combined sample of X's and Y's, where $N = m + n$.

If the X's and Y's are well-interspersed, one would tend to agree that $F_1 = F_2$. If they are not well interspersed, e.g.

$$XXXXYYYYXX \quad \text{or} \quad XXXXXYYY,$$

one tends to conclude that $F_1 \neq F_2$. All intermixtures of X's and Y's are equally probable if $F_1 = F_2$. However, if $F_1 \neq F_2$, then some rankings are more probable than others.

A paint chemist, F. Wilcoxon, who became an applied statistician, came up with the following idea for measuring the degree to which the X's and Y's are interspersed.

Let $U = \sum_{i=1}^{m} R(X_i)$, i.e. the sum of the ranks of the X's (or first sample values). A relatively large value of U indicates that the X's are generally larger than the Y's; while a small value of U indicates that the X's are generally smaller than the Y's. The sampling distribution of U is quite simple to compute. Before doing so it should be mentioned that the chronological order of the observations has no bearing on this analysis.

For the problem at hand the following rankings are equivalent:
$X_1 < Y_2 < Y_3 < X_2 < Y_1$; $X_2 < Y_3 < Y_2 < X_1 < Y_1$; $X_2 < Y_1 < Y_3 < X_1 < Y_2$, etc. They all lead to the configuration or ordering $XYYXY$, for which

$$U = \sum_{i=1}^{m} R(X_i) = 1 + 4 = 5.$$

Example 6.1.—For the case where $m = 2$ and $n = 3$, i.e. where there are 2 X's and 3 Y's, there are $\dfrac{5!}{3! 2!} = 10$ possible orderings.

$XXYYY$	$1+2=3$	$YXXYY$	$2+3=5$	$YYYXX$	$3+4=7$
$XYXYY$	$1+3=4$	$YXYXY$	$2+4=6$	$YYXYX$	$3+5=8$
$XYYXY$	$1+4=5$	$YXYYX$	$2+5=7$	$YYYXX$	$4+5=9$
		$XYYYX$	$1+5=6$		

If $F_1 = F_2$, i.e. if the X and Y populations are statistically equivalent, all orderings are equally probable. The sampling distribution of U is, then,

k	3	4	5	6	7	8	9
$P(U=k)$	.1	.1	.2	.2	.2	.1	.1

The important items here, as far as pre-college students are concerned, are that not only is the statistic U easy to visualize and manipulate; but also that tables for the sampling distribution of U can be constructed by the students in class. One class project should be devoted to constructing tables for the cases: $m=1, n=1; m=2, n=1; m=1, n=2; \ldots; m=5, n=5$.

In each case the construction of the table entails

1. Listing all $\dfrac{(n+m)!}{n!\ m!}$ orderings:

2. Summing the X ranks for each such ordering, and
3. Assigning to each integer k, a probability

$$P(k) = \frac{\{\text{number of orderings yielding } U=k\}}{\dfrac{(n+m)!}{n!\,m!}}$$

Students should also experiment with the various elementary properties of such tables. For example, if one sums Y ranks, then the resulting table is not the same as the U-table (unless $m=n$). However, there is a $1-1$ correspondence between two such tables.

The tests related to this statistic reject H_0 if U assumes a value "too large"; or "too small"; or "too extreme" depending on the alternatives of concern. The table is used to give precise significance levels.

Confidence intervals based on U are, in the author's opinion, beyond the scope of most pre-college students.

An equally elementary statistic can be applied to the problem below.

4.7. RANDOMNESS VS. TREND FOR A SINGLE POPULATION

A problem of great importance in many fields of endeavor is whether or not the population of interest is changing with time. A clothing manufacturer would like to know if the population of sizes of the clothes-buying public is changing with time. Everyone is concerned with whether or not the radiation level of the atmosphere is changing with time. Stock analysts, grocers and housewives have similar interest in the randomness or trend of various prices.

The data available for the analyses of such problems is quite often a sequence $X_1, \ldots, X_n$ of observations taken at hourly or daily or weekly, etc. intervals. (Here X_i represents the observation from the ith time interval.) The chronological order is essential to the analysis.

If one is primarily concerned with increase and/or decreases with time, i.e. upward and/or downward trends the nonparametric statistic $T' = \sum_1^m i R(X_i)$ is of interest. Large values of T' indicate that the X's are generally increasing, while small values of T' indicate the opposite.

A test for randomness vs. trend consists of rejecting randomness if the value of T' is "too large" and/or "too small". Precise significance levels, etc., must be obtained from tables.

Example 7.1.—For the case $n=3$, the possible $3!=6$ rankings of X_1, X_2 and X_3 with the corresponding T' values are: $X_1 < X_2 < X_3$ and $T' = (1) \cdot (1) + (2) \cdot (2) + (3) \cdot (3) = 14$; $X_1 < X_3 < X_2$ and $T' = (1) \cdot (1) + (2) \cdot (3) + (3) \cdot (2) = 13$; ...; $X_3 < X_2 < X_1$ with $T' = (1) \cdot (3) + (2) \cdot (2) + (3) \cdot (1) = 10$. The resulting table is:

k	10	11	12	13	14
$P(T' = k)$	$\frac{1}{6}$	$\frac{1}{3}$	0	$\frac{1}{3}$	$\frac{1}{6}$

Again the tables are quite simple to compute, and pre-college students can easily gain facility in their construction and use.

4.8. CORRELATION TESTS AND T'-TABLES

In many areas of science, one is interested in whether or not two types of measurements are correlated or not. For example, heights and weights of humans are correlated; as are the prices of stocks of companies in the same field (quite often). If one knows that the two quantities in question constitute a bivariate normal population, there are standard classical techniques available. However, the derivations and tables related to these tests are beyond the level of pre-college students. Further, in many applications the underlying population is not known to be normal.

The samples in such cases are of the form: $(X_1, Y_1), (X_2, Y_2), \ldots, (X_n, Y_n)$. For example, the X's could be prices of hamburger on successive days, and the Y's could be prices of eggs on the same days. The basic nonparametric statistic of interest here is $W = \sum_{i=1}^n R_x(X_i) R_y(Y_i)$, where $R_x(X_i)$ is the rank of X_i among the X's and $R_y(Y_i)$ is the rank of Y_i among the Y's. The hypothesis here is H_0: X and Y are uncorrelated.

Example 8.1.—On five successive days at a large supermarket the prices (X, Y) of 1 lb. of hamburger, and 1 dozen eggs respectively, were:

$$(.39, .64), (.40, .63), (.41, .65), (.38, .66), (.385, .62).$$

Here $X_1 = .39$, $X_2 = .40$, $X_3 = .41$, $X_4 = .38$, $X_5 = .385$

$$Y_1 = .64, \ Y_2 = .63, \ Y_3 = .65, \ Y_4 = .66, \ Y_5 = .62$$

Further, the ranks are

i	1	2	3	4	5
$R_x(X_i)$	3	4	5	1	2
$R_y(Y_i)$	3	2	4	5	1

Therefore, $W = (3) \cdot (3) + (4) \cdot (2) + (5) \cdot (4) + (1) \cdot (5) + (2) \cdot (1) = 44$.

About the above example, one should note two things. First one sees that there is no reason to rank the X's and Y's jointly. Here the X's are all smaller than the Y's, but this has no bearing on their correlation. Further in many applications, e.g., height and weight, the X's and Y's are measured in different units and, hence are not "naturally" comparable.

The second item of interest here is a computational one, which simplifies the construction of tables. In computing $W = \sum_{i=1}^n R_x(X_i) R_y(Y_i)$, one first rewrites the data in a manner such that $Y_1 < Y_2 < \ldots < Y_n$. In the example above, this means the data becomes

$$(.385, .62), (.40, .63), (.39, .64), (.41, .65), (.38, .66).$$

Then

$$W = \sum_{i=1}^n R_y(Y_i) R_x(X_i) = \sum_{i=1}^n i R_x(X_i),$$

since $\qquad\qquad R_y(Y_1) = 1, \ R_y(Y_2) = 2$, etc.

This means that the tables for the statistic T' in Section 4.7, can also be used for W. As far as the decisions go, large values of W indicate "positive correlation between X and Y, and small values of W indicate the opposite. Significance levels, etc., are treated here as in the case of T'. "Randomness" corresponds to "no correlation"; "upward trend" corresponds to "positive correlation"; etc.

A final nonparametric problem will be treated in terms of the preceding developments. One can use both methods for treating percentiles and 2-sample methods for the symmetry problem below.

4.9. MEDICAL TESTS AND SYMMETRY PROBLEMS

Consider testing whether or not a certain medication has an effect on blood pressure. One experimental program might consist of taking two random samples of human beings, giving the medication to one sample but not to the other. One would then compare the two samples as in Section 4.6. However, from a practical point of view one would soon learn that the variation of individual blood pressures is quite often greater than the effects of known medication. Hence, there is a good chance that the effect of the drug, if any, will be obscured.

The experimental program of interest here is one in which one random sample is taken. Each person's blood pressure is measured both before and after the medication is administered. The data then is of the form: (X_1, Y_1), $(X_2, Y_2), \ldots, (X_n, Y_n)$ where X's and Y's represent the blood pressures before and after medication, respectively. The hypothesis: "No Effect", then means that X and Y are symmetrically distributed. That is, if the medication has no effect, then (X, Y) and (Y, X) are equally distributed.

Many methods of treating this problem begins with forming the differences $D_i = X_i - Y_i$, the change in blood pressure of the ith subject. Two methods of handling the D's will be given.

Method (A).—(See Section 4.5.) If the medication has no effect, D is equally likely to be positive or negative. In fact, if one can measure accurately enough to eliminate ties, one finds $P(D_i < 0) = \frac{1}{2} = P(D_i > 0)$. Let S_n be the number of positive D's, or, equivalently, the number of subjects with lower blood pressures.

Then, S_n has a binomial distribution with parameters n and $\frac{1}{2}$ (as in tossing a fair coin, or in counting the number of exceedances of the median of a population). This means that

$$P(S_n = k) = \binom{n}{k} \left(\frac{1}{2}\right)^n \quad \text{for} \quad k = 0, 1, \ldots, n.$$

The tests here consist of rejecting the hypothesis of "No Effect" if S_n is "too large" and/or "too small". In fact, one can employ here all of the methodology of Section 4.5.

Moreover, one might be interested in the proportion p of the population which would have their blood pressure lowered (or raised) by the given medication. As in Section 5, one can give confidence intervals and tests for each value of p (not just the $p = \frac{1}{2}$ "No Effect" case).

The second method here is that of Section 4.6 and within the scope of pre-college students it can be applied to tests but not to confidence intervals.

66

Method (B).—(See Section 4.6.)

Example 9.1.—Consider tests of "shock-proof" packaging for electronic tubes. Let W be the "current" of a packaged tube before dropping, and Z be its "current" after it is dropped a specified distance. Suppose the data is

$$(1.3, 1.7), (2.1, 2.0), (1.9, 1.6), (3.6, 2.9), (3.2, 3.4)$$

$$(W_1, Z_1), (W_2, Z_2), (W_3, Z_3), (W_4, Z_4), (W_5, Z_5).$$

If $D_i = W_i - Z_i$ one has

$$D_1 = -0.4, D_2 = 0.1, D_3 = 0.3, D_4 = 0.7, D_5 = -0.2.$$

If the packaging is such that dropping has no effect on the current, then positive and negative values of D are equally likely. Further, the negative values should be distributed as a "mirror image" of the positive values. That is to say, the absolute values of the positive and negative D's have the same distribution.

The method here is to separate the D's into two-samples: D_1, D_5 and D_2, D_3, D_4, i.e., the negative differences and the positive differences. Then one takes the absolute values and tests $F_1 = F_2$. If the first sample values are called X's and the second sample Y's, then one has

$$X_1 = 0.4, X_2 = 0.2, Y_1 = 0.1, Y_2 = 0.3, Y_3 = 0.7.$$

Computing U as in Section 4.5, one finds

$$U = \sum_1^2 R(X_i) = 2 + 4 = 6.$$

The decision making process illustrated in the above example, consists of rejecting "no effect" if U is "too large" and/or "too small". The tables to be used here are exactly those of Section 4.6.

4.10. CONCLUDING REMARKS

From the preceding development, one sees that a variety of statistical problems can be treated in terms of counting and ranking techniques. The computation of the statistics and the construction of the tables are fully within the grasp of pre-college students. Further, "real world" problems and data can be handled by such methods. The introduction of such problems and data should give motivation to a large number of pre-college students.

In closing, one should reiterate the fact that these nonparametric statistics cannot be presented in a vacuum. Their use must be preceded by some basic statistics as given in the outline of Section 4.2.

REFERENCES

1. F. Massey and W. Dixon (1968), "Introduction to Statistical Analysis," Third Edition, McGraw Hill.
2. C. Kraft and C. Van Eeden (1969), Nonparametric Introduction to Statistics, John Wiley and Sons.
3. C. B. Bell and J. Donoghue (1969), "Distribution-Free Tests of Randomness," Sankhya (Journal of the Indian Statistical Society) p. 157–176.
4. G. Noether (1967), Elements of Nonparametric Statistics, Macmillan.
5. Section on Statistics in the "A-Level" Portion of the 1968 African Mathematics Program Report, Educational Development Corporation, Newton, Mass.
6. Section on Statistics of Goals for the Correlation of Elementary Science and Mathematics (1969). Published for Education Development Center, by Houghton Mifflin Co.

5. The role of practical experimentation in the teaching of probability and statistics

Hilda M. Davies

University of Sheffield
Sheffield, England

5.1. INTRODUCTION

My own interest in this subject began when I joined the staff of the University of Sheffield in 1953, working under Dr. G. H. Jowett,[1] who became Senior Lecturer in charge of the Department of Statistics on its creation a few years later. We ran three-hour practical classes for first and second year students of statistics, for which he evolved many ingenious ideas and I spent considerable time in those early days in trying out new experiments, making modifications and, in the case of group experiments in particular, planning the most suitable methods of class organization. The ensuing fifteen years have seen considerable development of Probability and Statistics as a subject in British education in general, and as a school subject in particular, and I have found school teachers all over the country to be keenly interested in such aids to teaching. Many of the ideas of the original experiments, simplified or modified, seem particularly suitable for school children, and these, together with some similar later additions, have the added advantage that no highly specialised equipment is necessary; only readily available or easily made apparatus is required so that no schoolteacher should be deterred by lack of funds. A list of such experiments is given in the Appendix and a glance through it at this point should illustrate and clarify the following discussion.

Let us first consider the *purposes* of such experimental work. In the main they are

1. To obtain data for analysis and/or to obtain a realization of a concept (e.g. the histogram—see Appendix III No. 1 and Appendix II).
2. To obtain experience of designing an experiment.

At the school level, (2) may involve only the simplest ideas, such as the need of randomising to avoid bias. But it will be found that even the seeming-

---

[1] Now Professor of Statistics at the University of Otago, Dunedin.

ly simplest experiment can involve the student in such knotty questions as "where does a pea pod begin and end?", "when is a pea not a pea?", and "when is an observer effect to be expected?" This final question crops up whenever it is required to "pool" observations from different observers. (e.g. Appendix III No. 1, 2, 5, and 8 and Appendix II.)

The main argument against such experimental work is that it can be very time-consuming. Data can be obtained in two ways

(*a*) by taking observations of a process already evolving (e.g. Appendix III, No. 5),

(*b*) by performing an experiment or *creating* a process from which the observations may be recorded.

Both these methods can involve a fair stretch of time; as can also the time required for the actual computation of the analysis. We must therefore face the question: "is this use of time justifiable?" The answer must involve consideration of the following points:

(i) the amount of time involved for *any one individual* pupil;

(ii) whether in the course of carrying out the experiment, any new aspects of basic statistical principles are brought to light, or possible dangers and pitfalls more clearly understood;

(iii) whether the exercise captures the enthusiasm of the participants, adding zest and interest to their study by personal involvement.

In most cases I believe that these three criteria are very much interrelated as regards methods of obtaining the desired results and that basically success depends on the amount of careful and imaginative thought that the teacher puts into designing and organizing the experiments. Let us consider this point by point.

(i) *Time taken for collection of data*

First ideas of histograms, their gradual build-up and a heuristic idea of the shape of the underlying probability distribution, can best be obtained from at least a hundred or more observations. For most pupils, however, the novelty of tossing dice, "shoving" a coin or counting the number of peas in a pod, can begin to wear off long before the hundredth trial, so I suggest that the data for such histograms be confined to such subjects as are suitable for class "pooling" of observations. Each student can count the contents of five or ten pea-pods, all students working simultaneously. (See also the experiment with matchboxes described in Appendix II.) In the case of dice, (Appendix III, 3), however, although they may be supposedly unbiassed, it is unwise to assume this, so the *same* dice should be used throughout an experiment, each *in turn* tossing the dice five or ten times, entering the results on a previously prepared tabulation sheet and then passing dice and sheet on to the next student. Meanwhile the class can either continue with some previous analysis or can be individually working out the "expected" probability or frequency distribution for the experiment. An experiment, such as "coin-shoving" must, on the other hand, be treated differently as this involves a certain element of personal skill, giving rise to an "operator" effect, each operator having his own personal probability distribution for the activity. The possibility of such differences may fruitfully be discussed with a class and the keenest pupils may feel it worth while to find their own such distribution at home in their spare time, but a class experiment using such a technique is better designed in such a manner that only small samples are required. (Appendix III, 4.) Time taken for the analysis is also a feature to be considered. This will be discussed in detail later.

(ii) *Aspects of Statistical Principles*
These include the idea of "operator effect" discussed above. In particular, when class results are to be combined, special emphasis must be laid on the need for a thorough shaking of the dice (III, 3) or mixing of the dried peas (III, 2). Similarly, by preliminary class discussions, agreement must be reached as to the limits of length of a pea-pod and which size of pea is to be considered "negligible" (III, 1). Thus students can learn to appreciate at the outset that no amount of elegant statistical analysis can counteract the effect of unsuitability of data for the investigation concerned.

(iii) *Personal Involvement*
Personal participation in obtaining the observations brings to the statistical analysis the zest of discovery. When the data is simply an exercise in a book, to the student the answer obtained may seem simply the answer to that specific exercise (and it is probably given at the back of the book anyway). In a subject such as physics an experiment simply *illustrates* an already known law and the excitement of seeing whether it does work is to some extent tempered by the anxiety of how to "cook" the results if things go wrong and the expected results are not obtained. On the other hand, in a statistical experiment there are two alternatives. In one, the expected outcome is *not* known (for example, in an experiment involving individual skill such as "coin-shoving") and some real discovery, however minor, is to be made. Furthermore, as in the above example and in the one on line drawing described below, it is a *personal* discovery—a small addition to the information the student has about himself—and this tends to be of peculiar interest so that the attention is that much more concentrated.

71

The other alternative is that in which the true parameters are known to the supervisor and given to the class, after completion of the experiment. The experiment then demonstrates how far the probabilistic methods work out in practice. In a fairly large class they may show not only that the most likely results (e.g. a parameter lying within a confidence interval) occur frequently but also that the less likely results do occur sometimes. For example, in a class in which more than twenty independent samples are taken from a large population having parameters known to the supervisor, it is likely that one or two of the 95 % confidence intervals computed from these samples will *not* cover the parameter in question. This helps to bring home the probabilistic nature of the exercise and is found to be more exciting than an unrepeated experiment which assumes that the parameter lies within the interval.

Many simple experiments of the type used in a practical psychology course for beginners can readily be adapted according to various alternatives. These alternatives make a suitable basis of discussion on simple design of experiment if required. I will describe one such experiment in detail. Basically the experiment consists of drawing a line of estimated length equal to a given line.

Possible designs could be devised to test whether (1) there is a consistent tendency either to underestimate or overestimate, (2) copying accuracy varies with

(*a*) the length of the given line,
(*b*) the distance of the copy from the original,
(*c*) the ordering of the attempt, i.e. investigation of a practice or a fatigue effect, or even
(*d*) which hand is being used.

It would be possible to discuss such alternatives with a class having as yet no knowledge of statistical methods. A more advanced class of, say, University level might devise an experiment to test all such effects simultaneously. At the early stages, however, the purpose of discussing the alternatives is two-fold; firstly, to choose among the possibilities and secondly, to ensure that the experiment is so designed that the effects of the alternative possibilities will not cause bias. Consider now one possible method in detail which I have tried out for myself but not as yet given to a class.

5.2. A LINE DRAWING EXPERIMENT

Instructions

The instructions for this experiment read as follows: Take several sheets or strips of plain (i.e. unlined) paper, preferably of foolscap length, (though

72

quarto will do). On the "master" page draw carefully, using a ruler, in a row parallel with the longer edges, lines of 1, 2, 3, 4, and 5 cm, with maximum spacing between them. Make a freehand copy of these lines on another sheet or strip of paper, at a distance of 10 cm from the originals, randomising the order of the line lengths copied. Label this copy "Trial 1". State clearly the method of randomisation used.

Repeat the process, taking a different random order each time, until six trials have been completed.

Measure the length of each copied line in mm (to the nearest mm) and tabulate the data as follows:

Line Lengths (mm)

Trial No.	Length of line copied (mm)				
	10	20	30	40	50
1					
2					
3					
4					
5					
6					

Make a similar tabulation for *differences* (deviations) between each copy and its original, paying due attention to sign.

Analysis

In the second table, the sign of the deviation determines whether the copy underestimates or overestimates the original, so the pattern of signs, as tabulated, can be considered.

Means and standard deviations for each set of six deviations should be calculated to give some idea of the answer to 2a. Copying accuracy includes both how closely the mean approaches the original value and how much variability occurs as measured by the standard deviation. Detail and sophistication of the statistical analysis will inevitably depend on the background knowledge of the class. A regression of mean deviation on line length can be considered quite simply "by eye" if least squares methods are unknown, by looking at the scatter of points drawn on a graph about the axis of line length: or by plotting the actual lengths, rather than the deviations, against original line length, putting in both individual and mean observations, (the latter, of course, being obtained from the mean deviations by adding each to the length of original line). Positions of these can then be compared with the line of the form $y = x$, for perfect copying.

Similarly, to consider the question 2c, means and standard deviations over each row (i.e. over each given distance) can be obtained and regression of deviation on trial considered to see whether either the mean or the standard deviation of deviations increases with trial number, as would be the case if practice does tend to make perfect.

For consideration of 2b, each trial must take place at a different distance from the original (e.g. 5, 10, 15, 20 and 25 cm) and the order in which these are taken should be randomised. To avoid over-complication it would probably be preferable, except for advanced classes, to copy only one line in any one experiment; the analysis would again be similar. Many other variations of this type of experiment can readily be devised and an alternative which has been successfully used in Sheffield involved estimating the midpoints of equal lines stamped on a sheet with a die-stamp.

5.3. CODING OF DATA

It will be noted that the method of using deviations has an effect similar to that of a coding system of reducing the data for greatest possible ease of computation. The choice of units and measuring accuracy is such that computation is confined to small integers. In my own trial the integers ranged between -3 and 6 inclusive, so that all computation was quick and easy. With a little thought and care all experiments used can be devised in such a way that, using suitable coding if necessary, the data for analysis is almost all in the range -12 to 12. If the original measurements have been taken with greater accuracy than will allow of such a reduction, the measurements can be rounded before coding to produce the desired effect. In such a case it will be found that, even with a sophisticated statistical analysis, the conclusions reached are not likely to be different, the values obtained for, say, a significance test being usually very little different when the rounded data replaces the original observations.

I am of the opinion that, for the beginner, the statistical ideas are so novel and demanding that the whole effort of the student is best concentrated on these until they have to some extent been mastered. A diffusion of the attention to cope with even two digit observations may both distract from the main purpose in hand and detract from the enthusiasm of the student by the tedium of the ensuing computations. Admittedly students thoroughly enjoy using hand-computing machines if these are available. They can still use them for the simple data, particularly for summations of squares, but they are by no means essential to the practical class.

There may however be a few occasions when a group experiment with pooled observations gives rise to larger or more complicated computations.

In such a case it is also possible to pool the effort. For example, long sums of squares can be subdivided among different groups of students. Several individuals in each group can perform the same computations as a check on the results obtained and then each group can sum the group sums to obtain a checked final result.

Additional incentive can be added to all such computation, whether individual or in groups, by encouraging the student to hazard a guess at the answer from a scanning of the data beforehand and to compare this estimate with the subsequent result obtained. This will train him in what might be termed as a "feel for figures", which can serve, among other things, as a useful check on the results. Otherwise obvious mistakes can be overlooked by the novice in computation who is overconcerned with the arithmetic, even to the slipping of a decimal point to give a supposed mean value which, all unnoticed, lies outside the range of all the figures involved.

This guessing competition can begin at an even earlier stage in the type of practical experimentation we are considering here. For example, many young people will be already sufficiently aware of their own capabilities to make a reasonable prediction concerning the outcome of the coin-shoving experiment (III, 4) already mentioned, particularly in regard to their likely accuracy of aim in shoving a coin "by hand" to cover a given distance. The exercise of guessing the result will also make the aim of the experiment more exactly clear and even make it possible to formulate a hypothesis to be tested. A situation in which one member of the class suggests testing the hypothesis "I am better by hand than by machine", while another wishes to test the opposite hypothesis, can instinctively give rise to the idea of the Null Hypothesis as being a useful starting point. This can lead eventually to a readier intuitive understanding of what is involved in the choice of an alternative hypothesis.

5.4. RANKING METHODS

It is debatable whether it is suitable to introduce ranking methods at the school level, on the grounds that approximate methods are better left until the student can appreciate the nature and degree of the approximation involved. Nevertheless there are some school syllabuses which already include the Spearman rank correlation coefficient and possibly also Kendall's coefficient of concordance and if such topics are being studied it is certainly worthwhile to obtain some class data for analysis. A set of a dozen or so pictures or picture postcards may be ranked by each student individually for two of such attributes as personal preference, colourfulness, intrinsic beauty, good design, according to the type of picture and type of class.

This might even be combined with an Art lesson. Each individual can compute his own correlation coefficient for the pair of attributes to be considered and the set of class observations for any one attribute can be analysed for concordance. Better still, perhaps, if co-operation with the Art class is possible, would be for each individual to rank the whole set of class drawings or paintings on one, two or several occasions to consider such questions as the following:

(i) Is the order of ability the same for each student on every occasion?

(ii) Is the student who is best at flower painting also best at object drawing or at landscape painting, or at design etc.?

(iii) Is there concordance between the judgements of individuals in the class?

Questions (i) and (ii) could be considered alternatively by product-moment correlation, without recourse to ranking methods, if marks are given by the Art teacher.

5.5. CO-OPERATION WITH OTHER SUBJECTS

The example above shows one possibility of applying even elementary statistical knowledge to other school subjects under study and such a practice must surely help to bring home to the student the universality of the application of statistical techniques. There would be ample scope for such co-operation in aspects of nature study, or botany, where, for example, any seed pods could be substituted for green peas (App. III, 1) or the petals of flowers such as the British wood anemone could be counted, having numbers ranging at least from 5 to 9. If an instrument such as the Mettler balance is not available, the process of weighing can be lengthy and tedious but, with a little forethought, this might be combined with the lesson on "learning to weigh" on a laboratory balance in a physics or chemistry lesson.

Opportunities for development of such practical work will vary according to the different school set-up and the interests of the individual teacher and this is one reason why I would not recommend too stereotyped a programme. Another reason is that the essence of statistical method is its use in the further investigation of something not as yet fully known and I believe that this excitement of inquiry can be brought to the student in some small measure by such practical methods, provided that these retain a certain explorative freshness; but that the same experiment, repeated in too identical a manner too often by the same instructor, might become in some way deadened by the repetition, even though the students participating were different on each occasion. For this reason, when I write or talk on this subject, my aim is primarily to stimulate ideas rather than to set out some specific programme of work. With this in mind I include in the Appendix (App. I) copies of some practical examination questions which in the past I have set for students at Sheffield and I would like here to record my thanks to the Senate of the University of Sheffield for giving me permission to use them. As they stand, most of these questions would be too difficult for most school children, but the ideas contained in them can be simplified and adapted according to the needs of the particular class.

I have since analysed the total resulting data from the matches experiment (App. I, No. 1) and Appendix II is devoted to discussion of a group experiment some of which could be done by a class with no previous knowledge of statistics, using boxes of matches in which the histograms can be built up visually from the matchbox lids.

Appendix III is devoted to a list of other experiments which have given good results, described only briefly here because I have dealt with many of them in more detail elsewhere. In each case the requisite reference number for the fullest description is given and, in any case, most are briefly described in the Appendix of Reference 1. Duplicated copies of all papers given in the references are available from me on request at the Department of Probability and Statistics, The University of Sheffield, Sheffield S3 7RH, England.

REFERENCES

1. G. H. Jowett and Hilda M. Davies, "Practical Experimentation as a Teaching Method in Statistics". Journal of the Royal Statistical Society, Series A (1960) 123, pp. 10–35.
2. Hilda M. Davies, "Practical Experimentation in the Teaching of Basic Statistics". The Mathematical Gazette, 1964, Vol. XLVIII, No. 365, 271–280.
3. Hilda M. Davies, "Practical Experimentation in the Teaching of Statistics at the Secondary School Level". Sigma. (Official Journal of the Mathematical Association of Western Australia) April 1967, 5–10.

Appendix I

PRACTICAL EXAMINATION PAPERS
(UNIVERSITY OF SHEFFIELD)

Set for first year (intermediate) and second year (Secondary) students for the degree of B. Sc.

1. From each packet of boxes of the six different varieties of matches supplied take a random sample of three boxes and count the number of matches

in each box. Analyse the variance of these counts and give your estimates of the between-variety and within-variety variances, placing 95 per cent confidence limits on the latter. Also obtain an alternative estimate of the within-variety variance using the mean range of your six samples of three. Comment on the agreement.

Weigh each of the eighteen boxes with the weighing device provided and carry out a regression analysis of number of matches on weight of box, assuming that a common relation can be used for boxes of all varieties. Draw a scatter diagram, inserting the regression line together with its 95 per cent confidence band. Is this confidence band of relevance in predicting the number of matches in a further *individual* box from its weight? Give reasons for your answer.

Two methods of estimating the average number of matches per box in a large number of boxes are suggested. In Method I all the boxes are weighed together but counts of the matches are made on only a few boxes. An estimate of the average count for all the boxes is then made by using a regression correction. In Method II counts are made on a proportion of boxes (not necessarily the same as in Method I) but no use is made of weights. Discuss the efficiencies of these two methods, taking different sample sizes to illustrate your answer, and using information obtained from your earlier investigation to assist your conclusions.

(Intermediate, June 1960)

2. Using the five needles, five threads and five background cards provided investigate whether the time taken to thread a needle is dependent on the size of the needle-eye, the colour of the thread and the colour of the background against which the needle is threaded.

Needle-threading time can be assessed by using equal short lengths of thread throughout (a length between two and three inches is recommended as suitable) and counting the number of times the thread can be pulled straight through the needle in one minute. Use a Graeco Latin square design, bearing in mind the possibility that your performance may improve with practice or deteriorate with fatigue.

Write an account of your experiment, explaining clearly with full reasons any special precautions taken both in the design and the execution. Criticise the limitations of the Latin Square type of design in this investigation and design and perform a further experiment or experiments to improve on this particular investigation.

Give a clear summary of your findings.

(Secondary General, June 1960)

3. Without using the needle threader and taking cotton lengths of 2 in., 4 in., 6 in., and 10 in., count the number of times the given needle can be threaded with each cotton in one minute, when the cotton is pulled right through the needle eye at each threading. Compute the regression equation of number of times per minute on cotton length and draw it in on a scatter diagram. Deduce from your graph the mean actual threading time of the needle in seconds (i.e. the time to thread a cotton of zero length) together with a suitable confidence interval. Repeat the whole process using the needle threader, drawing this second scatter diagram and regression line on the same graph in some distinguishable way. What do you deduce from these graphs about the advantages or disadvantages of using a needle threader?

Investigate this further by performing a series of five replicate counts, each with a cotton length of 6 in., both with and without the needle threader. (Take a new piece of cotton for each of the ten counts.) Compute the two mean counts and test the significance of the difference between them by performing a suitable analysis of variance on these data.

Are the results obtained by each of the investigations consistent in helping you to a conclusion as to whether or not it is better for you to use a needle threader? Give clear reasons for your deductions and write a report noting any difficulties encountered in making a valid estimate and any precautions taken to overcome such difficulties.

(Intermediate, Sept. 1960)

4. You are supplied with a sample of 25 boxes, each containing 10 rodlets from a manufacturing process. A rodlet is "defective" when it is too big for the "go, no-go" gauge provided, and not otherwise. Test the ten rodlets in each of the 25 boxes, note the number of defectives in each box, and draw up a frequency distribution and histogram of the data.

Compute the mean number of defectives per box and hence give an estimate of the proportion of defectives produced by the manufacturing process. Give two alternative 95 per cent confidence intervals for this estimate, obtained as follows:

(i) Using your estimated proportion, fit a Binomial Distribution to the data and test for goodness of fit. Compute the standard error of the proportion and use normal distribution theory to obtain an approximate confidence intervals for the proportion.

(ii) Using the mean number of defective per box as distribution mean fit a Poisson distribution to your data, and test for goodness of fit to see whether it is reasonable to accept the hypothesis that the data may be treated as a Poisson distribution. Test also whether the sample variance is in agreement with the expected value according to this hypothesis.

Assuming the hypothesis acceptable, obtain a confidence interval with the aid of Molina's Table II for your total count of defectives, by determining the mean count for the Poisson distribution having

(a) your observed count as its 2.5 percentile,

(b) your observed count as its 97.5 percentile.

Hence obtain the corresponding interval for the proportion.

Compare and contrast the two alternative confidence intervals, and state which you think is the more applicable in this case, giving reasons.

Using your estimated proportion of defectives in the process, and assuming that the lengths of the individual rodlets are normally distributed, estimate by means of normal area tables the population standard deviation σ for all the rodlets, given that the population mean is known to be 0.7500 inch, and that the width of the gauge is 0.7680 inch.

Choose one of your 25 boxes by a suitable random method (making a note of the method used) and measure each of the ten rodlets as accurately as possible, using a micrometer screw gauge. Compute the mean value and test whether it is significantly different from 0.7500 in.,

(i) using your estimate of σ from the total (large) sample,

(ii) using an independent estimate of the population standard deviation obtained from your measurements on the ten rodlets.

(See description in Ref. 2.)

(Intermediate, June, 1961)

5. The sample of ten limpet shells provided are a random sample of the species *Patella Vulgata* collected at a certain site. The data provided are measurements on a random sample of ten limpet shells of the species *Patella Aspera* collected at the same site on the same occasion. It is required to investigate the differences, if any, in both size and shape of the two species.

(i) Choose some form of base measurement which seems likely to be linearly related to the height measurement. Take the requisite measurements on your sample and carry out a regression analysis to test for linearity of the association.

(ii) If this appears to be satisfactory, investigate by means of analysis of covariance, how this regression line compares with that estimated by the corresponding set of measurements for the other species. Write a full report on your methods and conclusions.

(iii) Using your knowledge of multivariate analysis techniques, plan out a further investigation using two sets of base measurements, and write notes on this. Take the further measurements necessary, and proceed to carry out this analysis as far as time will permit.

(Secondary General, June, 1961)

6. You are provided with a random sample of ten limpets collected at a certain site and also with a sheet of measurements of a second random sample of limpets collected at the same site. One sample is of the species Patella *vulgata* and the other, Patella *aspera*.

Measure the lengths and heights of your sample of shells.

(*a*) Obtain from your sample the best estimate of the standard deviation of shell length for the population of these limpets at the site from which they were collected, and obtain 99 % confidence limits for mean shell length.

(*b*) Using your own data together with any relevant data from the sheet provided, determine whether there is a significant difference between the mean shell lengths of the two species.

(*c*) Plot a scatter diagram of height on length. Compute the least squares regression line of height on length and draw it on your scatter diagram. State whether you think the line appears to be a good fit and then test the significance of the regression coefficient. If significant, put a 99 % confidence band on the regression line.

(*d*) If any time remains, fit similarly a regression line to the corresponding data from the sheet for the other species of limpet. Compare the slopes of the two regression lines and comment on the result.

Write a report on what you have done, giving your conclusions clearly and fully.

(Intermediate, September, 1961)

7. The collection of balls provided are to be used for a certain game of bagatelle in which it is required that half the balls are able to circulate anywhere on the board and the other half are too large to do so. Perform the following tests to determine whether or not the true proportion of smaller balls is 0.5.

(*a*) Shake out a random sample of four, one after the other, and record the number of balls small enough to go through the gauge provided. Replace the sample, shake well, and take another sample in the same way. Repeat until 20 samples have been taken. Compute the total number of smaller balls recorded and hence the total estimated proportion.

(*b*) Using the Binomial approximation and assuming the true proportion to be 0.5, compute the expected frequencies of obtaining 0, 1, 2, 3, and 4 small balls in twenty repeated samples of four, and compare your observed frequencies with these by means of a χ^2-Goodness of Fit test.

(c) Assuming the total number of balls to be 100, so that 50 balls are small and 50 large, compute the exact expected frequencies using the Hypergeometric distribution. Would using these exact expected frequencies make any appreciable difference to the result of the test of significance carried out in (b)?

Note: At each stage of your work write a clear statement of your deductions and conclusions from the results obtained.

(Secondary General, June, 1962)

8. Boxes labelled A, B, and C each contain samples of five steel cylinders (spacing collars) manufactured by machines A, B, and C. Using the micrometer screw gauge provided, measure the height of each cylinder as accurately as possible. Simplify the data by some suitable coding and carry out an analysis of variance to obtain "Between machines" and "Within machines" components, and hence estimate the residual variation and test the significance of the difference between the sample means. What is the estimated standard error of a mean?

Give a 95 % confidence interval for the difference in mean values of machines A and B.

Give any further comments that may seem appropriate.

(Secondary General, June 1963)

9. You are provided with a copy of the first page of each of four papers from an international statistical journal, the articles being in English, French, German, and Italian respectively. For each copy in turn number each *complete* line of print and choose five of them by some random sampling method, making a clear statement explaining the method used. Count the number of letters in each word of any one line and hence calculate and tabulate the mean number of letters per word for each of the five sample lines for each of the four articles. (See note at end of question.)

Perform an analysis of variance on these data to determine whether there is a difference in mean word length per line between the four pages compared. If so, would it be reasonable to assume from this that there is a difference in mean word length per line between

(a) the complete papers
(b) the four languages under consideration?

Suggest any ways in which the experiment could be improved to obtain valid conclusions for (a) and (b).

(Note: Sometimes words are divided between the end of one line and the beginning of the next, so take care to observe, for the beginning of each line, whether the previous one ends with a hyphen. In all cases of a part of a divided word occurring at the beginning or end of a line of the sample, include the whole of the word in the sample unless *both* lines in which it occurs form part of the sample, in which case it should be included only in the line in which the larger number of letters occurs.)

(Secondary General, Sept. 1963)

10. (*a*) Practice a few shots with the "shove-halfpenny" catapult provided, then carry out a series of twelve shots using different tensions of the elastic band. For each shot note the initial position (x) of the chip on the scale and use the tape-measure to determine the distance y (inches) that the chip has travelled along the table from the scale point zero. Write a note stating in detail how you carry out this measurement.

(*b*) Compute the least squares linear regression of y on x and estimate from your regression line the position on the scale from which the chip should be catapulted in order to come to rest at a distance of 2 ft. from the zero mark.

(*c*) Draw a line across the scale at this point and carry out a series of ten shots from this line. Note the value of y for each shot; compute the mean $\bar{y}$ and estimate its standard error. Give a 95 % confidence interval for the population mean and note whether the specification distance of 2 ft. lies within this interval.

(*d*) Draw a chalk line across the table at a distance of 2 ft. from the edge and, after a little practice, carry out a series of ten "shove-halfpenny" shots "by hand" (i.e. without using the catapult). Measure the distance z (inches) that the chip has travelled along the table for each shot: compute the mean z and estimate its standard error. Give a 95 % confidence interval for the distribution mean and note whether the specification distance of 2 ft. lies within this interval.

(*e*) Test whether $\bar{y}$ is significantly different from $\bar{z}$. State any assumptions made in using your test and carry out a further test to see whether one of these assumptions is justified.

(*f*) Give a clear statement of your conclusions from this experiment. Comment on your results in (*b*) and give suggestions for improving on the estimated starting point.

(Secondary General, June 1964)

Appendix II

GROUP EXPERIMENT USING MATCHBOXES

In the experiment done by Sheffield students (Appendix I, No. 1) six different varieties of matches (A, B, C, D, E, F) were used, each box of the same price and having the same advertised content of 40 matches. Each student counted the contents of 3 boxes of each type, giving a total count of 60 boxes of each type.

For a simple group experiment to illustrate histograms and frequency distributions only two or three varieties need be considered and preferably boxes of each type should be purchased singly from separate shops or at different times.

The sort of variation to be expected between British makes of matches is illustrated by the data subsequently compiled from the Sheffield experiment, which can be tabulated as follows:

Matches analyses

Number of Matches	Coded number x	Type of Matches					
		A f	B f	C f	D f	E f	F f
22	− 18	1					
33	− 7		1				
35	− 5			1			
36	− 4	1	1				
37	− 3					1	
38	− 2		2	12		1	3
39	− 1	1	1	11		2	1
40	0	7	4	7	8	8	7
41	1	27	4	7	19	18	27
42	2	23	13	7	32	26	20
43	3		21	5	1	2	1
44	4		12	3		1	1
45	5		1	3			
46	6			2			
47	7			1			
48	8			1		1	
$\Sigma f_i x_i$		50	130	50	86	81	67
		0.83	2.17	0.83	1.43	1.35	1.12
Mean $\bar{x}$		40.83	42.17	40.83	41.43	41.35	41.12

It will be noted that computation is much simplified by considering the number *in excess* of the stated contents, which is equivalent to "coding about 40". The purpose of the investigation can be to determine which make of match is likely to be "best buy" when only one box of matches is to be purchased, and this experiment could be taken as an introductory one, with pupils of almost any age group, having no prior knowledge of statistics.

A simple framework of hooks, pins or some type of stand could be divised so that the actual matchbox lids can be built up into a histogram as the counting takes place. As a precaution, the number of matches in the box can be written on the lid as soon as the count has been made. The lid is then placed, sideways on, with suitable support from the framework, so that there will be no toppling when subsequent lids from boxes containing the same number are balanced on top.

Since one purpose of the experiment is to compare and contrast the shapes of the histograms for the different types, a pilot test is advisable on the types to be considered before giving this experiment to a class. For example, consider the situation were C and D to be chosen for such comparison, the dimensions of one lid being $2 \ 1/8'' \times 1 \ 1/2'' \times 5/8''$. In the case of D, the frequency of 32 would lead to a height of 48'' (approx 122 cm). This could be halved by a doubling-up to give a base of $4 \ 1/4''$, leading to a total base of reasonable length for this histogram of 17'' (approx 43 cm). This, however, would necessitate a considerably more inconvenient base span of almost 60'' (approx 152 cm) in the case of C.

This difficulty may to some extent be overcome by using the smaller type boxes such as the Swedish "Petite" (4 cm × 2.7 cm × 1 cm) if two or three types of identical dimensions can be found. This type of problem, however, illustrates my point concerning the desirability of careful planning and preliminary trials of such experimental work if maximum benefit is to be obtained.

Appendix III

LIST OF FURTHER EXPERIMENTS

Experimental Material	Statistical Concept	Reference No.
1. Green peas	Histograms	
	Frequency distribution	2, 3
2. Dried peas	Binomial distribution	2
3. Dice	Frequency distribution	
	Binomial distribution	2
4. Shove-halfpenny (coin-shoving)	Regression	
	Comparison of mean and variance	2, 3
5. Traffic survey	Poisson distribution	
	Negative exponential	2, 3
6. Model Factory	Quality Control	2
7. Roulette Wheel	Random sampling	
	Calibration of scale from distribution function	2, 3
8. Spacing Collars	Histograms	
	Random sampling	
	Confidence Intervals	2
9. Aspirins	Comparison of aspirin measurements, allowing for measuring accuracy. Comparison of aspirins from different bottles	2
10. Sparklers	Comparison of duration of sparkle for different varieties	2

6. Teaching probability in intermediate grades[1]

Arthur Engel

Stuttgart, West Germany

6.1. INTRODUCTION

Probability from K to 12 must be taught in four rounds. In this paper I will treat only the first and most important round, for by restricting myself I can offer considerable detail. But still this is far from a complete course as such a course would require a whole book. The reason for starting with grade 5 is simple: I have no teaching experience below that grade.

Let me first explain in some detail the aim of the First Round. One can best understand this aim by using an analogy with geometry.

We all think in geometrical terms and a significant part of mathematics is expressed in a geometric language. Geometric intuition directs our thoughts and it suggests new results. Geometry has always been a most fertile source of new ideas, and entire mathematical disciplines have sprung from it. This does not mean that we all are geometers. We use geometry not in the proper sense of the word (as a branch of mathematics) but as a way of thinking. We depend heavily on our eyes, and important ideas come to us by fiddling around with mental pictures and geometric diagrams.

There are other important ways of thinking; axiomatic thinking, algorithmic thinking, combinatorial thinking, and thinking in statistical terms. For applications, statistical thinking is an extremely valuable way of thinking. In the real world there is an unlimited number of probabilistic situations. The student should learn to regard probability not as a branch of mathematics, but as a way of looking at the real world. We teachers should use it constantly as motivation and inspiration, to direct our teaching and to suggest important mathematical results. Probability is second only to geometry in this respect.

What is the essence of statistical thinking? Although I am unable to predict the result of a single trial of an experiment, I can make "global" or average statements about what will happen "in the long run". So I adopt the following standpoint. I declare the individual case to be entirely devoid of interest and I replace my interest in the particular case by con-

[1] Approximately grades 5 to 7.

sideration of a great many cases which are copies of each other. I make average statements about the ensemble of these cases. What proportion of the cases go a certain way (or have a particular property)?

Why has probability not had the impact on mathematics that geometry has? Because we have a natural geometric intuition but no probabilistic intuition. The First Round aims at developing the intuitive background of probability. We can apply mathematics to the physical world only if we understand both mathematics and the physical world, and if we see the ties between the two. There are many ties between probability and the real world, and, what is more important, ties with the part of the real world accessible to the student in his everyday life. Therefore it is essential to develop the proper feeling for probability. The students get acquainted with random phenomena in many different settings through typical examples. If this intuitive background is missing, probability becomes a meaningless game, useless and dull, and the time wasted on it could be put to better use.

Let me summarize: I have a very ambitious goal. I do not want to teach formal theory in isolation for some short period of time. Rather, I want to change radically and permanently the thinking of the student. Such change can best be achieved if we start when the student is very young and his thinking habits have not yet become fixed. But this is not enough. To become a natural part of his thinking, probabilistic situations must be encountered continually. Hence the First Round—and later rounds also—must be completely integrated into the mathematics course to ensure a constant presence of probabilistic situations. For instance, in lower grades probability is completely absorbed into arithmetic, fractions, percentages, or whatever is done in these grades.

Now we turn to the First Round in which students learn thinking in statistical terms.

6.2. RANDOM DIGITS AND MONTE CARLO METHODS

6.2.1. *Random Digit Generators*

Students can get acquainted with random digit generators using different alphabets.

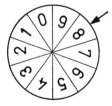

Fig. 6.1.

88

1. Here is a wheel of fortune. It is a *Laplace-wheel,* i.e. with congruent sectors. I spin it a million times and it will produce a long string of digits which can be called *decimal random digits.* Each student gets a list of 10,000 such digits.

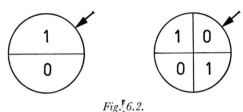

Fig. 6.2.

2. Here are two versions of a *Laplace-coin* (an L-coin) with faces 0 and 1. By flipping the coin many times I get a long string of *binary random digits.* Each student gets a list of 5,000.

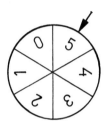

Fig. 6.3.

3. Here is an L-die. On a typical die relabel face "6" and call it "0". The die can be used to generate random digits in base 6. Each student is given a block of 5,000 digits.

Now these digits are explored with 30 or more students in a class. You can make extremely detailed investigations in a short time. In individual instruction the help of a computer would be very useful. The following is found by teamwork:

(a) All digits, all pairs of digits, all triples of digits appear with equal frequency.

(b) Equal frequency of longer blocks of digits is checked only for binary digits.

(c) *Lumping, Decimation, Cartesian Products.* Take decimal random digits, replace even digits by 0 and odd digits by 1, and you get the output of a coin. Strike digits 6, 7, 8, 9 and you get the output of a die.

The digits are most frequently used in blocks. Suppose that a random device uses an alphabet of q digits. Each pair of digits can be considered to

89

be one digit in a new alphabet with q^2 digits. Similarly for longer blocks. By lumping, decimation and by forming Cartesian Products any wheel can simulate any other wheel.

(*d*) From the equal frequency of all blocks of equal length one can deduce some important consequences. For instance (with decimal digits):

blocks of length two <37 appear with frequency 37/100 (37 in a 100).
blocks of length three <144 appear with frequency 144/1000 (144 in a 1000).

(*e*) If one looks at digits following even digits, following odd digits, following the digit 0 etc. one will find that the random devices have *no memory*. Knowing the present state does not help in predicting future.

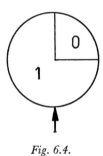

Fig. 6.4.

4. This binary wheel turns out a 0–1 sequence. You may call it a *lopsided coin* or simply a coin. A symmetric coin will always be referred to as an L-coin to stress that it is a special coin while a lopsided coin is an ordinary coin. It is interesting to note that this particular coin can be imitated by an L-coin. Take blocks of length two and use the mapping $00 \to 0$, $01 \to 1$, $10 \to 1$, $11 \to 1$. The coin can also be imitated with an L-die or decimal L-generator by suitable lumping or decimation. By considering numerals following 0's and 1's it is again found that a lopsided coin has no memory.

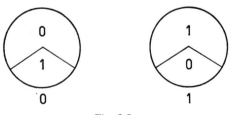

Fig. 6.5.

5. Now we turn to *Markov-coins*, i.e. wheels with memory. Consider these coupled spinners. Start with any one of the two wheels and spin it. The

result of the spin names the spinner to be used for the next spin. Below is the outcome of a sequence of 50 spins.

000000000000000 11 0 111 0 111 0 111111

00000 11111 0000 1 00 11 0 1 0

The result is a 0–1 sequence with equal long run frequency for both digits. But strong local clustering of equal digits is clearly visible. There is a deficiency of runs.

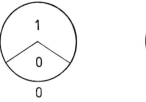

Fig. 6.6.

When these coupled spinners are used, they have an opposite effect. They generate a sequence that looks "pretty random". Both digits are equally frequent. Below is an example of sequence of length 50:

11011001010101100110101101010101100100100110010110

But, there are too many short runs. This is not optically apparent to a child since he does not expect long runs anyway. You get something like this if a student tries to forge outcomes of coin flipping. For both pairs of spinners above knowledge of the present state helps a lot in predicting future but knowledge of the past gives no additional advantage.

Now the student must be shown that the real world is a vast collection of interconnected random digit generators, producing long sequences of digits, mostly of a very complicated structure. Here are some examples:

(*a*) Look out of the window and watch people passing by. Use this coding to record your observations: Female→0, Male→1. Ignore couples. A record might start like this:

11000011101111001110...

(*b*) Record cars passing by. Use this coding: GM-car→1, any other car→0. You might get this sequence:

1000000000101010110010110110000000001...

(*c*) At the end of each day record the weather for that day. Use this coding: dry→0, wet→1. You might get this record:

00001110010001111011110000000...

91

(*d*) Open the Bible and replace each vowel by 0 and each consonant by 1. The binary sequence produced is very complicated, and in this case not only the present but also the past influence future.

int hebegi nni ngGodcr e at edth eheavenandtheeart h...
011101010110111 0111001011101001010111000111...

(*e*) Here are the daily numbers of deaths in Stuttgart, starting January 1, 1962:

14, 22, 12, 19, 11, 21, 14, 22, 16, 13, 21, 15, 20, 17, 24, 14, 26, 16,

23, 14, 21, 18, 14, 23, 19, 18, 18, 20, 15, 21.

(*f*) In fact the record of a long repetition of any experiment or observation is a string of digits in some alphabet.

After a dozen of similar examples an important idea should begin to emerge: The student should recognize that instead of a real process, it might be sufficient to study the output of some coin or other random device. Now it is time to start with Monte Carlo Simulation.

6.2.2. *Monte Carlo Simulation*

The student should be encouraged to learn the art of simulation because it is important in its own right and because this is the most natural place. You solve a problem by Monte Carlo methods if it is beyond your analytical skills and at this stage almost every interesting problem is beyond the analytical skills of the student. But the most important reason is this: *It is the best means to develop the intuitive background of probability and to learn to think in statistical terms.* The student can get acquainted with many typical problems of probability and he is able to solve them all by simulation. He should realize that with a table of random digits he can imitate any random phenomenon. Study of the real phenomenon can be replaced by a study of the table which is simpler and cheaper. Later he will discover that some problems can also be solved by reasoning. This will be a great step forward. Simulation gives him numbers, but no insights. Reasoning will give both numbers and insight. As reasoning power is developed more and more, it will replace simulation step by step.

6.2.3. *Examples of Pure Simulation*

As the student proceeds he should be asked to find probabilities, expectations and probability distributions by simulation. He should often be asked to perform an experiment "*at random*". This simply means he should use his table of (uniformly) random digits. Below I treat some examples in detail to show the style of presentation which is appropriate at this early stage. Random walk problems are the most important and the most instructive, but they will be treated later. Another extremely versatile example uses balls put at random into cells. A good example to start with is the "raisins in cookies" problem. I will use A. Rényi's version of the problem in the following example.

Example 1. Production of High Quality Bottles.—Suppose you have 100 pounds of molten glass and that you want to make 100 bottles of one pound each. In this molten glass there are 100 small solid particles, called "stones", distributed at random. If such a stone gets into the material of a bottle, that bottle is useless and must be discarded. How many bottles will be good?

To simulate the problem, the big square in the figure can represent all of the liquid glass and the 100 small cells represent the bottles. Now we start mixing 100 stones into the glass by using random digits. Every student can simulate one or two production runs by taking 100 pairs of decimal random digits from his private table, for instance:

47	82	24	68	78	06	33	70	36	09
42	32	22	38	70	74	73	96	46	96
34	52	00	82	01	31	18	57	16	48
94	22	58	75	82	68	68	04	79	81
67	69	23	71	74	99	16	08	68	31
85	14	35	61	76	84	07	84	50	62
77	74	23	91	44	94	49	37	08	92
56	99	50	05	18	05	84	91	91	94
05	41	26	17	37	45	22	82	20	01
28	37	78	07	52	91	25	32	18	61

This means that the first stone goes in cell (4, 7), the second stone in cell (8, 2) and so on. We get the following distribution.

stones/bottle	0	1	2	3	>3
bottles	37	39	14	7	3

By pooling their results, students come close to the theoretical distribution.

stones/bottle	0	1	2	3	>3
bottles	36.6	37.0	18.4	6.1	1.9

I predict this table by writing it in advance on the back of the blackboard.

In a way, this is an easy problem. A year later the student can write down the answer $(1 - \frac{1}{100})^{100} \approx 0.366$ for the fraction of good bottles, but

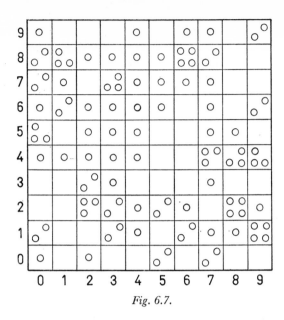

Fig. 6.7.

he cannot evaluate it. What we did was to find this number approximately by a Monte Carlo Method. The Monte Carlo Method belongs to probability, but even more to numerical mathematics.

I mention some related problems:

(a) In 100 days 300 cargo ships arrive in a certain harbor. Cargo ships do not run according to a fixed schedule. They arrive at random, but at an average rate of 3/day. It is important to know the distribution of arrivals: i.e. how frequently 0, 1, 2, 3, ... ships will arrive on a single day so that questions of practical importance, like total waiting time, can be answered. The arrival of the ships can be simulated by 300 pairs of random digits e.g.: 64 71 68 49 33 35 06 12 ... These represent days on which the ships arrive. Again I predict the distribution in advance.

(b) A biologist takes from a liquid 100 small samples of equal volume. One-half of the samples are free of bacteria. How many bacteria are there in these 100 samples? Again use the 100 cells of Figure 6.7 at random, until one-half of the cells is left empty. You will find that on the average 69 (100 ln 2) bacteria are present.

(c) Ten hunters, all perfect shots, are waiting for ducks to fly by. When a flock of ten ducks flies overhead, the hunters fire at the same time, but each chooses his target at random. How many ducks escape on the average if this experiment is repeated many times?

The ducks in each flock are numbered 0 to 9. Each student takes a string of 10 consecutive random digits in base 10. The missing digits can represent

94

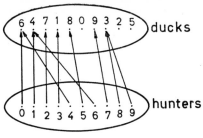

Fig. 6.8.

escaping ducks. It is found that 3.5 ducks on the average escape. A year later this number, $10(1 - \frac{1}{10})^{10}$ can be found by calculation.

One simulation of the duck experiment with outcome 6471684933 is shown in Figure 6.8. It is an arrow diagram of the function "fires at". Here $0 \rightarrow 6$ means: hunter number 0 fires at duck number 6.

(*d*) In the next simulation problem, the student must use 10,000 random digits. It is the famous *newsboy problem* (*inventory problem*): A newsboy has an average of 10 customers a day. He buys each paper for 2 dimes and sells them for 3 dimes. Unsold papers are a total loss to him. How many papers should he buy per day to maximize his profit over the long run?

We assume that customers arrive at random, with an intensity of 10/day. To simulate this situation we draw for each day a batch of 100 random digits. We use the zero's in the batch to represent the customers arriving on that particular day. It is handy if the digit 0 appears in red in the table for easy spotting. In simulating 100 days we use up 10,000 random digits. Here for example are the numbers of customers for 25 successive days (RAND-Table, p. 333):

$$9, 11, 10, 8, 8, 15, 9, 5, 13, 8, 8, 12, 12,$$

$$10, 8, 6, 13, 8, 12, 12, 9, 10, 17, 9, 10.$$

Assuming inventory size 8, 9, 10, 11 we get the total profits 185, 186, 175, 151. The optimal daily stock size seems to be 9. This is indeed the case, though 25 days are not enough to prove it with any certainty.

Example 2. A Percolation Problem.—At the lattice points of the plane, trees of an infinite orchard grow. Suppose that the tree at the origin gets sick and transmits the disease to one of its four neighbors with fixed probability p. The same is true for every sick tree.

The students can be told that one tree gets sick and starts an epidemic. Every sick tree transmits the disease at random with some fixed intensity p.

Suppose that $p=0.36$. Then for each healthy neighbor of a sick tree we pick a pair of decimal random digits. If this pair is <36 the neighbor gets infected, if the pair is ≥ 36 it stays healthy. The students should experiment to discover an interesting phenomenon. With $p<0.5$ (mild infection) the epidemic always dies out (local epidemic). But with $p>0.5$ (severe infection) the epidemic sometimes spreads to infinity (global epidemic). The critical intensity seems to be $1/2$, but to my knowledge no one has proved it as yet.

This example has one serious drawback. It is not easy to simulate and students get mixed up and make mistakes. The next example is far easier to simulate.

Example 3. Branching Processes.—(*a*) *Raising a critical tree.* Start by considering a tree stem one inch high and use random digits in the alphabet $\{0, 1, 2\}$. Use this coding: $0\rightarrow$stem dies, $1\rightarrow$stem grows one inch higher, $2\rightarrow$stem gets two branches of one inch each. Criticality is obvious to the student. If one generation has n branches, the next one has on the average

$$\frac{n}{3}\cdot 0+\frac{n}{3}\cdot 1+\frac{n}{3}\cdot 2=n,$$

i.e. the same number of branches. The generating function is

$$f(x) = \tfrac{1}{3}+\tfrac{1}{3}x+\tfrac{1}{3}x^2.$$

From the theory of branching processes follows that the probability of extinction is the smallest positive root of $f(x)=x$. This yields $x^2-2x+1=0$, $(x-1)^2=0$, $x=1$. Hence the tree dies with certainty, but the average height is infinite.

(*b*) *Raising a supercritical tree.* Start with a stem one inch high and use random digits with alphabet $\{0, 1, 2, 3\}$. Use this coding: $0\rightarrow$stem dies, $1\rightarrow$stem grows one inch higher, 2 or $3\rightarrow$stem gets two branches of one inch each. Supercriticality is obvious. If one generation has n branches, the next one has on the average the following number of branches:

$$\frac{n}{4}\cdot 0+\frac{n}{4}\cdot 1+\frac{n}{2}\cdot 2=\frac{5}{4}\cdot n$$

From the generating function

$$f(x)=\frac{1}{4}+\frac{x}{4}+\frac{x^2}{2}$$

we get for the probability of extinction

$$f(x)=x,\ 2x^2-3x+1=0,\ (x-1)\,(x-\tfrac{1}{2})=0.$$

96

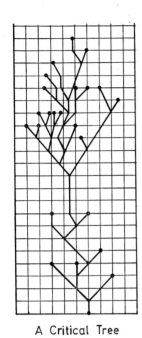

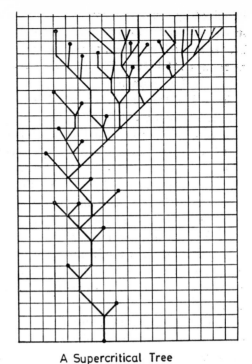

A Critical Tree   A Supercritical Tree

Fig. 6.9.

The smallest positive root is $\frac{1}{2}$. Hence the trees die eventually with probability $\frac{1}{2}$.

Needless to say these calculations are for senior high school. Figure 6.9 shows a critical and a supercritical tree. The critical tree died after 22 generations. The supercritical tree has 14 live branches after 25 generations. It could still die, but the probability is slim, $(\frac{1}{2})^{14}$.

Students like to raise random trees, especially critical trees. Subcritical trees are not exciting, because they die too soon. Supercritical trees are somewhat more exciting. They either die rapidly or they mushroom to gigantic dimensions and never die. But critical trees can keep you in suspense. Many die rapidly, but some linger on, sometimes on the verge of extinction, and assume strange and fascinating shapes.

Besides Monte Carlo simulation, the student should learn the important and completely different use of random digits in unbiased sampling.

6.2.4. Unbiased Sampling

The students should get acquainted with the classical "capture–recapture" method of estimating the size of a population. Here is an example that can be solved by common sense: On a small island the only inhabitants are a species of beetles living on the ground. A biologist brings 200 marked beetles and releases them to mingle with the native beetles. The next day he retraps 144 beetles, 120 unmarked and 24 marked. Estimate the size of the original population.

Since $\frac{1}{6}$ of the sample is marked, we assume that about $\frac{1}{6}$ of the whole population is marked. Hence the total population is about 1200 and originally there were about 1000 beetles on the island.

It is obvious to the student that for accurate results the marked beetles must be mixed uniformly all over the island in one day. The biologist can help to accomplish this by releasing them at many different spots. If he dumps them in one place the beetles will perform independent random walks. At each obstacle they will change course. If the island is long and narrow they will perform a symmetric random walk on a line with two reflecting barriers. If the island is not narrow we have a random walk in the plane with a reflecting boundary. It is instructive to study this slow diffusion of the beetles by Monte Carlo simulation. I will treat this problem later.

Simulation is important here if one is to see the reliability of the estimate even though in this particular case, simulation is time consuming. The students can be given jars with many small black balls. The number of the balls is known only to the teacher. Students add 200 red balls of the same size, mix well and draw a sample of 144 balls. The necessity of thorough mixing is again obvious to get reliable estimates.

But students are completely unaware that populations, as a rule, are not well mixed. That there is often lumpiness in the distribution of various characteristics: local irregular clustering of properties. To avoid such clustering, populations should be well mixed like balls in an urn, before drawing a sample. Casual selection of a sample can introduce a bias, i.e. a property can be over-represented or under-represented in the sample as compared to its importance in the whole population. This can be shown dramatically by a simple example. I ask 5th graders from Stuttgart this question: Consider all of the children in Stuttgart. Do you suppose that there are more boys or more girls among the children? (In Germany we have in general no co-education.) Most of the children have no opinion because they have never thought about this question. Some think there are more boys, others that there are more girls, and some think the numbers are about equal. Next I tell the class: Since you represent a sample of all Stuttgart families, let us see how many boys and girls there are in your families altogether. In a class of 27 boys I got this amazing result:

boys 56, girls 27

In another class of 36 boys I got:

boys 71, girls 34

What conclusion can we draw? Are there roughly twice as many boys as girls in Stuttgart? Think of the consequences if this were true. In a girl's school the results will be biased the other way around. We must not count ourselves.

Of course my samples are strongly biased. They are samples from those families which have a boy, 10 years old.

Students wonder how to draw an unbiased sample. They can learn to answer this question if they are taught how to select impartially one element from a finite set. This is simple: *label the elements of the set by a code and select the code number by an L-selector.* Suppose that a coin is used as selector, and that there are 32 students in the class. If one labels the students by a binary code (there are $2^5 = 32$ code words of length five), then one must use code length 5. I flip a coin 5 times and I get for example 10110. This is the code number of the selected student. With a die only two throws are usually needed, on the average 2.25. There are selectors with different alphabets. This leads to number systems in different bases.

As least a try should be made to label the elements of an infinite set. This is highly instructive. Take a segment of length 1. How do you select a point on this segment "at random"? Start tossing a coin. Let each flip eliminate one-half of the remaining segment according to this rule: $0 \rightarrow$ choose left half, $1 \rightarrow$ choose right half (endpoints are always included). As an example, a sequence of tosses starting with $x = .101001\ldots$ determines a point somewhere in the closed innermost interval of Figure 6.10. A finite block with d digits selects an interval of length $(\frac{1}{2})^d$. To select a point one must perform an infinite number of tosses. Such an infinite binary block determines a sequence of nested intervals and is the name of a point or real number. A point in the plane is best located by using two coins and a point in space by three coins.

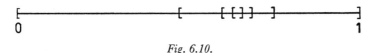

Fig. 6.10.

By fixing some digits, one determines subsets of the segment called "cylinder sets". Cylinder sets could become important only in senior high school. Here is a simple example: What can be said about the location of a point x if in its binary expansion a) the 1th digit is 1 b) the 2nd digit is 1 c) the first digit is 1 and the 3rd digit is 0?

99

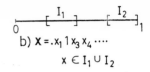

a) X = .1 $x_2 x_3 x_4$ ····

X ∈ I

b) X = .x_1 1 $x_3 x_4$ ····

X ∈ I_1 ∪ I_2

c) X = .1 x_2 0 x_4 ····

X ∈ I_1 ∪ I_2

Fig. 6.11.

6.2.5. Transition from Simulation to Reasoning

Now I turn to a problem which is awkward for simulation, but easy to solve by reasoning. In fact, the analytic approach is so obvious that even a 10 year old will think of it without much explicit help. In preceding lessons students made many selections and eliminations by performing sequences of coin tossing. This is excellent preparation for the problems to come. At this point eliminations by coin tossing are replaced by mental eliminations.

Example 1.—I have a boy in the 5th grade who has 5 brothers and no sisters. In our city there are 6400 families with 6 children. How many have 6 boys?

It is assumed that children are generated by spinning the L-generator in Figure 6.12. To simulate the problem, I would have to take 6400 blocks of 6 random digits (in any even base) and count the odd blocks. We are interested in a rare event, and rare events are difficult to simulate. It requires an excessive amount of work. This forces upon us an analytic solution.

Consider 6400 couples that start generating families of 6 children. On the first spin about 3200 are eliminated from the race for a 6-boy family, because they end up with a girl. On each successive spin, about one-half

Fig. 6.12.

100

of the remaining couples are eliminated. After 6 spins 100 couples remain with an all boy family. Here is a sieve diagram which displays the situation:

$$6{,}400 \xrightarrow{\frac{1}{2}} 3{,}200 \xrightarrow{\frac{1}{2}} 1{,}600 \xrightarrow{\frac{1}{2}} 800 \xrightarrow{\frac{1}{2}} 400 \xrightarrow{\frac{1}{2}} 200 \xrightarrow{\frac{1}{2}} 100$$

with downward arrows labeled 0 leading to $3{,}200 \quad 1{,}600 \quad 800 \quad 400 \quad 200 \quad 100$

In the same way the whole distribution of sexes among 6,400 families of 6 can be found. A sequence of 6 spins can be interpreted as a random walk on the lattice in figure 6.13. Because of the large numbers involved this can be handled as a deterministic walk. At each crossing, approximate splitting in two can be replaced by exact splitting in two.

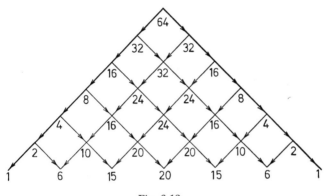

Fig. 6.13.

From now on problems are solved by reasoning, but in crude ways, since students cannot yet operate with fractions. Most of the problems are also solved by simulation, to check the computation and to see the fluctuations.

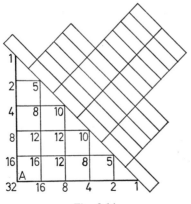

Fig. 6.14.

101

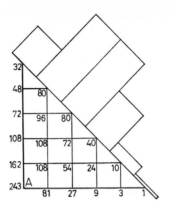

Fig. 6.15.

This approach is very effective in promoting statistical thinking. Instead of one stochastic process we consider a great number of processes which are copies of each other, evolving simultaneously or sequentially. Each process can be pictured by an indicator particle performing a random walk. Students make "global" or average statements about what will happen to these particles. The particles can be thought of as flowing in a network.

Example 2. Northeast Walks.—Figure 6.14 shows a street map. Suppose 32 people start at point A and walk to the north or east. At each crossing one-half goes to the east and the other half goes to the north. How many people arrive at the terminal crossings?

This deterministic problem is solved by simple mental arithmetic. Now we let 32 people walk at random through the maze, directed by an L-coin. Because of small numbers the resulting distribution can differ appreciably from the result of the deterministic walk. This difference can be cut down by increasing the number of walkers to 320 or by averaging the results of all students in the class.

Consider 234 ($=3^5$) people starting at point A. At each crossing 1/3 go east and 2/3 go north. The result is a skew distribution, Figure 6.15. Again these people are sent through the maze by a lopsided coin.

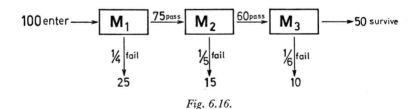

Fig. 6.16.

102

For each person arriving at a crossing students should put down a poker chip at that crossing. The result will be a histogram.

Following are some examples from the broad area of *reliability* theory. In these examples various devices either fail or survive during some operation (or some fixed interval of time). This is the first and most primitive round of reliability theory. Three more rounds will follow: in grade 7, in grade 8 in connection with the formal development of Boolean Algebra, and in grade 11 in connection with the exponential distribution.

Example 3.—A factory produces widgets. Before a widget is finished it must pass through three machines M_1, M_2, M_3. In M_1 $\frac{1}{4}$ of all widgets entering break and must be discarded. In M_2 $\frac{1}{3}$ breaks and in M_3 $\frac{1}{6}$ breaks. How many of 100 widgets survive the processing by all three machines?

Figure 6.16 shows the solution. Of course 50 is only an average value over many production runs. After all, the machines are random devices without memory. The only way to appraise fluctuations is by simulation.

Example 4. Quality Control.—The factory in example 3 produces 100,000 widgets per year. About 10,000 of these are defective. An inspector controlling quality overlooks about one out of ten defectives. How many defective widgets are sold to customers if there are 0, 1, 2, 3, 4 inspectors working independently of each other, each inspecting all widgets? An inspector has an annual wage of 12,000 dollars. Delivering a defective widget costs the factory 1, 1.2, 10, 13, 100, 130, 1000, 1500 dollars fine. How many inspectors should be employed in each of these cases? Here are the solutions:

number of inspectors	0	1	2	3	4
numbers of defectives passing inspection	10,000	1,000	100	10	1

The number of inspectors to be employed is 0, 0 or better 1, 1, 2, 2, 3, 3, 4.

Example 5.—A rocket has three stages. The first stage fails once in 6 times, the second once in 5 times, and the third once in 4 times. How many of 100 launches will be successful? (This is identical with example 3.)

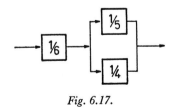

Fig. 6.17.

103

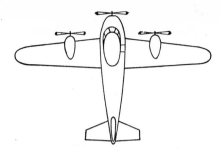

Fig. 6.18.

Example 6.—Certain electrical devices are made of three parts, which are defective and block current with respective frequencies $\frac{1}{6}$, $\frac{1}{5}$, $\frac{1}{4}$. The parts are connected as in Figure 6.17. How many out of 600 devices will fail to transmit current?

600/6 = 100 will fail at the entrance. Of the remaining 500 about 500/5 = 100 will fail on upper path, and of these 100/4 = 25 will also fail on lower path. Hence 100 + 25 = 125 devices will be defective.

Example 7.—Propeller driven cargo planes fly regularly over the Atlantic. Some fail and plunge into the ocean.

(*a*) The plane in Figure 6.18 has three engines. Either the main engine in the center or the side engines working together can keep the plane in the air. A main engine fails once in 200 flights. An auxiliary engine fails once in 10 flights. How many planes will go down in 20,000 flights?

Figure 6.19 shows the corresponding reliability diagram. In 19,900 out of 20,000 flights the main engine is working and these planes make the trip. Let us look at the 100 flights where the main engine fails. Of these 100/10 = 10 will go down because the left engine will fail. Of the remaining 90 planes 90/10 = 9 will go down because of the right engine. Altogether about 19 planes will be lost.

The plane in Figure 6.20 has four equally reliable engines, each of which fails once in 10 flights. The plane can be kept in the air

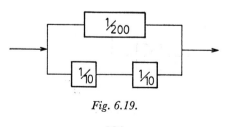

Fig. 6.19.

104

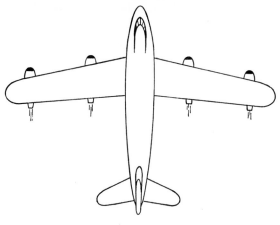

Fig. 6.20.

(*b*) by any two engines
(*c*) by any one engine on each side
(*d*) by any two symmetrically located engines.

How many planes will go down in 10,000 flights? Figure 6.21 shows the reliability diagrams for these three cases. By simple arithmetic one finds for the numbers of lost planes

$$(b) \ 37 \quad (c) \ 99 \quad (d) \ 361.$$

6.3. COMBINATORIAL THEORY FOR ELEMENTARY GRADES

6.3.1. *Introduction*

Combinatorial theory is a rapidly growing area with an amazing number of applications in diverse fields of pure and applied mathematics. Only a small part of the theory is indispensable for probability and fortunately this part is also very simple and can be covered in grade 6.

One can also teach combinatorial theory for its own sake or for use with nonprobabilistic applications. It is a fascinating and very difficult branch

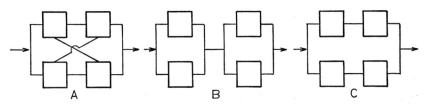

Fig. 6.21.

of mathematics. Selected topics can be treated later in two rounds: one round in grades 9–10 and another in grades 11–12. Some modern algebra is indispensable. In fact, most topics can be absorbed into an abstract algebra course as motivating and illustrative examples.

In early grades combinatorics should be taught in three rounds.

Round I (*age 7–10*).—Unsystematic counting by brute force. Children perform multistage experiments and they make exhaustive lists of all cases by which an event may happen or fail. The experiments deal with deterministic or stochastic situations in which they make a sequence of decisions. In a stochastic experiment the decisions are made by a random device. Through involvement in many combinatorial situations the children should gain a thorough familiarity with all important combinatorial problems.

Round II (*age 10–11*).—Outcome sets become huge by now and counting is done by the *RULE OF SUM*

$$A \cap B = \varnothing \Rightarrow \mathcal{N}(A \cup B) = \mathcal{N}(A) + \mathcal{N}(B)$$

and the *PRODUCT RULE*

$$\mathcal{N}(A \times B) = \mathcal{N}(A) \cdot \mathcal{N}(B),$$

$\mathcal{N}$ being the counting function assigning to each set its cardinal.

Round III (*age 11–12*).—Counting problems leading to Pascal numbers (binomial coefficients).

Combinatorial theory belongs to the theory of finite sets. Set theoretic terminology and its probabilistic counterpart should be used immediately and extensively. The most important teaching aids at this age level are pictures and graphs, because children may not yet reason well without some visual aid. I present some examples in the following without the visual aids since they take up too much space.

6.3.2. *Round I. Brute Force Counting*

This round consists of a long sequence of loosely connected examples. The aim of these examples is to create intuitive familiarity, to introduce terminology, and to develop statistical thinking. The first example I will treat in some detail.

Example 1.—An electric switch can be in one of two states: "ON" or "OFF". We denote these states by "1" and "0" (Figure 6.22). Now take a system of 2, 3, 4 switches. Make a list of all possible states.

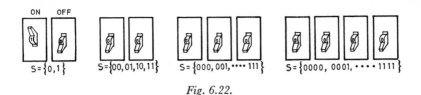

$S = \{0,1\}$ $S = \{00,01,10,11\}$ $S = \{000, 001, \cdots\cdots 111\}$ $S = \{0000, 0001, \cdots\cdots 1111\}$

Fig. 6.22.

Systems with 1, 2, 3 or 4 switches have $2, 2^2, 2^3, 2^4$ states respectively. The students are asked to guess the number of states for a system with 5, 6, 7, ... switches. Suppose one has a complete list of all states for a 3-switch system. How can we construct a complete list for a 4-switch system?

0000	1000
0001	1001
0010	1010
0011	1011
0100	1100
0101	1101
0110	1110
0111	1111

Fig. 6.23.

In front of each 3-state we can attach either the digit 0, or we can attach the digit 1 (Figure 6.23). In this way one gets all possible 4-states exactly once. Hence each additional switch doubles the number of possible states.

This kind of inductive construction process should be used whenever possible. Here is another example: Start with all permutations of 3 elements:

$$123, 132, 213, 231, 312, 321$$

How can we construct a list of all permutations of 4 elements? For each of these permutations we can form four others by inserting the number 4 in all possible places; e.g. 123 generates 4123, 1423, 1243, 1234. All permutations of four elements are obtained in this manner and no permutation is obtained more than once. General formulations using variables, like $p_n = n \cdot p_{n-1}$, are not well understood at this age. The students learn by numerical examples.

Now states can be classified according to digit sum, i.e. number of lamps burning. One gets the following:

$$
\begin{array}{ccccccccc}
 & & & 1 & & 1 & & & \\
 & & 1 & & 2 & & 1 & & \\
 & 1 & & 3 & & 3 & & 1 & \\
1 & & 4 & & 6 & & 4 & & 1 \\
\end{array}
$$

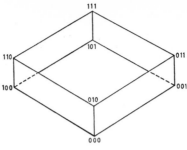

Fig. 6.24.

Take a 4-switch system. For switch number i an indicator variable I_i can be introduced, indicating the state of the switch. $I_i = 1$ means switch number i is on, and $I_i = 0$ means switch number i is off. By means of these indicators and their sum $B = I_1 + I_2 + I_3 + I_4$ various events of the state space can be defined and their elements counted. A student can for instance name (or count) all elements of these events:

$$I_3 = 0,\ I_1 I_2 = 1,\ I_1 + I_3 = 0,\ I_1 + I_4 < 2,\ I_1 - I_2 = 0,\ I_1 - I_2 = 1,\ I_1 I_2 = I_3 I_4,$$
$$(I_1 + I_2)\,(I_2 + I_3) = 0,\ I_1 B = 1,\ B = 3,\ B = 5,\ 1 \leqslant B \leqslant 4,\ \text{etc.}$$

In a short time students will solve dozens of these examples mentally.

Next the student should be handed a system of switches to play with. If a student starts playing the system makes transitions through a sequence of states. This can be pictured as a random walk of an indicator particle on a cube (Figure 6.24). For young children the indicator particle is described as a beetle and not some conceptual particle moving in an abstract phase space.

After some play the student starts in state 000 by putting a penny (beetle) on the corresponding vertex of the cube. To make a random walk he can use a digit generator with alphabet $\{1, 2, 3\}$. Suppose he generates the following sequence of digits:

23313 2322331 231 2121311112221 222322221 133111311113231

Digit 1 (2, 3) means that the state of the 1th (2nd, 3rd) switch changes. The walk is over when the beetle reaches state 111. The above sequence of random digits gives 6 walks:

000→010→011→010→110→111
000→010→011→001→011→010→011→111
000→010→011→111
000→010→110→100→000→001→101→001→101→001→011→001→
  →011→111

$000 \rightarrow 010 \rightarrow 000 \rightarrow 010 \rightarrow 011 \rightarrow 001 \rightarrow 010 \rightarrow 001 \rightarrow 011 \rightarrow 111$
$000 \rightarrow 100 \rightarrow 101 \rightarrow 100 \rightarrow 000 \rightarrow 100 \rightarrow 000 \rightarrow 001 \rightarrow 101 \rightarrow 001 \rightarrow 101 \rightarrow 001 \rightarrow$
$\rightarrow 000 \rightarrow 010 \rightarrow 011 \rightarrow 111$

The mean length of these 6 walks is 8.67. The expectation which is 10 will be found in grade 7.

Dozens of simple examples should be treated in the same spirit. By solving such problems the student will become familiar with some topics of central importance, e.g.

(*a*) sequential decision making and sequential counting, leading to tree diagrams,

(*b*) cartesian products: a hookup of several simple experiments is a new compound experiment,

(*c*) the sorting process, partitions and cross partitions, i.e. classification according to one or several categories,

(*d*) partitions of a set S induced by functions $X, Y, Z, ...$, defined on S,

(*e*) combinatorial investigation of strings of digits produced by random digit generators,

(*f*) distributions of sums of random variables.

Each problem should be reasoned out anew. Do not rush to get to rules or general principles!

Example 2.—Sequential decision making. At this point students are to learn the influence of previous decisions on subsequent ones. They begin to learn to recognize the situations where the product rule is applicable. Some suggestions follow:

Fig. 6.25.

(*a*) Here is a flag. Color its stripes with 3 colors (red, blue, and white) by using each color exactly once. In coloring, the student has to make a

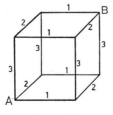

Fig. 6.26.

109

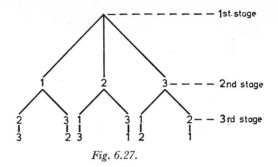

Fig. 6.27.

sequence of 3 decisions. At the 1st (2nd and 3rd) decision there are 3(2, 1) choices available.

(*b*) Think about a cube made of wire. A beetle in A wants to get to B in the shortest possible way by crawling along the edges of the cube. This is simply another version of problem *a*.

On its way the beetle has to make a sequence of 3 decisions. This can be pictured by a 3-stage decision tree (Figure 6.27). The important point to stress is this: *The number of choices available at each stage does not depend on decisions made at previous stages.*

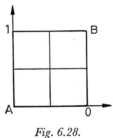

Fig. 6.28.

(*c*) Here is a very small street map. Suppose that you want to go from *A* to *B* by going EAST (0) or NORTH (1) only. You have to make a se-

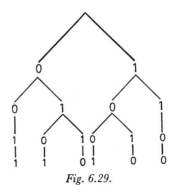

Fig. 6.29.

110

quence of 4 decisions. Figure 6.29 shows the decision tree in a binary code. Here the number of choices available at stage 3 does *depend on previous decisions*.

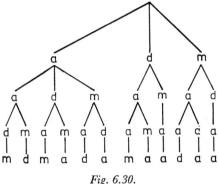

Fig. 6.30.

(*d*) Rearrange the letters of the word "adam" in all possible ways. Figure 6.30 shows the corresponding tree. The number of choices available at stage 2 and at stage 3 depends upon previous decisions. But in rearranging the letters of the word "Abel" the number of choices at each stage is independent of previous decisions. Draw a tree for "Abel". Explain the reason for the difference.

(*e*) You have two different coins a, b and you want to put them into four boxes. There are two decisions to be made and four choices for each decision. Make a list of all possible distributions (Figure 6.31).

(*f*) Next, if the two coins in (*e*) are copies of each other, list all possible distributions (Figure 6.32).

ab			
	ab		
		ab	
			ab
a	b		
a		b	
a			b
b	a		
b		a	
b			a
	a	b	
	a		b
	b	a	
	b		a
		a	b
		b	a

Fig. 6.31.

111

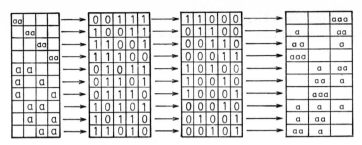

Fig. 6.32, 33.

(g) Three coins, which are copies of each other, are put into three boxes List all possible cases (Figure 6.33). If we draw a tree for case (e) we will find that its subtrees starting at any level are copies of each other. In (f) and (g) this is not the case. The equal number of cases in (f) and (g) is no coincidence. By a suitable coding these two examples become identical. We use this coding: coin → 0, separating wall between neighboring boxes → 1. By this coding each case in (f) is coded into a binary number with 2 zero's and 3 one's, while each case in (g) translates into a binary number with 2 one's and 3 zero's.

Example 3.—Ordered samples can also be viewed as functions (Bourbaki). For counting purposes this point of view is not good, at least not for young children. But it provides some more examples for the function concept. This is reason enough to give some attention to this point of view, but a systematic treatment in this vein should be postponed for the combinatorial round in grades 9–10.

Suppose that some books are to be given to a set of children under various restrictions.

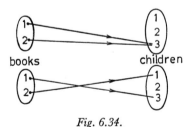

Fig. 6.34.

(a) Two books {1, 2} are given to three children {1, 2, 3}. In Figure 6.34 are two possible assignments. Display all of them. To draw an arrow diagram one has to make a sequence of two decisions: who gets the first book? who gets the second book? There are three choices for each decision.

112

(*b*) Look at the related problem with 3 books and two children. Now there are three decisions with two alternatives for each.

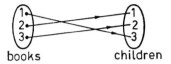

books   children

Fig. 6.35.

(*c*) Next consider assignments with various restrictions. Suppose that three books are given to three children and each child gets exactly one book. In Figure 6.35 is one case. Draw arrow diagrams for the remaining cases. Variations of these examples are obvious.

Example 4.—Given the set $S=\{A, N, G, L, E\}$, a subset T of 3 letters is to be selected. In how many ways can this be done?

We discribe a selection by a binary code. Below each selected letter write 1 and below each rejected letter write 0. Here is an example:

$$A \quad N \quad G \quad L \quad E$$
$$1 \quad 0 \quad 1 \quad 0 \quad 1$$

Hence to the binary code 10101 belongs the subset $T=\{A, G, E\}$. To get a subset of 3 letters the code must have digit sum 3. Make a list of all these binary codes. Map the codes into paths in the plane lattice by this assignment:

$$0 \rightarrow \text{one step to the right}$$
$$1 \rightarrow \text{one step up}$$

Figure 6.36 shows the path corresponding to 10101.

Example 5.—At this point, or later one can start with the combinatorial exploration of strings produced by random digit generators. Blocks of fixed

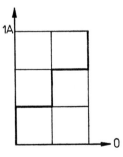

Fig. 6.36.

```
                    1   1   1
                1   2   3   2   1
            1   3   6   7   6   3   1
        1   4  10  16  19  16  10   4   1
    1   5  15  30  45  51  45  30  15   5   1
```

Fig. 6.37.

length should be classified according to their digit sums and frequency tables and frequency diagrams made. Take for instance an L-generator with alphabet {1, 2, 3}. Let us generate blocks of length 1, 2, 3, 4 and count the frequencies of the possible digit sums. The frequencies will be given approximately by the first 4 rows of the "numerical triangle" in Figure 6.37.

Now let us look at the corresponding frequency diagrams in Figure 6.38. We see how the central limit theorem starts working. Of course this is no surprise, since we are plotting the distributions of sums X_1, $X_1 + X_2$, $X_1 + X_2 + X_3$, $X_1 + X_2 + X_3 + X_4$, ... of independent random variables with identical distribution. Already a sum of three terms is well approximated by the normal distribution. Coins and dice problems should be explored in a similar way with similar results. The shape of the frequency diagrams in Figure 6.38 is found to be a general property of all random digit generators.

Next, we want to explain the resulting frequency distribution of digit sums. Here brute force combinatorics will be used. Since we know already that all digit blocks of equal length appear with the same long-run frequency,

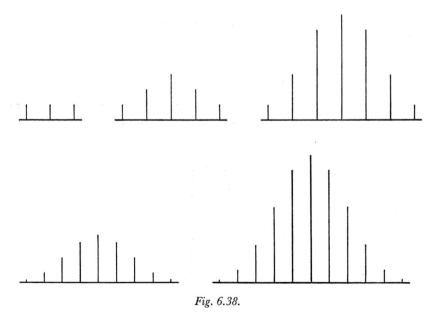

Fig. 6.38.

114

we can take all blocks of 4 and count how many have digit sums 4, 5, 6, ..., 12. A class working as a team should come up quickly with a table similar to the table below.

Digit Sum n	4	5	6	7	8	9	10	11	12
Types of Blocks with Digit Sum n	1111	1112	1113 1122	1222 1123	2222 1223 1133	2223 1233	1333 2233	2333	3333
Number of Blocks with Digit Sum n	1	4	$4+6=10$	$4+12=16$	$1+12+6=19$	$4+12=16$	$4+6=10$	4	1

Such a table explains the observed frequencis of digit sums of 4-blocks.

6.3.3. *Round II. Rule of Sum and Product Rule*

Eventually big outcome sets are encountered, whose elements cannot be counted by exhaustive enumeration. Counting is done by the *Rule of Sum*:

$$A \cap B = \phi \Rightarrow \mathcal{N}(A \cup B) = \mathcal{N}(A) + \mathcal{N}(B)$$

and the *Product Rule (Sequential Counting Lemma)*:

$$\mathcal{N}(A \times B) = \mathcal{N}(A) \cdot \mathcal{N}(B)$$

Children can learn these trivial rules by solving many numerical examples which illustrate the rules. Their general formulation is not necessary at this stage.

For a start of systematic counting *route problems* are probably the best. Here are some typical examples:

(*a*) How many routes lead from A to C via B in Figure 6.39? To select

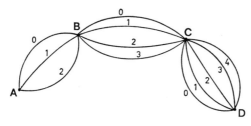

Fig. 6.39.

115

a route A–B–C, a sequence of two decisions is made, which can be put down on paper by filling two boxes as follows:

First decision → goes here | | | ← Second decision goes here

Does the first decision influence the number of decisions at the second stage? No. How many route descriptions start as follows:

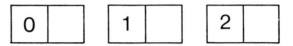

Hence there are 3·4 different routes. Such situations can be iterated by adding a fourth city D (Figure 6.39). Now you have to make three decisions. But the first two decisions can be viewed as one (compound) decision, and hence the number of routes is (3·4)5. After a few similar examples the Product Rule is easily grasped. More trouble is caused by problems in which both rules must be used. For instance:

(*b*) What is the number of routes from A to D in Figure 6.40?

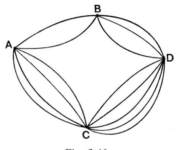

Fig. 6.40.

Here the number of decisions at the second stage depends on the previous decision. Observe, however, that the set of routes can be partitioned into subsets: those via B and those via C. These subsets must be counted separately and the numbers added. There are 2·3 routes via B and 4·5 routes via C. Hence there are 2·3 +4·5 different routes from A to D.

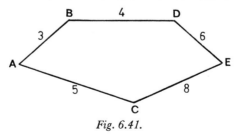

Fig. 6.41.

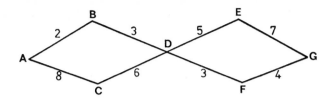

Fig. 6.42.

(c) In Figure 6.41 there are $3 \cdot 4 \cdot 6 + 5 \cdot 8$ routes from A to E.

(d) In Figure 6.42 there are $(2 \cdot 3 + 8 \cdot 6) \cdot (5 \cdot 7 + 3 \cdot 4)$ routes from A to G.

Now many problems should be solved by the rule of sum and the product rule, so that the students becomes familiar with additional combinatorial situations. The material used should appeal to the imagination of the student.

Problems about perforated cards, combination locks (sequential locks and safes), searching, guessing, dialing, switching, path counts for various nets, generation of pseudo-random digits etc. are all appropriate at this stage.

Dialing.—There are six-place phone numbers in a big city. To call someone you must push 6 buttons in the correct order on the dial in Figure 6.43. A few hints will show how to exploit this situation with profit: To phone a specific person you have to make a sequence of 6 decisions with 10 choices for each decision. Hence you can phone to 10^6 persons. Each of the people with whom you can converse are elements of a 6-dimensional outcome set. After the first push you have eliminated 900,000 people and a 5-dimensional set of 100,000 people is left. On the next push you eliminate 90,000 people and a 4-dimensional sub-space of 10,000 people is left, and so on.

Switching.—Figure 6.44 shows a system of 6 switches. What is the number of possible states of the system? How many of these states will transmit current?

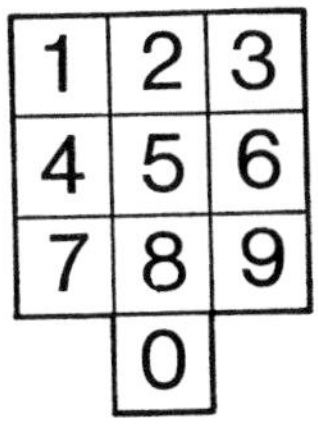

1	2	3
4	5	6
7	8	9
	0	

Fig. 6.43.

117

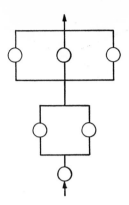

Fig. 6.44.

To select any one state one has to make a sequence of 6 decisions with two alternatives, ON or OFF. Hence there are $2^6 = 64$ states. The system is conducting current if in each of the three subsystems at least one switch is ON. Hence there are $(2-1)(2^2-1)(2^3-1) = 21$ conducting states.

Figure 6.45 shows another system with 64 states. Let us count the conducting states. Let I_i be the *indicator* of switch number i. We partition the conducting states into two subsets: the subset with $I_1I_2I_3 = 1$ has 8 elements. The subset with $I_1I_2I_3 = 0$ and $I_4I_5I_6 = 1$ has 7 elements. Altogether 15 states are conducting.

Counting Paths on Various Lattices. Northeast Walks.—Below each of the lattices in Figure 6.46, the number of shortest paths from A to B is given.

Road System in San-Fibonacci.—Figure 6.47 shows the road system of San-Fibonacci. There are only one way roads from A to B. To count the total number of routes, one has to use repeatedly the rule of sum. On the graph of the road system one can play an interesting game. Put a coin on A. Two players in turn move the coin in the direction of the arrows to a neighboring

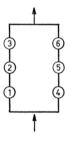

Fig. 6.45.

118

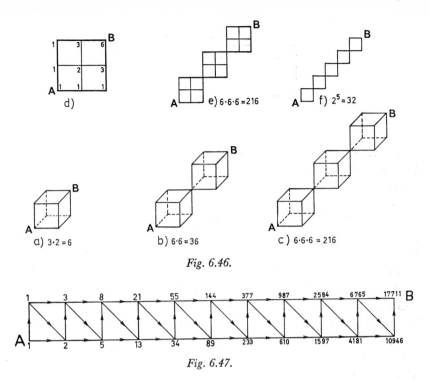

Fig. 6.46.

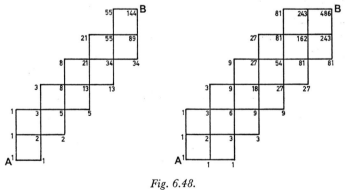

Fig. 6.47.

point. The player who first reaches B is the winner. It is also the graph of a simple countdown game. Start with a pile of 21 stones. Two players in turn take away one or two stones. Winner is the one who takes the last stone.

Generation of Pseudo-Random Digits.—Is it possible to construct a simple machine which grinds out binary random digits?

Fig. 6.48.

119

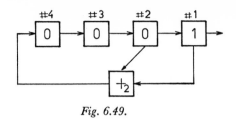

Fig. 6.49.

Let us try. Figure 6.49 shows a shift register. Load its registers by 4 binary digits (except 0000), for instance 1000. To the beat of a clock the content of each register is shifted to the next one on the right, and register #4, which becomes empty, is loaded by the mod 2 sum ($+_2$) of the registers 1 and 2. Each time unit another digit is produced, and we get the endless string 100010011010111..., which looks "pretty random". What is the number of possible states of the shift register? Obviously $2^4 - 1 = 15$, since we excluded state 0000. Why must the period of the string be $\leqslant 15$?

Figures 6.50–6.51 show some more shift registers. What is the possible maximum period for each register? Load the registers by non-zero binary blocks, generate strings of digits and find their actual period. Devise your own shift registers and find the periods.

In fact there are only three combinatorial problems which are indispensable for elementary probability theory. Two of these are handled in 5th

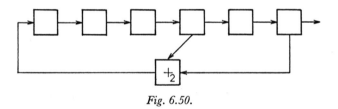

Fig. 6.50.

grade by a straightforward application of the product rule. The third is best postponed until grade 6.

These problems concern sampling: E.g. in an urn there are 15 balls numbered 1 to 15. A sample of 6 balls is drawn. This sampling can be done in

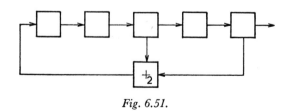

Fig. 6.51.

many ways but there are three procedures that are especially important to explore.

I. *Ordered Sampling with Replacement.*—A ball is drawn and its number noted. Then it is put back and the urn is thoroughly mixed. This is repeated 6 times. The number of possible samples in this case is by the product rule 15^6.

II. *Ordered Sampling without Replacement.*—Six balls are drawn one at a time without replacement and the number obtained on each draw is recorded. In this case there are

$$15 \cdot 14 \cdot 13 \cdot 12 \cdot 11 \cdot 10 = 15!/9!$$

different samples. If all 15 balls are drawn, we get a permutation of 15 different object. Hence there are 15! different permutations of 15 objects.

III. *Unordered Sampling without Replacement.*—Six balls are drawn at a grab. The number of possible subsets containing exactly 6 elements is denoted $\binom{15}{6}$. This number cannot be found by a straightforward application of the product rule. Hence it is tough for children. The easiest way is to view drawing of an ordered sample as a two-stage experiment: draw a subset (unordered) and then order it.

$$\boxed{\begin{array}{l}\textbf{Picking an ordered}\\ \textbf{sample of 6}\end{array}} = \boxed{\begin{array}{l}\textbf{Pick a}\\ \textbf{subset of 6}\end{array}} \times \boxed{\textbf{Order it}}$$

$$\begin{array}{l}\text{Number}\\ \text{of ways}\end{array} \quad \dfrac{15!}{9!} \quad = \quad \binom{15}{6} \quad \times \quad 6!$$

$$\text{Hence} \quad \binom{15}{6} = \frac{15!}{6! \, 9!}$$

Unordered sampling with replacement is not so important and can be put off until considerably later.

Let me stress again that no variables need be used at this stage. Also I give no more combinatorial examples since many are available in standard texts on the subject.

6.4. PROBABILITY

6.4.1. *Introduction*

Bona fide probability should begin as soon as students can multiply fractions. In a German high school this happens in grade 6. At this point weights with total sum 1 can be assigned to the outcomes of single stage experiments.

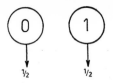

Fig. 6.52.

As usual this should be motivated by referring to the stability of relative frequencies.

A symmetric coin with faces 0 and 1 is flipped many times. Both faces appear with almost the same frequency. To describe this behavior we assign to each face the same weight $\frac{1}{2}$. When the same weight is assigned to each face of a coin, we call it a Laplace-coin. This is an exceptional case. The standard case is that of a lopsided coin, e.g. as with the tack in Figure 6.53.

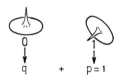

Fig. 6.53.

If the long run relative frequencies of the outcomes 0 and 1 are q and p, $p+q=1$, then we make the assignments $0 \to q$ and $1 \to p$. The die is treated similarly. An urn with n ball is a model for a Laplace-experiment with n outcomes.

Here is a wheel with circumference 1. It is divided into n sector s_1, s_2, ..., s_n whose arcs have lengths p_1, p_2, ..., p_n. This is a model for the most general finite probability space (S, P). We have a finite set $S = \{s_1, s_2, ..., s_n\}$ and a function p on S: $s_i \to p_i$ with the restrictions $0 \leqslant p_i \leqslant 1$, $\Sigma p_i = 1$. By means of the point function p we can define a set function P on the subsets of S by

$$P(A) = \sum_{s_i \in A} p_i, \quad P(\phi) = 0.$$

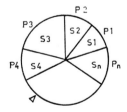

Fig. 6.54.

122

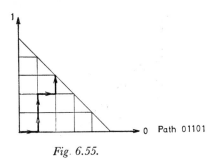

Path 01101

Fig. 6.55.

In a Laplace-experiment the function p is a constant function, i.e. $p_i = 1/n$ for all i, and we have

$$P(A) = \frac{N(A)}{N(S)}.$$

So far we can get along with addition of fractions alone, but single stage experiments are pretty trivial and one should not waste too much time on them. So we turn to multistage experiments. Start with *independent repetitions of an experiment*. Consider a coin which is tossed n times. The whole sequence of tosses is one *compound experiment* whose outcomes are strings of binary digits, for instance 01101. These strings can be mapped into paths in the plane lattice (Figure 6.55). Now we must assign a weight to each string of digits (or to each path) in a reasonable way. The assignment $01101 \rightarrow qppqp = p^3q^2$ is easy to motivate and has already been done many times with 5th graders.

Similarly one proceeds with all independent and Markovian sources.

Now we are through. From this point on a substantial part of the indispensable skill in operating with fractions and percentages is acquired by solving probabilistic and statistical problems.

The problems, which students solve, often lead to the binomial distribution. These problems can mostly be solved by use of a lattice.

Example 1.—Bob and Jim are fine ping-pong players. If they would play a long series of games with each other Bob would win the fraction $p = 0.6$ of the games and Jim the remaining fraction $q = 0.4$. Suppose however that they do not know who is better, and they decide to find out by playing a series of games. The one who wins a majority of the games is declared the better player. What is the probability that the weaker player (Jim) wins the competition if 1, 3, 5, 7 games are played?

(a) If one game is played Jim wins with probability $q = 0.4$.

(b) If Bob wins a game we write 1, if he loses we write 0. A series of 3 games will result in one of these 8 outcomes: 000, 001, 010, 011, 100, 101,

123

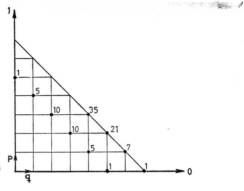

Fig. 6.56.

110, 111. The outcomes 000, 001, 010, 100 lead to a victory by Jim. The probability for this event is

$$q^3 + 3q^2 p = 0.352.$$

(*c*) A record of the competition when 5 games are played is a binary digit block of length 5. It can be interpreted as a path in the lattice starting at the origin and ending on the line $x + y = 5$ (Figure 6.56).

All paths leading to (5, 0), (4, 1), and (3, 2) result in Jim's victory. Their total weight is

$$q^5 + 5q^4 p + 10q^3 p^2 = 0.31744.$$

(*d*) With 7 games we get by the same method

$$q^7 + 7q^6 p + 21q^5 p^2 + 35q^4 p^3 = 0.290,$$

still a sizable chance. This shows a strong dependence of sports decisions on pure chance.

Example 2.—A binary symmetric channel (Figure 6.57) transmits the digits 0 and 1. Suppose that because of noise a 0 is changed into 1 and vice versa with probability $q = 0.2$. (This is very strong noise, as is found for instance in space communication.) Suppose that we want to transmit an important message consisting of one binary digit. To protect it from corruption by

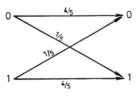

Fig. 6.57.

124

noise we transmit 00000 instead of 0 and 11111 instead of 1. The receiver of the message uses "majority" decoding. What is the probability that the message will be wrong when decoded. This is obviously example (1c). Hence the probability of an incorrect reading of the message is

$$q^5 + 5q^4p + 10q^3p^2 = 0.05792.$$

Suppose that it costs one dollar to send each digit, and that a wrong interpretation causes costs at 1000 dollars. How many digits should we send in order to minimize the costs? It can be shown that with 15 digits the loss is minimal, 19.24 dollars.

After a while the support of the lattice may be dropped, as shown by the next example.

Example 3. Chicks Pecking at Imitation Grain (Hypothesis Testing).—Does a newborn chicken recognize grain, or does it learn this by experience? To decide this question we could give it imitation grain made of paper in both round and triangular shape of equal size and number. If the chick pecks on a round shape we would write 1, and for each peck on a triangular shape we would write 0. Suppose that we record the following sequence: 1111011101. Then the chick stops pecking. What does this mean? There are two competing hypotheses.

H_0: $p = \frac{1}{2}$, i.e. a newborn chicken is a Laplace-chicken. It has not yet learned that grain is round.

H_1: $p > \frac{1}{2}$, i.e. chicks prefer round objects looking like grain, without ever having trasted grain.

Suppose the first hypothesis is true. Then something unexpected has happened. Laplace-coins produce long blocks with about equally many 0's and 1's in the overwhelming majority of cases. Now very surprisingly we have results that we simply do not believe. In fact, we will be tempted to reject H_0. But is such an outcome really that rare! Suppose we decide in advance to reject H_0 if it implies that the observed result falls into a region whose total weight is < 5 %. What is the total weight of all outcomes that are at least as unexpected as the observed result? There are altogether $2^{10} = 1024$ different pecking sequences, when 10 pecks are observed all having the same weight (under H_0). Among these outcomes we have

$$\binom{10}{0} + \binom{10}{1} + \binom{10}{2} = 1 + 10 + 45 = 56$$

with either 0, 1, 2 zero's. Since $56/1024 = 5.5$ % the sequence we recorded is not as unexpected as we thought it to be. Hence with 10 pecks recorded we cannot be sure and must continue collecting data.

Fig. 6.58.

Now suppose 20 pecks are observed and result in the following sequence:

$$11111001111110101 11001$$

Here the proportion of zero's is considerably higher than in the first example, so this result would seem even less surprising. But the block is longer. This time there are $2^{20} = 1,048,576$ possible pecking sequences. Let us count the extreme sequences with 0, 1, 2, 3, 4, 5 zero's:

$$\binom{20}{0} + \binom{20}{1} + \binom{20}{2} + \binom{20}{3} + \binom{20}{4} + \binom{20}{5} = 1 + 20 + 190 + 1140$$

$$+ 4845 + 15664 = 21860$$

Now $21,860/1,048,576 = 0.02069 = 2.069\%$. This time we reject H_0 with confidence.

6.4.2. *Expectation of a Random Variable*

Most textbook problems are concocted for the sole purpose of providing drill. We can replace such problems by problems familiarizing the student with important concepts, such as probability, random variable and expectation, and which in addition help develop skill in manipulating fractions. Of course we must restrict ourselves to specific numerical examples. General proofs will not work. (By the way, this is an advantage.) I give some typical examples, though I cannot go into any detail.

Example 1.—In the casino of Monte Bello there are many roulette wheels with different rules and offering different ways to lose money. One wheel looks like Figure 6.58.

For 10 dollars you may spin it once and you will be paid the number of dollars determined by the pointer. Now the notion of a *random variable* is explained. Your gain X is a random variable. The expectation $E(X)$ of X is defined as the weighted average of the values of X, each value being weighted by its probability. It is motivated in the usual way as average winnings per game over a long series of games. Both versions

126

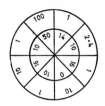

Fig. 6.59.

$$E(X) = \Sigma X(s_i) \, P(s_i) \quad \text{and} \quad E(X) = \Sigma x_i P(X = x_i)$$

are used. In our case above we have

$$E(X) = \tfrac{4}{10} \cdot 2 + \tfrac{3}{10} \cdot 11 + \tfrac{2}{10} \cdot 4 + \tfrac{1}{10} \cdot 50 = 9.9.$$

Thus in the long run the casino makes a small profit of a dime per game. You can also play "Double" for 20 dollars or "Double plus Five" for 25 dollars. In the first case you are paid $2X$ and in the second $2X+5$. Now $E(2X), E(2X+5)$ are computed and it is found $E(cX+d) = cE(X) + d$.

Popular among gamblers is the split wheel shown in Figure 6.59. For 16 dollars you can bet on the inner number X or on the outer number Y, and for 32 dollars on $X+Y$. Find $E(X), E(Y), E(X+Y)$ and compare with $E(X) + E(Y)$.

$$E(X) = \tfrac{3}{8} \cdot 10 + \tfrac{1}{8} \cdot 14 + \tfrac{1}{4} \cdot 16 + \tfrac{1}{8} \cdot 50 = 15.75$$

$$E(Y) = \tfrac{1}{2} \cdot 1 + \tfrac{1}{4} \cdot 10 + \tfrac{1}{8} \cdot 2.4 + \tfrac{1}{8} \cdot 100 = 15.80$$

$$E(X+Y) = 31.55 = E(X) + E(Y)$$

On New Year's Eve, people were in a spending mood. The manager of the casino decided to take advantage of their mood and speed up his winnings. He announced: Let us play X^2. If X comes up on the inner wheel you get paid X^2. But of course a spin will cost you $16^2 = 256$. Before the night was over he was out of business. Let us see why by computing the expectation of X^2:

$$E(X^2) = \tfrac{3}{8} \cdot 100 + \tfrac{1}{8} \cdot 196 + \tfrac{1}{4} \cdot 256 + \tfrac{1}{8} \cdot 2500 = 438.5$$

The expectation of the square is considerably bigger than the square of the

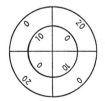

Fig. 6.60.

127

Fig. 6.61.

expectation: $E(X^2) > [E(X)]^2$. Now find $E(XY)$ and compare with $E(X)E(Y)$. We get $E(XY) > E(X)E(Y)$. Devise a wheel with $E(XY) < E(X)E(Y)$. Figure 6.60 shows one.

Devise a wheel with $E(XY) = E(X)E(Y)$. Figure 6.61 shows one. Here X and Y are independent. Knowing the value of one does not help in predicting the value of the other.

Next, the new casino manager introduced the product game, played on two different wheels simultaneously. You can bet on the outcome X of the first wheel and pay a, or you can bet on the outcome Y of the second wheel and pay b, or you can bet on the product $Z = XY$ and pay c. Find a, b, c if all three games are fair.

$$E(X) = \tfrac{3}{5} \cdot 5 + \tfrac{1}{5} \cdot 10 + \tfrac{1}{5} \cdot 100 = 25$$

$$E(Y) = \tfrac{1}{4} \cdot 3 + \tfrac{1}{4} \cdot 5 + \tfrac{3}{8} \cdot 8 + \tfrac{1}{8} \cdot 120 = 20$$

Hence $a = 20$, $b = 25$. Using product measure, which was discussed earlier in detail one gets

z_i	15	25	30	40	50	80	300	500	600	800	1200	12000
$P(Z = z_i)$	$\tfrac{3}{20}$	$\tfrac{3}{20}$	$\tfrac{1}{20}$	$\tfrac{9}{40}$	$\tfrac{1}{20}$	$\tfrac{3}{40}$	$\tfrac{1}{20}$	$\tfrac{1}{20}$	$\tfrac{3}{40}$	$\tfrac{3}{40}$	$\tfrac{1}{40}$	$\tfrac{1}{40}$

We find $E(XY) = 500 = 25 \cdot 20 = E(X)E(Y)$. Now you can consider coupled wheels. The choice on the second wheel depends on the outcome of the first spin, etc.

Example 2. Guessing Numbers.—In an urn there are 10 balls numbered 1 to 10. Someone draws a number and you try to guess it by questions with

Fig. 6.62.

128

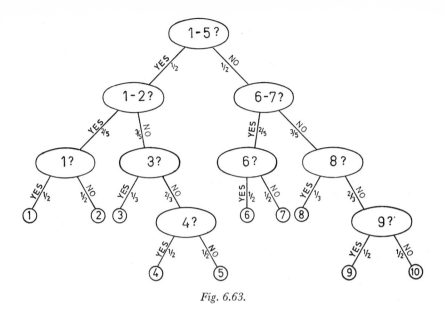

Fig. 6.63.

"yes–no" answers. The number of questions necessary is a random variable X and its expectation depends upon our strategy of asking questions. Let us analyse two strategies:

Simple-minded strategy.—I ask: Is it 1, 2, 3, ..., 9? Obviously

$$E(X) = \tfrac{1}{10}(1+2+3+...+8+9+9) = 5.4.$$

On the average 5.4 questions would be needed to guess the number by this strategy.

Sophisticated strategy.—With each question I try to eliminate one half of the remaining numbers, as nearly as possible. The tree in Figure 6.63 shows all possible outcomes of this experiment.

There are 10 paths through the tree, and each has weight 1/10. Six paths are of length 3 and 4 of length 4. Hence the expected path length is

$$E(X) = \tfrac{1}{10}(6 \cdot 3 + 4 \cdot 4) = 3.4.$$

With this strategy only 3.4 questions are needed on the average instead of 5.4 with the former strategy.

We change the game slightly. The urn still contains balls with number 1 to 10, but the different numbers appear with frequencies shown by the following table:

Number of the ball	1	2	3	4	5	6	7	8	9	10
Frequency	512	256	128	64	32	16	8	4	2	2
Probability	$\tfrac{1}{2}$	$\tfrac{1}{4}$	$\tfrac{1}{8}$	$\tfrac{1}{16}$	$\tfrac{1}{32}$	$\tfrac{1}{64}$	$\tfrac{1}{128}$	$\tfrac{1}{256}$	$\tfrac{1}{512}$	$\tfrac{1}{512}$

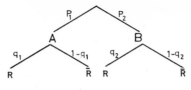

Fig. 6.64.

A ball is drawn at random and you try to guess its number. By means of the sophisticated approach you need about 3.22 questions on the average. Let us be simple-minded and call: 1?, 2?, 3?, ..., 9? With this strategy the expected number of questions needed is:

$$E(X) = \tfrac{1}{2} + \tfrac{2}{4} + \tfrac{3}{8} + \tfrac{4}{16} + \tfrac{5}{32} + \tfrac{6}{64} + \tfrac{7}{128} + \tfrac{8}{256} + \tfrac{9}{512} + \tfrac{9}{512} = 2 - \tfrac{2}{512} < 2$$

This is considerably better than by the sophisticated strategy.

Conditional probabilities and the total probability rule are not explicitly formulated. Rather the problems are solved by using trees or other directed graphs and then using multiplying along paths. Here are some examples.

Example 1.—Suppose that widgets are produced by two machines A and B. The reliabilities of the widgets are q_1 for those from A and q_2 for those from B. A and B produce the proportions p_1 and $p_2 = 1 - p_1$ of the total output. The products are mixed at random before sale. When you buy a widget what is the probability $P(R)$ that it is reliable?

From Figure 6.64 we get at once

$$P(R) = p_1 q_1 + p_2 q_2.$$

The formal approach

$$R = (R \cap A) \cup (R \cap B), \ P(R) = P(A) P(R|A) + P(B) P(R|B)$$

would probably not work at this stage, though I have never tried.

Example 2.—A hungry Laplace-driver on the lookout for a restaurant starts at 0 (Figure 6.65) and drives in the direction of the arrows. R_1, R_2, R_3, R_4,

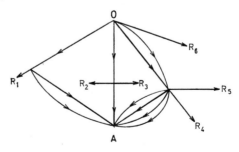

Fig. 6.65.

130

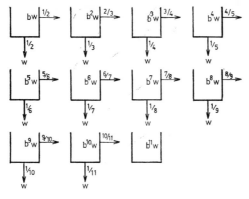

Fig. 6.66.

R_5, R_6, and A are restaurants. What is the probability that he will dine at restaurant A?

We get at once

$$P(A) = \tfrac{1}{5} \cdot \tfrac{2}{3} + \tfrac{1}{5} \cdot \tfrac{1}{3} + \tfrac{2}{5} \cdot \tfrac{2}{3} = \tfrac{2}{15} + \tfrac{1}{15} + \tfrac{4}{15} = \tfrac{7}{15} = 0.47$$

Example 3.—Monte Bello again. The new manager of Monte Bello never stops inventing games. One day he hit upon the BALL GAME: Initially in the Ball Game, one white ball and one black ball are put into an urn. One ball is drawn at random. If it is white the game stops. If it is black two black balls are put into the urn. This is repeated until either a white ball is drawn, or the number of draws reaches 10 (or more general N). The number X of draws necessary to stop the game gives your winnings in dollars. It costs three dollars to play the game.

Draw a complete tree of all possible evolutions of the game and find the expectation and distribution of X.

Here I use N instead of 10. Students use 10. By looking at the tree we get the following distribution:

n	1	2	3	4	...	$N-1$	N
$P(X=n)$	$\dfrac{1}{1 \cdot 2}$	$\dfrac{1}{2 \cdot 3}$	$\dfrac{1}{3 \cdot 4}$	$\dfrac{1}{4 \cdot 5}$	$\cdots$	$\dfrac{1}{(N-1)\,N}$	$\dfrac{1}{N}$

Now we get

$$E(X) = 1 + \frac{1}{2} + \frac{1}{3} + \frac{1}{4} + \ldots + \frac{1}{N}$$

For $N=10$ we have $E(X) = 7381/2520 = 2.929$. Again the house makes a small profit over the long run.

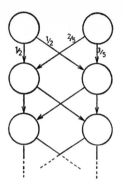

Fig. 6.67.

The probabilities should add to 1. Let us check.

$$\frac{1}{1\cdot 2}+\frac{1}{2\cdot 3}+\frac{1}{3\cdot 4}+\frac{1}{4\cdot 5}+\cdots+\frac{1}{(N-1)\,N}+\frac{1}{N}=\frac{1}{1}-\frac{1}{2}+\frac{1}{2}-\frac{1}{3}+\frac{1}{3}-\frac{1}{4}$$

$$+\frac{1}{4}-\frac{1}{5}+\cdots\frac{1}{N-1}-\frac{1}{N}+\frac{1}{N}=1.$$

This is a completely artificial example. Why did I use it? Because it contains a lot of good mathematics: a telescoping series, the harmonic series, and practice with fractions. What happens if only a white ball can stop the game? The expectation $E(X)$ becomes infinite because the harmonic series diverges. This situation can be discussed in later years. Even artificial constructions are justified if they lead to good and interesting mathematics.

6.4.3. Markov Chains

I treat Markov chains first from an algorithmic point of view. This point of view is rich in applications and should be developed in a systematic way. Give students problems for individual exploration. For young children iterations are easiest to understand. They get a recipe T. They choose a starting point v and they apply T repeatedly to v. They get a sequence

$$v,\ Tv,\ T^2v,\ T^3v,\ \ldots$$

What is the long run behavior of the sequence? How does it depend on the starting value? There are many interesting and instructive number theoretic problems of this kind. Students soon discover the possible patterns of behavior.

(a) There is a run away (to infinity).
(b) A cycle appears.
(c) The sequence remains at a fixed point.

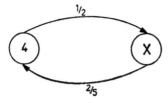

Fig. 6.68.

(d) The sequence approaches a fixed point without ever reaching it. Sometimes there is dependence on the starting point, but very often the process seems to "forget" its initial state.

Consider a *stationary mixing process*. Initially one gallon of some fluid is distributed among two tanks. The initial distribution is given by a vector $v=(p, q)$ with $p+q=1$. At regular intervals the contents of these two tanks are pumped into two thanks below according to some fixed mixing proportions (Figure 6.67). This operation will be called T. To calculate v, Tv, T^2v, ... is an excellent and unusual training in fractions. The mixing proportions in Figure 6.67 are very handy and the student soon discovers a pattern. If this is not the case, ask him this question: Is there a *stationary distribution* v, such that $Tv=v$? Let us look at another representation of the same mixing process, shown by Figure 6.68.

Now we have a mixing of two tanks. After each time unit 1/2 of the first tank flows into the second and 2/5 of the second tank goes into the first. Put four gallons into the left tank and x gallons into the right tank. Can x be choosen in such a way that a stationary distribution results? For the left tank we write down the condition

$$OUTFLOW = INFLOW$$

and get $\frac{1}{2}\cdot 4 = \frac{2}{5}\cdot x$, or $x=5$. Hence $v=(\frac{4}{9}, \frac{5}{9})$ is a stationary distribution. It is unique because of total volume 1.

What happens if the process is started with a distribution which devi-

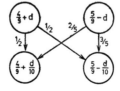

Fig. 6.69.

133

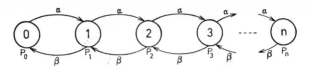

Fig. 6.70.

ates by d from the stationary distribution? Let us start with

$$v = (\tfrac{4}{9} + d, \tfrac{5}{9} - d).$$

For the first component of Tv we find

$$\frac{1}{2}\left(\frac{4}{9} + d\right) + \frac{2}{5}\left(\frac{5}{9} - d\right) = \frac{4}{9} + \frac{d}{10}.$$

Hence

$$v = \left(\frac{4}{9} + d, \frac{5}{9} - d\right), \quad Tv = \left(\frac{4}{9} + \frac{d}{10}, \frac{5}{9} - \frac{d}{10}\right), \quad T^n v = \left(\frac{4}{9} + \frac{d}{10^n}, \frac{5}{9} - \frac{d}{10^n}\right).$$

Thus there is geometric convergence to the stationary distribution, *independently of the initial distribution.*

Markov chains with more than two states must be postponed until the student is able to solve systems of linear equations. Considerably later in 11th grade, the most important stochastic service systems can be explored (Erlang-Palm theory). For instance, let us look at the mixing graph in Figure 6.70. We have $n+1$ states, numbered $0, 1, 2, ..., n$. Find $p_0, p_1, p_2, .., p_n, \Sigma p_r = 1$, such that a stationary distribution results.

This leads to simple but instructive algebraic manipulations. One gets with $x = \alpha/\beta$ for Figure 6.70

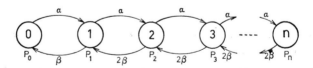

Fig. 6.71.

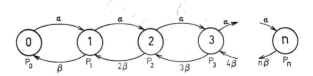

Fig. 6.72.

$$P_r = x^r p_0, \quad p_0^{-1} = \frac{1 - x^{n+1}}{1 - x}, \quad r = 0, 1, \ldots, n$$

and for Figure 6.72

$$P_r = \frac{x_r}{r!} p_0, \quad p_0^{-1} = \sum_{r=0}^{n} \frac{x_r}{r!}, \quad r = 0, 1, \ldots, n.$$

Figure 6.70 is a graph of a single server queue with maximum length n. Here α and β are the intensities of arrival and service, both completely random (e.g. waiting at a doctor's office). Figure 6.71 shows a double server queue, like in a bank or post office. And finally figure 6.72 shows an n-server queue, e.g. a parking lot. Here the geometric and exponential series appear with their tails chopped off. If we idealize slightly by dropping the restriction on queue length, we have excellent motivation for studying convergence, limits, and infinite series.

6.4.4. *Reliability*

Reliability problems have much merit: they are easy to understand, easy to construct, and they can be treated on different levels of difficulty. Some caution is necessary so that in the future they are not used out of proportion to their actual importance. I have already shown by several examples how to treat them in grade 5. In grade 6 problems in the same vein are treated more elegantly by means of fractions. In grade 7 variables can be used and in grade 8, reliability problems provide examples for extensive algebraic manipulations and for applications of Boolean algebra.

A system is made up of n parts. At any moment t each part is in one of two states:

$$\text{functioning} \to 1, \quad \text{not functioning} \to 0.$$

The state space S of the whole system consists of 2^n states. We partition S into two subsets: $S = F \cup W$. If the system state is in W, the system works, if the system state is in F it fails. As time goes on the individual parts of the system change their states and the whole system can be considered as performing a random walk on the subset W of the n-cube. It stops as soon as it hits F, that is F is the set of absorbing states. At this level of generality, the problem is treated in grade 11, when the exponential function is available and students are familiar with the exponential failure law.

For work in lower grades the time factor must be eliminated. For the short remarks here I even make the (unnecessary) assumption that each part has the same probability p of functioning and $q = 1 - p$ of not functioning. Needless to say, independence is also assumed.

Reliability $R(p)$ of a system is the probability that the whole system is operative (current flows from L to R).

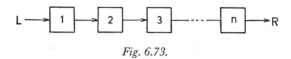

Fig. 6.73.

Series System.—Parts can be connected in series. By definition a series system fails if any of its parts fails. 111 ... 11 is the only state in W. Hence

$$R(p) = p^n.$$

Parallel Systems.—Parts can be in parallel. By definition a parallel system fails only if all of its parts fail. 000 ... 00 is the only state in F. The failure probability is q^n and the reliability

$$R(p) = 1 - q^n = 1 - (1-p)^n.$$

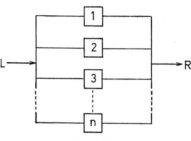

Fig. 6.74.

Series and parallel systems can be iterated to get *series-parallel* and *parallel-series* systems. These are the simple systems a sixth grader can handle if p is some specific number. For other systems he must write down all states, find those in F (or W) and compute their total probability. This is forbidding for $n \geqslant 5$. We start with 3 simple systems and use them as subsystems for more complicated systems (Figure 6.75).

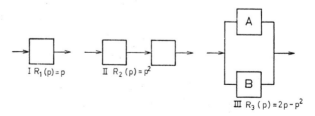

I $R_1(p) = p$ II $R_2(p) = p^2$ III $R_3(p) = 2p - p^2$

Fig. 6.75.

136

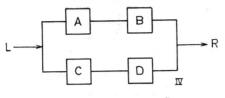

Fig. 6.76.

The general solution for system III already presents some difficulty. Its reliability is $1 - q^2 = 1 - (1-p)^2$. German students learn in grade 8 how to simplify this to $2p - p^2$, but before that time they know some Boolean algebra and some formal probability, and they can handle it this way

$$P(A \cup B) = P(A) + P(B) - P(A \cap B) = p + p - p^2 = 2p - p^2.$$

Examine Figure 6.76. This system is obtained if we replace each part in system III by system II. Hence its reliability is $R_4(p) = (R_3 \circ R_2)(p) = 2p^2 - p^4$, where $\circ$ denotes functional composition.

System V in Figure 6.77 is obtained by replacing each part in II by III. Hence

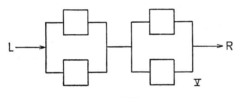

Fig. 6.77.

$$R_5(p) = (R_2 \circ R_3)(p) = (2p - p^2)^2 = 4p^2 - 4p^3 + p^4$$

The system VI in Figure 6.78 is obtained by hooking up system II and system I. Hence

$$R_6(p) = R_3(p) R_1(p) = (2p - p^2) p = 2p^2 - p^3.$$

By Boolean algebra system IV could be handled this way:

$$W = (A \cap B) \cup (C \cap D), P(W) = P(A \cap B) + P(C \cap D) - P(A \cap B \cap C \cap D) =$$
$$P(A) P(B) + P(C) P(D) - P(A) P(B) P(C) P(D) = 2p^2 - p^4.$$

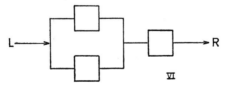

Fig. 6.78.

137

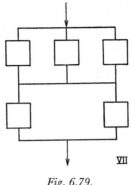

Fig. 6.79.

To summarize we can say: A system like VII in Figure 6.79 is easy to handle since it is a series of two parallel systems. Its reliability can be written down by inspection:

$$R_7(q) = (1 - q^3)\,(1 - q^2)$$

But a system like VIII in Figures 6.80 is tough for the student. Here conditional probability considerations are helpful. Separate the two alternatives: E is functioning and E is not functioning.

Note. I used capital letters like A in a dual sense, to denote components of a system, and to denote sets. A is the subset of the state space S of a system for which component A is working.

6.4.5. *Countably Infinite Outcome Sets*

As soon as students can solve linear equations in one variable we can turn to infinite processes. *The infinite process is simpler analytically since it possesses an invariant aspect over time.* For instance, we deal with beetles performing random walks. These beetles have no memory. Whenever they return to

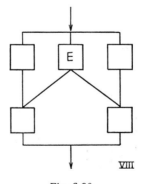

Fig. 6.80.

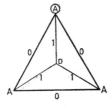

Fig. 6.81.

the starting state, they are in the same situation as far as future is concerned. This will be used to set up equations for probabilities and expectations. Here are some examples.

Example 1.—(a) Figure 6.81 shows a regular tetrahedron made of wire. There is a Laplace-beetle at Ⓐ. To traverse one edge, it takes one minute. At D there is a strong insecticide which kills the beetle at once. What about the lifetime X of the beatle? X is a random variable. Let us find the expectation and distribution of X. The event $X=n$ corresponds to the path $000 \ldots 01$ and consequently it has weight $P(X=n) = (\frac{2}{3})^{n-1} \cdot \frac{1}{3}$. The event $X>n$ corresponds to $000 \ldots 0$ and has weight $P(X>n) = (\frac{2}{3})^n$. For the complementary event $X \leqslant n$ we get $P(X \leqslant n) = 1 - (\frac{2}{3})^n$. The expectation of X cannot be found in the usual way since students lack the analytical and conceptual maturity to sum the geometric series $\sum_1^\infty n(\frac{2}{3})^{n-1} \cdot \frac{1}{3}$. It should first be found by a clumsy, but highly intuitive method. For reasons of symmetry the expected time from any vertex A to D is the same, say a. Suppose 300 beetles start on 300 copies of this solid. Their total lifetime will be $300 \cdot a$ minutes. Consider the situation after one minute. The beetles as a group lived a total of 300 minutes, 100 reached their destiny at D and 200 will be in the same situation as at the start, and will live a total of $200 \cdot a$ minutes more. Hence $300 \cdot a = 300 + 200 \cdot a$ which gives $a = 3$. This clumsy method is for grade 6. A Monte Carlo run gives very satisfactory results.

(b) By eliminating edges we get new problems. Figure 6.82 shows the same solid with one edge missing. Suppose the expected life when beetles start from position Ⓐ is x. Then from B it is $x-1$. The tree in Figure 6.83

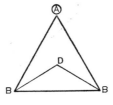

Fig. 6.82.

139

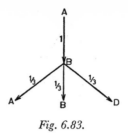

Fig. 6.83.

shows the possible life histories of the beetle during the first two minutes after the start.

We get

$$x = \tfrac{1}{3} \cdot 2 + \tfrac{1}{3} \cdot (2 + x - 1) + \tfrac{1}{3}(2 + x)$$

which gives $\qquad x = 5.$

(c) Let us eliminate another edge (Figure 6.84). From the corresponding tree in Figure 6.85 we get for the expected life x

$$x = \tfrac{1}{2}(x + 1) + \tfrac{1}{6} \cdot 2 + \tfrac{1}{2} \cdot \tfrac{2}{3}(x + 2)$$

$$x = 9.$$

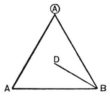

Fig. 6.84.

Example 2. A Symmetric Random Walk With Two Absorbing Barriers.—Only trivial special cases are treated. The general solution could be found by some ingenuity, but it should not be done. The amazingly deep results probably cannot be understood or appreciated at this early age. A thorough treatment of random walks in one, two and three dimensions belongs to grades 10/11 and is an excellent prelude to calculus. Here the concepts of

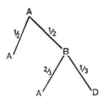

Fig. 6.85.

140

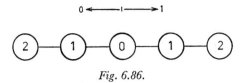

Fig. 6.86.

estimation, approximation, convergence, and limits arise in a highly motivated setting.

A chip is put on state 0 in Figure 6.86, and a sequence of binary digits is generated by an L-coin. For each "0" the chip moves one step to the left and for each "1" one step to the right. The game stops as soon as state 2 is reached (gambler's ruin). Find the expectation and distribution of the duration X of the game. Students have studied the problem in 5th grade by Monte Carlo. The evolution of the game can be represented in many different ways:

(a) As a random walk on the 2-cube (Figure 6.87). Starting state is 00 and 11 is absorbing state.

Fig. 6.87.

(b) As a Markov chain graph (Figure 6.88).

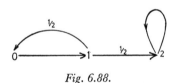

Fig. 6.88.

(c) By a path in the plane lattice starting at the origin and stopping on the lines $y=x-2$ and $y=x+2$ (Figure 6.89). Here it is easy to count the paths by the rule of sum.

(d) By an infinite tree (Figure 6.90). By multiplying along the corresponding path in the tree one finds the distribution of X,

$$P(X=2n) = \frac{1}{2^n}$$

To find the expectation a we truncate the tree by chopping off the infinite tail.

141

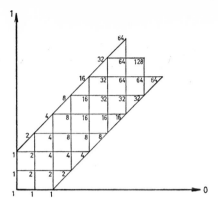

Fig. 6.89.

From Figure 6.91 we get

$$a = \tfrac{1}{2} \cdot 2 + \tfrac{1}{2}(2 + a), \; a = 4.$$

The event $X > 2n$ is represented by the path $010101 \ldots 010$ in the tree with $2n + 1$ digits and $2n$ transitions. Hence

$$P(X > 2n) = \frac{1}{2^n}.$$

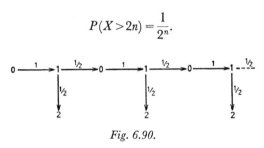

Fig. 6.90.

Now probabilities of various events like the following are found:

$$X < 4, \; X > 10, \; 8 < X < 16 \text{ etc.}$$

One class played a total of 100 games and one student got a walk of length 22. Is this surprising? How strong a case do we have in suspecting that the coin used is lopsided?

$$P(X > 20) = 1/2^{10} = 1/1024.$$

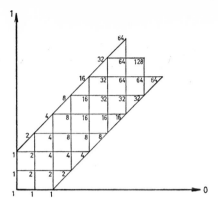

Fig. 6.91.

142

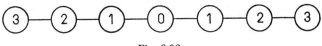

Fig. 6.92.

We have 100 trials, each with probability 1/1024 for success. Students think the probability for at least one success is 100/1024. This is approximately correct. Hence a walk of length 22 in 100 is not very surprising at all.

Next we can generalize slightly. A Laplace-rat starts in state 0 of Figure 6.92.

For a transition to a neighboring state the rat needs one minute. In each of the states 3 there is a hungry cat waiting. Let X be the life time of the rat. Let us find the expectation and the distribution of X.

By looking at the tree in Figure 6.93 we can set up an equation for the expectation a

$$a = \tfrac{1}{2}(2+a) + \tfrac{1}{4}(3+a-1) + \tfrac{1}{4}\cdot 3, \quad a = 9.$$

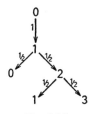

Fig. 6.93.

We get the distribution from the Markov chain diagram in Figure 6.94.

$$P(X=3) = \tfrac{1}{1}\cdot\tfrac{1}{2}\cdot\tfrac{1}{2} = \tfrac{1}{4}, P(X=5) = \tfrac{1}{4}[\tfrac{1}{2}+\tfrac{1}{4}] = \tfrac{1}{4}\cdot\tfrac{3}{4},$$

$$P(X=7) = \tfrac{1}{4}\cdot\tfrac{3}{4}[\tfrac{1}{2}+\tfrac{1}{4}] = \tfrac{1}{4}(\tfrac{3}{4})^2,$$

$$P(X=2n+1) = \frac{1}{4}\left(\frac{3}{4}\right)^{n-1} = \frac{1}{3}\left(\frac{3}{4}\right)^{n}, \quad n=1,2,3,\ldots$$

$$P(X>2n+1) = \left(\frac{3}{4}\right)^{n}$$

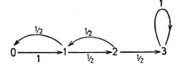

Fig. 6.94.

143

One of my classes performed 1000 trials and the event $X > 49$ occurred twice. The class was unanimously of the opinion that the coins were lopsided. But

$$P(X > 49) = \left(\frac{3}{4}\right)^{24} = 0{,}001$$

approximately. Again this is by no means surprising.

To reach the absorbing states at distance 2 and 3 the random walker requires on the average 2^2 and 3^2 steps. This suggests that he needs n^2 steps on the average to reach the barriers at distance n. But to prove this for $n = 4$ requires the solution of a system of linear equations with two variables. The general solution is best done in grade 10, but we could solve a related problem.

Let us look at this game: A player starts at the origin and makes 10 random steps. The square of his final distance from the origin is his gain in dollars. What is the average gain per game? A class performed 100 games with these final distances from the origin resulting:

$$4, 2, 2, 8, 2, 2, 2, 6, 6, 2, 4, 4, 2, 0, 2, 8, 0,$$
$$4, 4, 8, 0, 0, 2, 2, 0, 2, 4, 2, 2, 0, 2, 6, 2, 0,$$
$$2, 0, 2, 2, 0, 2, 4, 4, 8, 2, 0, 0, 0, 4, 4, 0, 2,$$
$$4, 2, 4, 2, 0, 0, 0, 4, 4, 2, 2, 2, 0, 4, 4, 2, 4,$$
$$2, 4, 2, 8, 2, 2, 2, 4, 0, 2, 4, 0, 4, 4, 2, 0, 2,$$
$$2, 2, 6, 0, 4, 0, 2, 4, 6, 2, 0, 0, 0, 4, 2.$$

The average gain is $1060 : 100 = 10.6$. The expected gain is 10. In fact we can show that for each step, the expected square of the distance from the starting point increases by 1. This follows easily from the algebraic identities

$$(x+1)^2 - x^2 = 2x + 1, \ (x-1)^2 - x^2 = -(2x-1).$$

Consider the random walker at the moment at x. After the next step he will be at $x+1$ or $x-1$, each with probability $1/2$. His distance squared

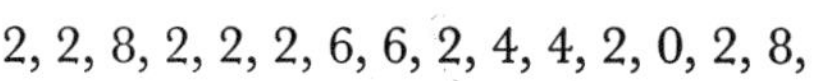

Fig. 6.95.

will be either increased by $2x + 1$ or decreased by $2x - 1$. The average net increase in $\frac{1}{2}(2x+1) - \frac{1}{2}(2x-1) = 1$. Hence, after n steps, his expected square distance from the starting point will be n.

Example 3. Waiting time for the first success.—Here is a simple but important problem with an intuitive result. I shoot at a target until I hit it for the first

144

time. The probability for hitting is p. Let X be the number of shots necessary. What is the expectation a of X?

Fig. 6.96.

A look at the tree gives

$$a = p \cdot 1 + (1-p)(1+a), \quad a = \frac{1}{p}.$$

Now we can solve the *coupon collector's problem*: A die is tossed until a complete set of points is made. The expected waiting times for the next new points are successively

$$\tfrac{6}{6}, \tfrac{6}{5}, \tfrac{6}{4}, \tfrac{6}{3}, \tfrac{6}{2}, \tfrac{6}{1}.$$

The total waiting period is

$$6(1 + \tfrac{1}{2} + \tfrac{1}{3} + \tfrac{1}{4} + \tfrac{1}{5} + \tfrac{1}{6}) = 14.7.$$

From a decimal random digit generator I sample digits one by one until I have a complete set of 10 different digits. I need on the average the following number of digits:

$$10(1 + \tfrac{1}{2} + \tfrac{1}{3} + \ldots + \tfrac{1}{10}) = 29.29.$$

6.4.6. *Wasps, Molecules and Ehrenfest*

Here is an example suggested by the Ehrenfest model. Figure 6.97 shows two rooms 0 and 1 with a connecting door, which is shut. In 0 there is a man and there are also three wasps flying around furiously and at random.

This is rather unpleasant company and the man wants to get rid of it. He opens the door and waits until all the wasps are in 1. Then he shuts the door. On the average once a minute a wasp flies through the open door. How long must he wait to get rid of the wasps?

The waiting time X is a random variable, and we want to find $E(X)$ and the distribution of X. In this form the problem is intractable. Hence we idealize: we replace the wasps by three numbered balls. Each minute

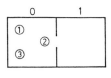

Fig. 6.97.

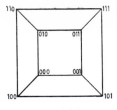

Fig. 6.98.

one ball is chosen at random and transfered to the other room. Now we simulate the situation to see what is going on:

$$000 \rightarrow 100 \rightarrow 000 \rightarrow 100 \rightarrow 000 \rightarrow 010 \rightarrow 011 \rightarrow 010 \rightarrow 110 \rightarrow 111.$$

In each binary block the i-th digit from left shows the location of ball number i. Now it becomes obvious that we are dealing with a random walk on a 3-cube. The student has met this situation many times before.

Figure 6.98 shows a cube. Suppose that a beetle starts in state 000 and takes one minute to travel one edge of the cube. As soon as it reaches state 111 it is absorbed. We are interested in the life span X of the beetle. Earlier work dealt with *microstates*. The binary blocks described completely which wasp was in which room. Now it is useful to lump all states with equal

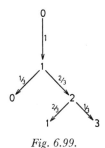

Fig. 6.99.

digit sum, i.e. to shift our interest to *macrostates* which merely specify the number of wasps in each room. The expectation $a = E(X)$ we get as usual from a truncated tree (Figure 6.99) and the distribution of X from a Markov chain diagram (Figure 6.100).

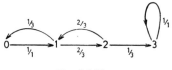

Fig. 6.100.

146

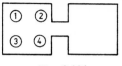

Fig. 6.101.

We get

$$a = \frac{2}{9} \cdot 3 + \frac{4}{9}(3 + a - 1) + \frac{1}{3}(2 + a), \ a = 10$$

$$P(X=3) = \frac{1}{1} \cdot \frac{2}{3} \cdot \frac{1}{3} = \frac{2}{9}, \quad P(X=5) = \frac{2}{9}\left(\frac{1}{3} + \frac{4}{9}\right) = \frac{2}{9} \cdot \frac{7}{9}$$

$$P(X=2n+1) = \frac{2}{9}\left(\frac{7}{9}\right)^{n-1} = \frac{2}{7}\left(\frac{7}{9}\right)^n, \quad n = 1, 2, 3, \ldots$$

Before any calculation is made the class should perform 1000 trials so that theoretical and empirical results can be compared. The following table shows the results of such an experiment. The empirical mean was 10.12.

Life span	3	5	7	9	11	13	15	17	19	21	>21
Observed frequency	225	167	140	99	71	58	42	49	34	27	88
Theoretical frequency	222	173	135	105	82	63	49	38	30	23	81

This experiment is the famous Ehrenfest model for 3 molecules. The wasps are merely stand-ins for molecules. In general an even number of molecules is used, but the case with 2 molecules is trivial and cases with more than 3 cannot be handled technically by 13 year olds. Still some important aspects can and should be discussed.

Consider 4 wasps, initially all in room 0. Now we are dealing with a random walk on a 4-cube. Take a 3-cube and label its vertices by binary

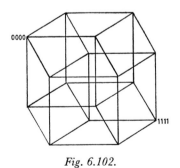

Fig. 6.102.

147

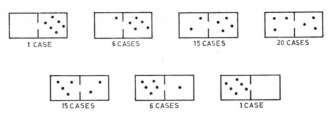

Fig. 6.103.

blocks of length 3. Now project the cube in any direction. Prefix 0 is to each label of the original cube and a 1 to each label of the projected cube (Figure 6.102). Now you have a labeled picture of a 4-cube. Pictures of higher dimensional cubes are a mess and are not recommended.

To find the expectation for the transition $0000 \to 1111$ one must solve a system of two equations. The students cannot do this, but they can and do like to find a rough estimate of the expected time for this transition by a Monte Carlo method.

The expected time is desparately long, $21\frac{1}{3}$ minutes on the average. Suppose that there are 6 wasps in both rooms. At regular, but not too short intervals snapshots of the rooms are taken. Each of the pictures will show a situation like one of the 7 pictures in Figure 6.103. After a great many pictures are taken, what proportion of them will show each possible situation? Suppose that the wasps fly around independently of each other. Then you could just as well determine by a coin in which room each wasp is to be found. Hence the 7 possible pictures should occur with frequencies in the following proportion $1 : 6 : 15 : 20 : 15 : 6 : 1$.

Next we start with 10 wasps in room 0 and simulate this situation for a few steps, just to see the flow into room 1. Take a string of decimal random digits: e.g.

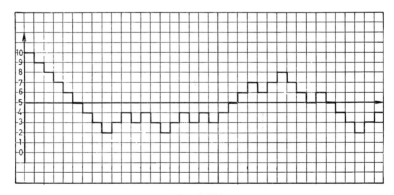

Fig. 6.104.

148

$$40982 \quad 17521 \quad 22630 \quad 61308 \quad 90794 \quad 17845 \quad 30646$$

The successive digits can be used to represent which wasp changes room. Figure 6.104 shows how the number of wasps in room 0 changes with time.

After a uniform distribution is reached there remains a small fluctuation around this equilibrium distribution. The 10-cube has $2^{10} = 1024$ vertices. The beetle returns very seldom to its initial condition, about once in 1024 minutes. With 100 wasps we have a random walk on a 100-cube with $2^{100} = (1,024)^{10} > 10^{30}$ vertices. After a few steps the beetle gets lost and for all practical purposes never finds its way back. Compare that if our planet was made of sand only, 10^{30} would be the number of grains of sand.

6.4.7. *The End of Naivety*

The Petersburg Paradox.—In the casino of St. Petersburg there is a popular game. You are handed a coin and you flip it until 1 comes up for the first time. Payment is made according to the following table.

Outcome	Gain
1	2
01	4
001	8
0001	16
.....	..
00..01	2^n
$\underbrace{\qquad}_{n}$	

The coin you are handed is not an L-coin. The probability of 1 is $p = 0.6$. What do you win on the average per game? Call the average gain x. On the first toss you either get 1 and gain 2 rubles or you get 0 and your future expected gain doubles. Hence

$$x = 0.6 \cdot 2 + 0.4 \cdot 2x, \quad x = 6.$$

The result looks respectable and it is easily confirmed by simulation.

Now suppose you are in desparate need of money and you decide to cheat the bank. Up your sleeves you bring your own coin which has probability 0.4 for 1, and you substitute it for the official coin of the bank. Your

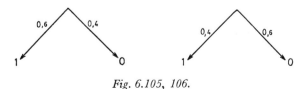

Fig. 6.105, 106.

149

expected gain x per game should increase since you have to wait longer for the arrival of the digit 1. The same reasoning as above gives

$$x = 0.4 \cdot 2 + 0.6 \cdot 2x, \ x = -4.$$

This is a highly unpleasant surprise. Your dishonesty is punished by a negative gain. But this is impossible. Something must be wrong. It can only be the method of finding expectation. Simulation results in another surprise: tremendous fluctuations and big gains. The average gain is infinite. For an L-coin we get the equation $x = 1 + x$ which has obviously no solution. The average gain is still infinite but grows very slowly in simulations.

A few more such examples (e.g. returns to the origin in symmetric random walk) and the confidence of the student is shattered. This is the end of intuitive probability. In the 8th grade a new start is made in a completely new style.

7. The aims of teaching probability

Hans Freudenthal

Mathematical Institute
Utrecht, Netherlands

Probability as a branch of mathematics was born in the Pascal–Fermat correspondence, with two famous problems, which we are told were raised by the Chevalier de Méré.

De Méré knew that it was advantageous to bet on the occurrence of at least one six in a series of four tosses of a die—maybe this was an old experience. He argued it must be as advantageous to bet on the occurrence of at least one double-six in a 24 toss series with a pair of dice. As Fortune disappointed him, he complained to his friend Pascal about preposterous mathematics which had deceived him.[1]

You know Pascal's answer. The probability of one six in one toss is $\frac{1}{6}$, the probability of no six in one toss is $\frac{5}{6}$, the probability of no six in four tosses is $(\frac{5}{6})^4$; at least one six in four tosses is the negation of no six in four tosses, hence the probability is $1 - (\frac{5}{6})^4 \approx 0.516$ which is a bit more than one half. Analogously, the probability of no double six, when tossing a pair of dice is $\frac{35}{36}$, and finally the probability of at least one double-six in 24 tosses is $1 - (\frac{35}{36})^{24} \approx 0.491$, which is less than one half. So de Méré had lost his money according to the rules of, and in perfect agreement with mathematics. Thus shall it be done to everybody who calls down curses on mathematics.

De Méré's other query was the "problème des partis". A and B have contracted to play a set of games with equal chances for both of them. He who first reaches five points, would take the stakes. Owing to circumstances beyond their control they are compelled to stop playing at a point where A has won 4 games and B has won 3 games. How should the stakes be divided? Some people said 4 : 3 was fair, others were in favour of $(5 - 3) : (5 - 4)$. Who was right? Neither, said Pascal as an arbiter. Suppose two more games were played. There are four possibilities:

A wins, A wins
A wins, B wins
B wins, A wins
B wins, B wins.

---

[1] There are other versions of this story, too.

151

In three of these cases A takes the stakes, in one case only, B wins. A has three chances against one of B. The stakes should be divided in the ratio of 3 : 1.

There are a lot of examples to explain to generally educated people what mathematics is, but for many reasons I prefer these two queries which de Méré posed to his friend Pascal. The irrationality of $\sqrt{2}$, the cardinality of the continuum, the complete induction, the existence of an infinity of prime numbers, the theorem on the bisectors of the sides of a triangle—these are excellent examples but, except for the last, too far from reality, too abstract: they fail to show that mathematics, though a transcendent way of thought, is immanent in the real world. But there is another still more important reason: de Méré's problems shed a sudden, unexpected light on the great problem of mathematics education. Chevalier de Méré certainly was an educated man, no doubt he had learned mathematics, yet as soon as he was dropped in a situation where he needed apply it, he was not able to do so. He applied the mathematics he knew, the mathematics of what in my infancy was called the rule of three: if I may bet on one specific result out of *six* in *four* tosses, I may bet on one specific result out of *thirty-six* in *twenty-four* tosses, because 6 : 4 = 36 : 24. And in the second problem, since the data are 3, 4, 5, and something has to be distributed among two persons, one concludes that it must be done in some ratio like 4 : 3 or $(5-3) : (5-4)$. Poor de Méré, like a faithful student he applied the mathematics he had learned and nevertheless he was punished. Maybe he would have performed better if he had never learned mathematics. Then there would have been some chance that he would have applied not the mathematics he had learned but the mathematics he made himself.

De Méré is not so much a historical figure. He is a paradigm, the ancestor of a prolific offspring, of all the poor de Mérés of our days who have learned mathematics they cannot apply. Each of us will once have played Pascal's part when he was consulted by people confronted with mathematics they did not understand.

I like the two de Méré problems, not only because these are jewels of mathematics and highlights of the history of mathematics, but even more because they reveal profound characteristics of teaching and learning mathematics. From the oldest times the rule of three or in modern terminology, the linear function has been an important mathematical tool of explaining and mastering phenomena in physics, chemistry, astronomy, economics, and in any field of human activity. It is a cheap procedure in experimental science to fit observational data to a linear function, and even before any experimentation has taken place, the linear function is the cheapest mathematical model. Using it dispenses with rethinking a situation, and such a dispensation is gladly accepted. Of course, from the oldest times people knew about inverse proportionality, but even Plato utters at least three times the surprise of the common man that not all functions are linear, namely at the example of the area of a circle as function of the circumference, the hypotenuse as a function of the other sides of a right triangle, the geometric mean as a function of its terms. Though today everybody would consider it as a matter of evidence that the luminosity caused by a light source of distance r is proportional to r^{-2}, Oresme still assumed a piecewise linear function, which vanished at a certain distance, depending on the strength of the source.

Teaching arithmetic can boast of an old and healthy tradition, but from fractions onward teaching mathematics meant and very often still means implementing some techniques such as linear functions, quadratic equations, solving triangles, trigonometry, differentiating and integrating. Even more modern subjects as sets, relations, and logic are no better taught than as formal techniques. Quite a few published courses show that teaching modern mathematics can be even worse than teaching old mathematics.

Take our two examples. What is of mathematical and educational impact in these problems? Not the ready-made mathematics which is applied in solving them but the mathematics reinvented for finding the solution, and the fact that to be solved these problems are to be tackled as new problems with no precedent whatsoever. Of course, in history they were solved by Pascal, but history does not mean old hat. A young student has his own history to which such problems should belong, not as facts related from three centuries ago, not as parts of a well-organized theory of probability with their analysis and solutions firmly attached, but as though they were new problems which have never been raised or solved before.

Teaching methodologies of the past, and in particular teaching geometry, have evoked the idea that mathematics is a deductive system. Of course this is true. It is true of all parts of mathematics which have afterwards been systematized. Mathematics, if it comes into being in research, in solving real problems, in teaching and in learning, is not a deductive system; it is no system at all. It is rather something which asks to be put into a system and this systematizing may be profound mathematics. It has been generally recognized that mathematizing a non-mathematical situation is essentially a mathematical activity but if I look to the greater part of mathematical texts, I should say that no more than lip service is paid to this principle. It is true that sets and relations usually are introduced by examples, but the fact that most of these examples are either wrong or irrelevant shows that the realistic context of such subjects has not even been considered. Mathematizing is even less exercised in new mathematics than it was in old. Eliminating geometry is a dangerous step away from reality and from a field where precious lessons in mathematizing can be learned.

If probability is mentioned in discussion as a possible subject of new mathematics teaching it always appears in one context, as an example of set and measure theory. In fact, in a few recent texts it has been dealt with in this frame, which means as a new lump of indigestible mathematics that the students will never be able to apply. I like probability for quite different reasons: because it is the best opportunity to show students how to mathematize, how to apply mathematics—not only the best, but maybe even the next and last opportunity after elementary arithmetic, since a rage for formalism seems to have spoiled all other teaching matter. I like probability and I teach it to college freshmen but I should say I would hate it to be introduced into high school teaching because I fear it will also be spoiled, as it has been in quite a few experiments which actually have been done. I know that many probabilists and statisticians share my view.

I teach a short course on probability of about 10–12 lessons to college freshmen with about the same number of periods for exercises. I do not teach it as part of measure theory, but as useful mathematics, and in the hope that students will be able to apply what they have learned in these lessons a bit better than what they learned in other courses. I will not tell you the content of this course. I will rather report teaching experiences, which, though obtained on college level, may apply to pre-college education, too.

Of course, I do not start by telling the students what probability is. In fact, there is as little need to do this as there is to tell what a point is in a course on geometry. The reason, however, why there is no need to do so is even more profound in probability than in geometry. It is logical in probability rather than ontological as it is in geometry. Any question on probabilities can be replaced with one on betting rates. Instead of asking somebody whether he estimates one probability larger than the other, or how large he estimates some probability, I can propose him a wager. Behavioristic definitions instead of logical ones are completely legal and trustworthy in elementary probability since every deviation from what is the logical background would be severely punished by material losses. This was, in fact, the argument which convinced de Méré even before he consulted Pascal. I will come back to this point later on.

If I did not start with a definition of probability, I must confess that I always started with examples of probabilities, but now I know that even this is wrong. I learned it when, at a weekend conference on primary education in mathematics, the participants were asked to sit together in groups of four and to elaborate a lesson of primary mathematics out of a choice of forty subjects. The group I belonged to chose "Toto". I am not sure whether Americans know what "Toto" means in Europe, but European children of primary school level know it. "Toto" is an abbreviation of "totalisator", the betting office of the classical horse races, which now handles organized betting on soccer contests. The gambler fills out a form with 13 lines corresponding to 13 soccer games and three columns which mean win, loss, and tie. According to a fixed pattern the betting total is divided among the correct guessers, those who have missed one, and those who have missed two answers.

Our group chose Toto and decided to elaborate a lesson for 10–11 year olds. The lesson should be started by asking the children what Toto means. But then, what should the next question be? To ask how large the probability (or the chance) is of having one's form filled out at random and nevertheless correctly, as somebody proposed? No. After a few less successful attempts we decided not to use the words "probability", "chance", and "at random" at all. The teacher would ask the children to draw Toto forms and to fill them out. Then the forms would be compared with one filled out by the teacher; forms which agree with the teacher's would be considered winners. Of course most likely nobody will win (there might be identical ones among the children's forms, and if this happens it is worth discussing). The next question would be: would there possibly have been a winner if we had played this in a class of 100 students? 1000 students? 10,000 students? and so on. Teachers in our group claimed that 10–11 year olds are so well acquainted with Toto that they would, correctly, wait for the million bracket to give a positive answer. The next steps would be in a more mathematical setting and would deal with a Toto of one contest, of two contests, and so on, to find what finally could be called the probability of guessing correctly the result of 13 contests.

This experiment has been a precious lesson for me. If next academic year I teach probability, I will start in an analogous way, that is by letting the students guess some probabilities. Actually I will start with de Méré's first problem or rather with the experience which provoked the problem. My first question will be: how many times must a die be thrown to get an equal chance of at least one six? I always asked this question, but this used to happen at the end of the first lesson. The students always answered: three. Next year if they again answer "three', I will perform the experiment of tossing a die thrice and I will repeat it a few times. We will record from those series of three the favorable cases though actually there is no need to do so. Within a few attempts we will get a series with a six first or second. I will ask whether we should continue such a series of three or not. This is a first indication against the guess that three tosses would be sufficient for an equal chance of at least one six. If this indication is accepted, we would start computing the probability of at least one six in 1, 2, 3, ... tosses in the crude natural way, which leads to the expression

$$\frac{1}{6} + \frac{5}{6} \cdot \frac{1}{6} + \left(\frac{5}{6}\right)^2 \cdot \frac{1}{6} + \cdots$$

To arrive at a more intelligent computation method we would consider the square and cube pattern representing the possible and the favorable dice results x, y and x, y, z. This undoubtedly leads to the insight that "at least one six" is better replaced with its equivalent "not without six". I think it is the first profound and convincing example, not of the equivalence of "there is an x with the property ..." and "not all x lack the property ...", but of the fertility of this equivalence of "sometimes" and "not never", which in logic should be mentioned along with others such as "somewhere" and "not nowhere", "somebody" and "not nobody", and so on. As you know, in probability, interpreting "at least one ..." via its negation is an important technique. It should be taught by leading the student to reinvent it instead of deriving it in a measure theoretic context. After these preparations, de Méré's proper question on two dice is merely a routine problem. A nice example I would add is the advertising (quoted by de Moivre) of a gambling club which for an event with a probability $\frac{1}{32}$ paid only 28 times the stakes; they justified the claim that this was fair by offering a bet that the event would occur at least once in 28 trials.

One query I usually raise in this context is whether, instead of tossing one die four times as is needed in the solution of the previous problem, I would be allowed to toss four dice together. Of course, I ask what "at least one six" now means. Too little attention is paid in traditional courses to the fact that probability problems can be often formulated in many equivalent ways. To get a feeling for how probability is applied the student should become acquainted with a variety of disguises under which one problem can be hidden. In mathematics the isomorphism of *problems* is as important a teaching subject as that of *mathematical entities* and this notion is not acquired by formal definitions but by having the student confronted with such isomorphisms.

As a simple and illustrative example consider the following. Ask someone to compare the chance that a person chosen at random has his birthday a given day, with the chance that two people chosen at random have the same birthday. Those without mathematical experience will tell you that the latter chance is much smaller. Strangely enough, if afterwards you ask them to compare the chance of throwing six with one die and the chance of throwing doublets with a pair of dice, they will not hesitate to estimate them as equal. It will cost you some trouble to make it clear to them that these problems are isomorphic as soon as their numerical differences are disregarded.

I have had another experience many times. People will tell you that in the usual system of phone numbers the figure 0 has a larger frequency than the other numbers owing to the fact that so many redundant zeroes are added in the vacant places at the left. In contrast, in the usual system of numbering pages of a book they consider the distribution uniform. Even quite a few freshmen do not realize what is wrong in these statements. It is useful to have them compute the probabilities of a digit 0 and of a digit 1 in the usual system of writing down the integers from 1 to 100 or from 1 to 100,000.

One of the first problems I deal with in my freshman course is that of the probability of the different outcomes of the sum of points of three dice. It is a tremendously useful exercise in showing students how to write down the possible combinations systematically. If the computation has been done, it strikes us that 10 and 11 have the same probability $(\frac{1}{8})$ as do 9 and 12 $(\frac{25}{216})$ and so on. How to understand this symmetry? After a few attempts to explain it a solution is proposed. If you turn a die upside down, the result x is changed into $7-x$, so if all dice are turned, the sum s is changed into $21-s$ which consequently arises with the same probability as s. Fine, I agree, it is a fact that our dice bear on opposite sides the pair of numbers 1 and 6, 2 and 5, 3 and 4. It is possible, however, to imagine the numbers 1 to 6 distributed over the sides of the die in a different way. Old Etruscan dice have been found showing 1 and 2, 3 and 4, 5 and 6 on opposite sides. With such dice, would the result be the same? I mean, would 10 and 11, 9 and 12, and so on show the same probability?

The reaction to this question is the same every year. A few students smile, a few laugh, and a vote taken shows a vast majority in favor of equality of the results. Nevertheless, a closer interrogation proves that all of the students are heavily disoriented, as disoriented as the poor boy who in a high school examination was asked whether the Trojan war was before or after the deluge. When I posed the question about the three dice to a group of mathematics teachers the consternation was as heavy but there nobody dared to answer. There is indeed a good reason for disorientation Everybody feels that the distribution of the numbers 1 to 6 over the sides of the die should not matter, but it is not easy to understand how it influences the former argument of turning the dice upside down. I think it is extremely useful to analyze this situation. The argument of turning the dice upside down is as correct as, for instance, the argument if $x^2 - 3x + 2 = 0$

157

and the earth is round, then $x = 1$ or $x = 2$. It is correct in formal logic but not if arguments are required to reveal the very essentials. The former argument should run: since with one die x and $7 - x$ have the same probability, with three dice the probability of s and $21 - s$ is the same. It does not matter whether the transition from x to $7 - x$ in every die is performed by turning it upside down, and therefore relying on this realisation of the function $x \to 7 - x$ is operationally wrong. It would not be difficult to find more examples of such "wrong" proofs but I think that this one is particularly illustrative.

Simple combinatorics is the backbone of elementary probability and our teaching of probability should take account of this fact. Serious mistakes in simple combinatorial problems are very common, maybe as common with our freshmen who have been taught a lot of mathematics at high school as with yours who have learned less. It is a characteristic of combinatorial problems that the mathematics they require is extremely simple. The essential thing to be done is to mathematize the problems since they are not usually encountered with mathematized wording. This mathematizing is something which is taught in our high schools as little as in yours. The main point of difficulty is the strange and multifarious disguises in which isomorphic problems can present themselves.

The number of ordered pairs (a, b) taken from two finite subsets A, B of cardinalities m and n is of course $m \cdot n$. The union of such subsets, if disjoint, has $m + n$ elements. This is as simple as it can be but it is an utterly worthless abstract theory if forming and recognizing products and unions have not systematically been exercised.

Take the following example. There are three rooms with two beds in each and three married couples to be assigned to these six beds such that husband and wife sleep in different beds in the same room. In how many ways can this be arranged? The students will rightly argue that first there are $3! = 6$ ways of putting the three couples into the three rooms, then there remain two ways to assign the couple in the first room to the two beds, two ways in the second room two ways in the third, and finally $6 + 2 + 2 + 2 = 12$, so there are 12 solutions to the problem. If such answers are given at college level, something, or rather much, has been wrong in mathematical education at the high school level and I must confess in this respect I do not expect much improvement from new mathematics if it is interpreted as it has been in quite a number of texts I have seen. The educational problem of acquiring simple combinatorial techniques is not solved by teaching set theory but by having the student disentangle complex situations in which such combinatorics play an essential part. Such situations are usually found within probability but there are enough outside it too. Finite groups often require such techniques. For instance, to find the automorphisms of the symmetric group of four permutands, one would consider that an automorphism is known by its action upon the six 2-cycles (ij), that (12) can pass onto everyone among them, that after fixing (12), (34) is also fixed, and (13) can still pass into (13), (14), (23), (24), which data fix the automorphism. After all these steps have been done correctly, students will still conclude that there are $6+4$ instead of $6\cdot4$ automorphisms.

In my freshman course on probability I deal with various occurrences of combinations in a systematic and logically connected way. I start with the well-known Galton board, a vertical isosceles right triangle of pins which are numbered as follows: one pin in the highest, 0th row; two pins numbered 0, 1 from the left in the next, 1st row; three pins numbered 0, 1, 2 from the left in the 2nd row, and so on. Balls are introduced through a slot to fall upon the topmost pin at which they rebound and are deflected to arrive with equal probabilities at the two pins in the first row where they are again deflected to the pins in the 2nd row, and so on. After a zigzag path the balls come to rest between partitions under the bottom row. I do not show a concrete Galton board, but students readily understand that most of the balls will accumulate near the center of the bottom row and only a few of them will fill the cells in the wings. I suggest the distribution of the balls by sketching the well-known de Moivre curve which will be dealt with at the end of the freshman course.

To find the distribution of the balls mathematically, we imagine that one ball is introduced into the slot and that instead of rebounding at every pin it divides into two balls which go to the next pins in the next row to be divided again. At every pin the number of passing balls is noted. This leads to the Pascal triangle which is numerically exhibited. Its generation is described recursively: the number of balls passing at the k-th pin of the n-th row is called $\binom{n}{k}$. Then the Pascal triangle is defined by

$$\binom{n+1}{k+1} = \binom{n}{k} + \binom{n}{k+1}$$

and a few boundary conditions. From these definitions the expression

$$\binom{n}{k} = \frac{n!}{k!\,(n-k)!}$$

is easily derived.

The numbers $\binom{n}{k}$ are afterwards easily identified with the binomial coefficients in the binomial formula. The equality

$$\sum_{i=1}^{n} \binom{n}{i} = 2^n$$

is also noted.

The number of zig-zag paths from the top to the k-th place in the n-th row is $\binom{n}{k}$. But what is a zig-zag path? To describe a zig-zag path of length n, the ball makes n choices of "right" or "left". A zig-zag path is a mapping Φ of the number set $\{1, \ldots, n\}$ into the set $\{\text{right, left}\}$, indicating the two possible choices. The path Φ ends at the k-th element of the n-th row after n choices among which k are "right", in other words if the Φ-pre-image of "right" has cardinal k. Hence

$$\binom{n}{k} = \begin{array}{l}\text{number of mappings of } \{1, \ldots, n\} \text{ into } \{\text{right, left}\} \text{ with } k \ \Phi\text{-orginals}\\ \text{of "right".}\end{array}$$

A zig-zag path Φ is completely known if the Φ-pre-image set of "right" is given, because the others are necessarily the Φ-originales of "left". Consequently,

$$\binom{n}{k} = \text{number of subsets of } k \text{ elements out of } \{1, \ldots, n\}.$$

A traditional term for such a subset is "combination of k out of n"; this term has to be mentioned but its use is perhaps better avoided.

Blackening k out of n circles or drawing k cards out of a deck of n cards may or may not be examples of forming a subset of k out of the given set of n things. If I get the task to blacken k circles or to draw k cards, I can ask whether the order of executing the task matters or not. If the order does not matter, the mathematical description of this procedure is: take a subset of k elements. If the order does matter, then I should say: take a sequence of k elements avoiding repetitions, that is, make a one-to-one mapping ϑ of the set $\{1, \ldots, k\}$ into the given set of n elements. Obviously the number of such mappings is $k!$ larger than the number of subsets of k out of a set of n. (The traditional term for a k-sequence out of n is "variation of k out of n".)

The task of seating k persons upon n chairs is the same kind of problem. Indeed, it is performed by mapping the set of people one-to-one into the set of chairs. However, if I am only interested in whether a chair is occupied though not by which person, then I have to look for subsets of k rather than for sequences of k out of n. It depends on the problem whether a choice of k out of n is to be considered as a subset or as a subsequence. Often it does not matter. The probability of finding at least three of a kind among five cards taken at random from a deck of 52 cards is the quotient of the favorable and of all cases. It does not matter whether a "case" is interpreted as a sub*set* or as a sub*sequence* of five cards; the second interpretation would mean an extra factor 5! both in numerator and in demoninator, which finally cancels out. This is paradigmatic for what usually happens in such problems.

To explain the difference between what are traditionally called combinations and variations, the language of sets and mappings, such as I have used here, may be of great help. In fact, I believe combinatorics can be in school mathematics one of the first convincing and profound examples for the use of sets and mappings.

For instance, dividing a set S of n elements into a set of k_1 elements, a set of k_2 elements, ..., a set of k_p elements, all disjoint but with $k_1 + k_2 + ... + + k_p = n$, is more clearly formulated as mapping S onto $\{1, ..., p\}$ such that the pre-image of $i(= 1, ..., p)$ consists of k_i elements. It is well known that the number of this kind of mappings equals $n!/(k_1! \, k_2! \, ... \, k_p!)$. It is worthwhile to analyze what actually happens if a deck of 52 cards is divided into four piles of thirteen. According to our previous definition I should take a function Φ which assigns to every $x = 1, ..., 52$ one of the numbers 1, 2, 3, 4 (or N, E, S, W) such that $\Phi(x) = i$ (i.e. $\{1, 2, 3, 4\}$) for exactly thirteen x. Usually the cards are dealt according to a fixed function Φ_0, e.g., defined by $\Phi_0(x) = x \pmod 4$, but before dealing the cards have been shuffled, i.e., subjected to a random permutation π. Consequently the actual Φ is the product $\Phi_0\pi$ of the two mappings. It is easily proved but not trivial that as a means of randomization Φ and Φ_0 are equivalent.

Leaving combinatorics and turning to probability proper, the first important concepts are stochastic dependence and independence and conditional probability. In my experience their implementation is an easy enterprise because they can be introduced and illustrated by numerous and multifarious examples. This experience, though well established, is met with serious doubts by people who are committed to an axiomatic approach; it shows one of the didactic reasons why the axiomatic approach has to be rejected. I am in the habit of introducing a bag assumed to be filled with the numbers 1, ..., 1000 and the subsets of multiples of 4, 5, 10, 20 in order to investigate dependence and conditional probabilities. But this is only one possibility out of host. A complete understanding of dependence is quickly acquired. In this process conditional probabilities are used as a means of reformulating the notion of independence, but I should say that I never dealt with conditional probabilities as such by independent difficult problems.

There is, however, one kind of disappointment that surprises me every year. Take the following problem. A bag contains the four numbers 1, 2, 3, 4 which are drawn in random order (permutation), every number in the correct place being paid one dollar. Compute the expectation of this promise. Students always answer the question by figuring out all permutations x_1, x_2, x_3, x_4 of 1, 2, 3, 4 with the corresponding payments:

1 2 3 4 ; 4	2 1 3 4 ; 2	3 1 2 4 ; 1	4 1 2 3 ; 0
1 2 4 3 ; 2	2 1 4 3 ; 0	3 1 4 2 ; 0	4 1 3 2 ; 1
1 3 2 4 ; 2	2 3 1 4 ; 1	3 2 1 4 ; 2	4 2 1 3 ; 1
1 3 4 2 ; 1	2 3 4 1 ; 0	3 2 4 1 ; 1	4 2 3 1 ; 2
1 4 2 3 ; 1	2 4 1 3 ; 0	3 4 1 2 ; 0	4 3 1 2 ; 0
1 4 3 2 ; 2	2 4 3 1 ; 1	3 4 2 1 ; 0	4 3 2 1 ; 0

(I always ask why there are no payments of 3.) The sum of the payments is 24, the expectation is 1 dollar. A curious result.

Is there not an easier way to find it? Of course, among the 24 permutations you must have 1 in the first place 6 times $(x_1 = 1)$, 6 times a 2 in the second $(x_2 = 2)$, a 3 on the third $(x_3 = 3)$, a 4 on the fourth $(x_4 = 4)$, though these coincidences can occur in combinations.

Note that I have proved the general theorem on the expectation of a sum of random variables

$$E(\sum_1^n x_i) = \sum_1^n E(x_i)$$

before, and when I proved it I stressed that it holds with no regard to questions of dependence and independence of the involved variables. But nobody hits on the idea that this can be applied to the four variables x_1, x_2, x_3, x_4 which take the values 1, 2, 3, 4 with equal though dependent probabilities, or rather to the payments

$$y_i = \begin{cases} 0 \\ 1 \end{cases} \text{ for } x_i \begin{cases} \neq i \\ = i \end{cases}$$

to compute the desired

$$E(y_1 + y_2 + y_3 + y_4).$$

If I draw the attention to this general theorem, students object that the variables are dependent. If I recall the generality of the theorem and its proof they agree but in their heart they do not believe that this trick is sound.

The next problem of this kind is separated from the first by at least one week. Given a bag containing two quarters, two dimes, two nickels, you are allowed to draw at random three coins out of this bag. What should you pay for this opportunity?

Again they start figuring out the 20 cases of drawing three coins out of six and the corresponding incomes to arrive at the expectation $20 + 10 + 5$

which would not have been different if the bag had contained every kind of coin just once. They recognize that their method was wrong again but I am convinced that in their heart the majority still do not believe what logic tells them—reasons of the brain which the heart does not know (to invert a famous saying of Pascal's).

I think I now understand what has been wrong in my teaching. I should not start with the general theorem but with one example or even with both and prove the theorem first in the special case of the example and then in general. I believe this would be more convincing than the old method which is classical and which dominates our traditional teaching philosophy from the first classes of mathematics upwards. Possession of a general theorem almost never guarantees its application and the fact that one learned it too early may even frustrate easy applicability. (I should tell you, but please, this is a secret—that quite a few people working professionally in probability and statistics can apply the addition law only in abstract, not in concrete contexts.)

Of course to apply the addition law to *variances* one has to suppose independence. The foregoing examples can be used to make this clear. I like to state the law a bit differently. I speak about dispersion (square root of the variance) and I say that dispersions are added according to "Pythagoras". This is not just a nice formulation, but touches the very profound reason of this unusual behavior of the dispersion.

Too little attention is usually paid to this property of the dispersion and, in particular, to the fact that the dispersion of the sum of n independent copies $x_1, \ldots, x_n$ of a variable x,

$$D(\Sigma x_i) = \sqrt{n}\, D(x)$$

is $\sqrt{n}$ times the dispersion of x. In other words, that the dispersion of the average of the $x_1, \ldots, x_n$

$$D\left(\frac{1}{n} \Sigma x_i\right) = \frac{1}{\sqrt{n}} D(x)$$

is $\sqrt{n}$ times smaller than that of x.

The $\sqrt{n}$-law is a striking feature wherever probability is applied in nature. There are textbook writers who never noticed this fact. In my opinion, students have to learn and understand it in a mathematical course and not to wait for some theoretical physicist or an experimental physics instruction book in order to get acquainted with this law.

Many mathematicians would not agree. They object that expectation and dispersion are only two parameters of a distribution and they would pass as quickly as possible to higher moments, Fourier transforms, or to

163

special families of distributions with indeed no more than two parameters. People applying probability in statistics or in sciences know that in many cases these two parameters carry all useful, and often even all relevant, information. I like to stress the use of expectation and dispersion and to make do as long as I can with these simple tools.

One of the most important applications of the $\sqrt{n}$-law is absent in almost all textbooks on probability. The daily number N of births in a country, the number N of responses of a Geiger counter per second, the number N of molecules in a cubic millimeter of gas, the number N of electrons passing in a milli-ampere current in a second is dispersed around its average $\bar{N}$ with the dispersion $\sqrt{\bar{N}}$ (as soon as $N \gg 1$). The probabilistic reason of this phenomenon should be explained in any college freshman course on probability, maybe even in high school courses. As mathematicians we simply cannot afford to leave such fundamentals to physicists. Therefore, it is a sad story that in almost all modern textbooks on probability applications to physics are never mentioned. Even error theory is usually neglected or passed over. There is no need to connect it to the normal distribution. In observational data the dispersion is a suitable measure of the error even if the distribution is not normal. Error calculus is still the most important and most frequent application of probability. It should figure in any course on probability, even at the high school level. Again we cannot afford to leave error theory to the instruction pamphlets of the physics laboratory. I will tell you a story about what may happen if we allow this. One of the prescriptions of such a booklet is to draw 400 times a card from a deck of 52 cards and to count the spades. Such a series of 400 has to be taken ten times. Though many thousands of students have worked with this booklet, a series with less than 75 or more than 125 spades never occurred in their reports because according to the prescriptions, observational data out of the 3σ-bounds are to be rejected. Still worse, even the variance of the ten results of the ten series of 400 should fit into bounds prescribed by this booklet and since these bounds were badly chosen some students had to waste their time with 40,000 instead of 4000 drawings. When these probabilistic experiments were discussed with the physicists they finally admitted that while it was not very sound mathematics, it was just the mathematics experimental physicists had to learn rather than the highbrow mathematics of mathematicians.

No doubt the weak law of large numbers, proved under the condition of finite dispersion, belongs to the fundamentals of slightly advanced probability. The law is easily proved, it shows again the importance of the expectation and the dispersion, and it is the best departure to arrive at the principles of statistical inference. Better than the more efficient, but rather

164

clumsy, central limit theorem. Only when the law of large numbers has been understood are the normal distribution and the central limit theorem didactically justified, though of course their proof can be omitted. To explain the subject I go back to the Galton board. It exhibits the sum of n independent copies x_i of a stochastic variable x which takes the values 0, 1 with equal probabilities. The arrangement of the Galton board suggests the variable Σx_i to be diminished by its expectation $n/2$, which means that the center of the basis is accepted as the origin of the scale. To make things converge it is natural to divide $\Sigma x_i - n/2$ by its dispersion $\frac{1}{2}\sqrt{n}$, that is to reduce the scale by a factor $\frac{1}{2}\sqrt{n}$. The stochastic convergence of the variables $(\Sigma x_i - n/2)/\frac{1}{2}\sqrt{n}$ is now suggested by the normal curve drawn in the picture of the Galton board.

Afterwards students may be told that the normal law applies, not only to the Galton board, but under broad conditions, to any sum of a large number of stochastic variables. A closer analysis shows three kinds of occurrences of the normal law: first, as a law for computing the distribution of sums of stochastic variables such as are formed in processing observational data; second, as an error law thanks to the unconscious summing of elementary error sources in the process of observation, and third, as a natural law applying in cases where extra-human nature has already formed such kinds of sums, as in the length of maple leaves or in the velocity of molecules in a gas.

Among the subjects I would add to my freshman course if there were more time available are games theory and stochastic processes. They would also fit into a high school course on probability. Both fields are a tremendous treasure of beautiful examples. As an example of games theory, take the following. A writes down one of the numbers 1, 2, 3, 4, 5 and B must guess the number. If the number that A has written down is i and B has guessed correctly, B receives i cents from A. If B makes a wrong guess, he receives nothing. Of course, B must also put a stake in the game, but the main question at this stage concerns the strategies that A and B should follow. You know what the problem is. If A writes down many fives he will have to pay out many fives. If he shuns fives, then B, if he notices it, will name no fives; he will confine himself to 1, 2, 3, 4 and increase the chance of a good guess. Such dilemmas were known in probability from the beginning of the 18th century. They were solved by von Neumann's discovery of the minimax principle: A can, and should, play so that B's maximal gain expectation is minimized. It is rather easy to explain this principle in the underlying example, simple arithmetic suffices to understand it.

The principles of stochastic processes can be explained by simple games, in fact the "problème des partis" is an example of a stochastic process.

165

Stochastic processes as a teaching subject has the advantage of providing valuable opportunity to practice matrix operations.

Probability is so close to its applications that it can even boast of a theory about how it is applied, I mean mathematical statistics. Should we deal with statistics in a college freshman course or in a high school course on probability? The principle of statistical inference is easily demonstrated with nice, simple examples which do not require sophisticated techniques of probability. Sign test, or double dichotomy, are sufficient material to explain the two hypotheses pattern and to analyze it profoundly. There is little need and it would be rather misleading to tie the principles of statistical inference to the normal distribution.

In any case I would never recommend that we teach any technique of mathematical statistics to college freshmen or high school students. All textbooks including statistics that I know are written as if to train future statisticians and indeed, it seems as if everybody who has learned a few statistical formulae believes he is a statistician. No part of mathematics is applied with less judgment than is statistics. Statistics, as it is usually taught, is the worst source of misinterpretation of mathematics. Mathematical statistics, though invented to handle numerical data with a critical mind, is often used to substitute mechanics for criticism. If we teach statistics to people who are not supposed to become statisticians, we are advised to educate their critical mind by showing them principles rather than to mislead them with superficial techniques. Of course this is a general principle in teaching mathematics to which everybody will pay at least lip servie. Therefore, I simply do not understand the philosophy of those who propose to teach a bunch of statistical techniques to high school students and I consider this philosophy as a most dangerous menace to teaching meaningful mathematics.

The last particular question on teaching probability you expect me to answer is: how about axiomatics? My answer can be as short as the question. What kind of axiomatics?

Measure theory axioms? But as Kolmogorov rightly pointed out, probability is much more than measure theory. To measure theory probability adds the use of a variety of measures instead of one, and the multiplication of measures. Hence the multiplication law of independent probabilities should be among the axioms. Of course such an axiom could only be understood if the students have learned before that stochastic independence is defined by the validity of the multiplication law. How is one to explain to these students who are not very experienced in axiomatics the strange fact that now the multiplication law is stated under the condition of independence?

166

A second aspect of my question is: probability axioms on *finite* or on *in-finite* universes? A finite system would not involve the generality we aim at in the axiomatizing business. An infinite system would not work if no integration theory is available.

Altogether, I am sure that if probability is taught through its applications, axiomatics of probability at the college freshman or high school level would not work, it would be a meaningless ornament. And on a higher level, where linear functionals tend to supersede old measure theory, Huygens' expectation or betting axiomatics looks more adequate than Kolmogorov's measure axiomatics.

Let us summarize. Probability is that part of mathematics which, after elementary arithmetic, is the most directly applied, without the intervention of any profound physical theory. If there is disagreement on arguments of elementary probability, it can usually be decided by a wager. Financial arguments can sometimes be more convincing than logical ones. Probability applies in every day situations, in games, in data processing, in insurance, in economics, in natural sciences. There is no part of mathematics that is as universally applied except, of course, elementary arithmetic. On the other hand, there is a particular probabilistic climate. In no mathematical domain is blind faith in techniques [more often denounced than in probability; in no domain is critical thought more often required.

These data should determine the teaching philosophy of a course in probability. Such a course should be a workshop where the student gets acquainted with as many applications of probability as possible, with the spirit of applying probability, with analyzing probabilistic situations, with creating probabilistic tools and with critical assessments.

Until this is recognized as the aim of teaching probability I would continue to pray: Please, do not spoil one more mathematical subject!

8. The role of mathematics in conceptual models

J. Gani

University of Sheffield
Sheffield, England

> New directions of thought arise from
> flashes of intuition bringing new ma-
> terial within the scope of scholarly
> learning.
> A. N. Whitehead: *Adventures of Ideas*

8.1. INTRODUCTION

The ability to create conceptual models is a gift to which man owes some
of his most basic intellectual advances. Through their practical applications, such models have proved a formidable weapon in the struggle for the
mastery of Nature.

It is one of the aims of this paper to illustrate the universality of the human
urge for model building. In psychological, social, mathematical, and probabilistic models, similar structural patterns recur, enriching our intelligence
and extending our environmental control. This natural human activity
appears to have deep psychological roots in children's efforts to develop a
personal working model of the world. Some details of this process are discussed in the brief account of the psychological researches of Jean Piaget.

A paradoxical point is that while in practice, children may operate with
sureness within the assumptions of their personal models, these need not be
logical or conceptually clear. The same appears to be true of subjective
models of society as perceived by adults. For example, members of a household in which descent and property rights are traced through the female
line are able to discuss the most complex relationships within their own
social framework. They may not necessarily grasp its conceptual principles, or the possibility of alternative schemes of personal relationships
and property rights.

A further aim of the paper is to suggest that in mathematical models,
the consequences of conceptual relations may be worked out to their logical
limits. The value of mathematics lies first in its capacity to express con-
cisely the links between the components of a model. Once this is done, the
model builder finds available a symbolic language which permits of prompt
logical calculus as well as arithmetical computations. The use of mathematics leads to results which may be tested against Nature; mathematical

models are then said to "explain" natural phenomena if their predictions accord with reality. It is precisely in this predictive capacity that their practical use lies, as we shall see when the development of Newton's model for the planetary system is described.

Perhaps the most difficult of mathematical models are those involving randomness. But precisely because so many real problems contain an element of chance, here too prediction becomes important, as for example in forecasting the spread of an epidemic.

If, as this paper maintains, model building is indeed a natural human activity, intellectually stimulating and practically useful, it must have a strong claim to a place in our school curriculum. I hope to present some suggestions for the possible teaching of this skill to students as an integral part of their mathematical training.

8.2. A PSYCHOLOGICAL MODEL: PIAGET'S RESEARCHES ON THE MENTAL GROWTH OF CHILDREN

It is commonplace that conceptual as well as cardboard scale models are used by mathematicians, scientists, architects and engineers. What seems to be less fully understood is that each of us carries within him a personal model of the world, however fragmentary. Forethought and planning are based on the manipulation of components of this model, and their projection into real situations. Mostly, these occur without conscious difficulty, and are barely noticed. Only when a serious discrepancy arises between the personal model and harsh reality is one forced to become aware of the conceptual framework, its possible falsity and the need to modify it. The construction of such a model begins in childhood; it is this process, duly refined, which sometimes emerges as the physical or cosmological world-system of the scientist.

Jean Piaget, a Swiss psychologist born in 1896, has been concerned since 1920 with the philosophy and psychology of the mental development of children. As a layman in the area, I could not possibly hope to give a critical evaluation of his research. But the experimental nature of his later studies [1], [2], carries considerable conviction, and the main outline of his findings leads to a consistent theory of how children create a personal working model of the universe around them [3], [4]. Here is a brief account of his main results, as I understand them.

Piaget argues that a child, from the beginning of his life, is at work creating a model of his surroundings. He will note that objects, though frequently moving, have persistence and continuity, that certain events

170

have a way of recurring. Once the framework of a personal model is built, it is expanded and enriched by experience throughout the child's life.

In his first eighteen months, the child arrives at a rudimentary understanding of spatial relations: by trial and error he learns that his rattle is *here*, not *there*. He also begins to grasp the basis of time sequences: he may expect, for example, to be powdered after a bath. He begins to recognize certain objects and persons, and expects them to persist, to move in space-time and to display certain recurrent patterns. By the age of eighteen months, the purposive behaviour of the child indicates the existence of a structured world-model.

From then up to the age of five years, imaginative play, experiment and constant questioning increase the child's understanding of space-time relations. This is the stage of intuitive thought: many of his concepts and images remain vague, unstable, illogical. For example, length will be confused with movement, or time with speed. However, from about the age of five up to eight years, the structural concepts of the child's world-model stabilise. Schemes of connected rational thinking become possible, chains of reasoning which lead to the logic of mathematics and the sciences are now conceived. By the age of eight, children are capable of dealing with experimental situations much as adults would, though their capacity for full abstract reasoning is usually reached only between the ages of 11 and 14.

To give an example of the methods used by Piaget to reach his conclusions, a simple experiment is described in which he elicits children's responses to the concept of *distance traveled*. Children between the ages of $5\frac{1}{2}$ and $8\frac{1}{2}$ are presented with lengths of wire AB and CD tacked to a board, and a cardboard strip to use for measuring lengths. They are told that the beads α, β threaded on the wire represent trams traveling along each tramway route AB, and CD respectively. The experimenter moves β and asks the child to move α by an equal distance. Three stages of understanding emerge in the children.

At the first stage of conceptualisation, children between the ages of $5\frac{1}{2}$–6 feel that if the beads are opposite each other, as in Figure 8.1, they have traveled the same distance. At the second stage, between 6–7, discussion with the experimenter enables the child to distinguish between distances traveled and the position of points of arrival; however, any suggestion that the cardboard strip be used for measuring is disregarded. At the final stage, between 7–$8\frac{1}{2}$, the child actually measures, at first hesitantly but later with assurance, to establish whether distances traveled by α and β are the same.

What this progression clearly shows is that in constructing his conceptual model, one of the child's most important steps is the realization of what is

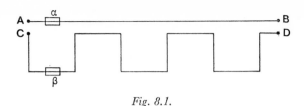

Fig. 8.1.

relevant in a problem. In his first stage, the child seems to suggest that his conception of *distance traveled* refers merely to progress in the direction from left to right. Only as he matures does he grasp that the distance traveled refers to the total length of path covered by a bead, and only later still that the cardboard strip can be used to measure such distances along paths. This notion of relevance recurs as a major factor in the success of more sophisticated models conceived by scientists and mathematicians.

One finding of Piaget's of particular importance is that the growth of children's understanding of numerical relations runs parallel to their grasp of logic. Thus, the persistent endeavour of man to construct mathematico-logical models of the real world may perhaps be considered as the limit of a natural psychological process. The remarkable success of such models in scientific explanation and prediction continues to reinforce the value set upon them.

8.3. AN ANTHROPOLOGICAL MODEL: MALINOWSKI'S MATRILOCAL HOUSEHOLD

But I must digress a little from the main theme of this paper to emphasize a special point. This is that while a model may be used with sureness by the person who has constructed it, as a basis for thought and action, it need not be conceptually logical, nor its principles abstractly understandable to the user. An example of my meaning will be illustrated by the following account of relations within a particular type of household first described by Malinowski ([5] pp. 233–238), and reported by Schusky ([6] pp. 22–23).

In describing a society of horticulturalists, Schusky outlines the structure of a *matrilocal* household as follows:

Here the women spend most of their time with the domestic crops. Men do some clearing and some harvesting, but women take the major interest in the fields. Daughters inherit their mother's fields and their knowledge of agriculture. Women may provide 80 or 90 percent of the subsistence. Mothers have a vested interest in the important factor of land. They could pass on their land to their sons' wives, but the daughters are already familiar with the land. Assume they choose their daughters. Sons must go to live with their wives who are inheriting land from their mothers. The society practises what is known as matrilocal residence. A household

172

consists of a woman, her daughters, their daughters, and any unmarried sons. All of these are consanguine relatives. The husbands of these women are in the household through affinal ties; possibly none of the men are related to each other. One must study this situation to appreciate fully the positions of men and women. An adult male marries and moves into a household occupied by his wife, her mother, her sisters, and her unmarried brothers. Most other adult males in the household are in the same position as he is—a virtual stranger. If trouble occurs with the wife, the man has a host of consanguine relatives allied against him. For solace he must remain tied to his mother's household and his own lineage; the situation re-emphasizes the importance of the female line.

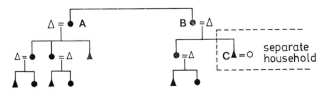

Fig. 8 2. ○ is a female, △ is a male, and = indicates marriage.

Suppose such a household consists of 2 sisters whose parents are dead. Both are married to men whose parents are also dead: the first sister A has 2 married daughters and an unmarried son, each of the daughters having an unmarried son and daughter. The second sister B has a married daughter with an unmarried son and daughter, and a married son C. A conceptual diagram of the relationships as drawn by an anthropologist might look like Figure 8.2. In this figure all the blood (consanguine) relations of the 2 sisters are darkened. Because of the simplicity of the diagram, and the conceptual clarity of the relationships involved, we can see directly that everyone except the married son C on the right will live in the 2 sisters' household. This married son will have moved into the household of his wife's relations.

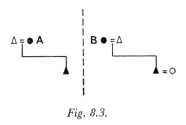

Fig. 8.3.

But this is surely not how the structural model is perceived by members of this society, clear as it must be subjectively to each of them. Every man and woman will be able to state without hesitation, the household to which a daughter or son should belong on the matrilocal concept. But it appears that if asked to replace the *matrilocal* by the *patrilocal* basis, considerable dif-

173

ficulty is experienced by members of the household in grasping the new ties which would obtain. We, with the simple conceptual principles of Figure 8.2 at hand, know the 2 sisters would find themselves in the separate family groups of Figure 8.3; it is the married son C who would now be in his father's household, while all married daughters would have moved into the households of their husbands' relations. To members of the matrilocal household, without the benefit of such conceptual principles, this conclusion would come only as the result of lengthy reflection.

Thus, while a subjectively well-defined model is adequate for immediate action within a familiar structure, it is not sufficient for a reorganisation of the concepts on which the model is based. For this, a fundamental grasp of the relevant principles is necessary. There is a parallel here between action based on accepted usage, and action based on the thorough understanding of basic ideas. Perhaps I might be allowed a very brief additional illustration of this point.

We use paper money as a measure of economic value and a means of exchange, while certain South Sea Islanders prefer cowrie shells. In both cases, we and the Islanders may operate efficiently within our own economic systems without a full understanding of the conceptual nature of our currencies. For neither paper nor shells really have value *per se*; they are only accepted counters for work done or goods purchased. So it may be hard to explain to the Islanders the value of a dollar bill until they have grasped the concept of 'currency' as against the (irrelevant) particular usage of cowrie shells in their local economy. To those who believe such conceptual discoveries trivial, I need only point out the "discovery" in Medieval Europe of the principles of modern banking.

8.4. A MATHEMATICAL MODEL: THE NEWTONIAN PLANETARY SYSTEM

The points so far made are that men tend to create models of the world, and that these models can be subjectively well-defined and usable without a full conceptual understanding of their principles. With the introduction of mathematics into a conceptual model, the relations between its analytical components become more clearly defined. A highly developed calculus is now available which leads to prompt logical deductions as well as arithmetical results. These can be checked against reality, and if they are verified, the mathematical model is held to "explain" reality. I would not wish to become involved here in a philosophical disquisition as to the *meaning* of such explanations. Let us agree for the moment that the power of mathematical models lies in their predictive achievements.

174

Fig. 8.4. Cycles and epicycles.

What I should now like to outline is the haphazard way in which a mathematical model for a scientific theory can grow; gradually, as an interplay of observation, experiment and guesswork, nursed with that mixture of intuition and logic which Koestler describes so well in his *Sleepwalkers* [7]. No story can illustrate this development better than Newton's derivation of the Law of Gravitation to account for the orbital paths and periodic times of our planetary system.

We shall not delve too closely here into astronomy or dynamics. Suffice it to say that the geometrical constructions of Ptolemy in the second century of the Christian era, with the Earth at the centre of the planetary system, and the Moon, Mercury, Venus, the Sun, Mars, Jupiter and Saturn in increasing concentric spheres about it appeared to fit the existing astronomical records [8]. The necessity of motion in circular orbits was regarded as obvious, though the method of epicycles allowed non-circular orbits to be constructed.

In Figure 8.4, for example, a point moving in a clockwise direction around the smaller circle, whose centre is simultaneously moving in an anti-clockwise direction around the larger circle produces an elliptic orbit. The point goes once round the smaller circle in the same time that its centre takes to travel round the larger circle.

Not until the axioms set out by Copernicus (in his *Book of the Revolutions*) in the mid-16th century postulating that the Earth was not the centre of our universe, but revolved around the Sun and its own axis, was the Ptolemaic conception questioned. Even so, Copernicus continued to deal in complex circular and epicyclic motions to explain the motion of the planets.

With Kepler, more accurate observation and calculation at last uncovered the elliptic nature of planetary orbits. But it would be wrong to think of Kepler as a cool scientist whose acute experimentation and cold logic led to the formulation of his famous three laws. When not immersed in the casting of astrological horoscopes, at which he was most adept, or indulging in mystical visions of the Harmony of the Spheres, Kepler conducted his researches into the planetary system to the tune of much acrimonious con-

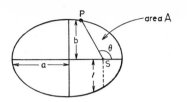

Fig. 8.5. Elliptic orbit of a planet.

troversy. In his *Astronomia Nova* in 1609, he gave the first two of his laws, to be followed in *Harmonice Mundi* in 1619 by his third law. Restated in modern terminology (see Synge and Griffith [9]), and illustrated in Figure 8.5, these are

Law 1. The orbits of planets (P) are ellipses with the Sun (S) at one of the foci.

Law 2. The rate at which area (A) is swept out by a vector from the Sun to an orbiting planet is constant. $(dA/dt = \frac{1}{2}r^2 d\theta/dt = \frac{1}{2}h$, a constant, say.)

Law 3. The squares of the periods of revolution (τ) of the planets are proportional to the cubes of the semi-axes major of their orbits $(\tau^2 = ca^3)$.

But it was still not clear to Kepler why these laws should hold. It remained for Newton in his *Principia*, published in 1687, to provide the mathematical model which would account for them. Briefly, the key lay in the concept of gravitation whereby, alone, a force proportional to Mm/r^2 towards the Sun S (mass M) acting on a planet P (mass m), sufficed to account for the elliptic orbit as well as the other properties. Newton's achievement was monumental for his time; the scope of his synthesis cannot but strike us, even today, as incredibly imaginative [10], [11], [12]. We who have recently witnessed the U.S.A.'s Apollo-8 moonshot, the docking manoeuvres of the U.S.S.R.'s Soyuz 4 and 5, and the testing of the lunar module during the U.S.A.'s Apollo-9 spaceshot, still have good reason to appreciate his work.

Given Kepler's laws, the problem as it presented itself to Newton was to prove that such a gravitational force, inserted in a mathematical model, adequately accounted for the observable phenomena. Consider the elliptic orbit in Figure 8.5 postulated in Kepler's Law 1. This orbit can be represented in polar coordinates (r, θ) in the form

$$l = r(1 + e \cos \theta)$$

where e is the eccentricity, a specific property of the ellipse, and $l = b^2/a$ the

176

length of the vertical line drawn through the focus S. If for convenience we denote $u = r^{-1}$, then the transformed polar equation is

$$u = l^{-1}(1 + e \cos \theta).$$

Using his laws of motion, Newton could now write the attracting force per unit mass acting on the planet P as

$$\frac{d^2r}{dt^2} - r\left(\frac{d\theta}{dt}\right)^2 = -h^2 u^2 \left(\frac{d^2u}{d\theta^2} + u\right) = \frac{h^2 u^2}{l},$$

where the latter result follows directly from Kepler's empirical Law 2 $(r^2 d\theta/dt = h)$, and the transformed polar equation for u in terms of θ. Since $u = r^{-1}$, we see that the total force acting on the planet must be of the form $\mu m/r^2$ where m is the mass of the planet.

There remained only to show that μ was the same for *all* planets: this Newton deduced from Kepler's Law 3. For, the period τ of any one planet could readily be shown from his mathematical analysis to be

$$\tau = \frac{2\pi a b}{h}$$

where a, b are the semi-axes shown on Figure 8.5, and h was the constant angular momentum per unit mass of the planet. Now Kepler's Law 3 stated that

$$\tau^2 = ca^3$$

with the same c for all planets. Hence, from the previous equation

$$\frac{\tau^2}{a^3} = \frac{4\pi^2 b^2}{ah^2} = \frac{4\pi^2 l}{h^2} = c$$

so that $h^2/l = \mu$ must be the same for every planet.

The entire system now hung together; all that was required in Newton's opinion was an explanation of the origin of the solar system. He saw in it the deliberate design of a Creator whose plan it was that it should continue forever in an orderly manner. "This most beautiful system of the sun, planets, and comets" he wrote "could only proceed from the counsel and dominion of an intelligent and powerful Being." There we must leave Newton's speculations to turn to our final construct, a probabilistic model for the spread of epidemics.

8.5. A PROBABILISTIC MODEL:
THE SPREAD OF EPIDEMICS

Of all mathematical models of reality, the ones which possibly present the greatest conceptual difficulty are those involving the notion of a random

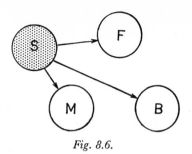

Fig. 8.6.

event. Quite apart from any complexity in the internal stochastic structure of such models, there is also the apparent contradiction of enunciating laws for them which are not followed deterministically, but exhibit themselves in a probabilistic manner. However, the importance of probabilistic models in the biological, physical, social and technological sciences is such that I shall attempt to illustrate their construction by describing a typical model for the spread of an epidemic disease.

Suppose that a child (S) brings home from school a virus infection; on arrival he meets the rest of his family consisting of a father (F) and mother (M), and a younger baby (B). We shall assume them to be represented by the various circles in Figure 8.6, and imagine that each person in the family will be in contact with all the others. Thus, on arrival home from school, the infective S can pass the virus on to any one of the susceptibles B, M, F; if B also becomes infected, S and B can each infect either of M, F, and so on. The number of possible infective encounters in the first instance is 1×3, and in the second 2×2, generally, the number of such encounters equals the number of infectives $\times$ susceptibles.

If we can make certain assumptions about the probability of passing on the virus at each encounter, then we can formulate a simple stochastic model. This was, in fact, first done in detail for this case by Bailey [13]. Let us assume that from time $t=0$ onward, an infective will, on encountering a susceptible, infect it independently of previous events with probability, $\beta \delta t$ (to order $o(\delta t)$) in time δt where β is a constant infection parameter. Then, if at any time $t > 0$ we have $i = 1, 2, 3, 4$ infectives and $s = 4 - i$ susceptibles in the home, the probability of the transition from i to $i + 1$ infectives in $(t, t + \delta t)$ will, independently of previous events, be

Transition	Probablilty
$i \rightarrow i+1$	$\beta i(4-i)\,\delta t$

all other transitions being impossible, or having probabilities $o(\delta t)$ in the interval δt. It follows, after some simple calculations for $i = 1, 2, 3$, that we can obtain for the probabilities

178

$p_i(t) = Pr\{i$ infectives at time $t > 0\,|\,1$ infective at $t = 0\}$, $(i = 1, 2, 3, 4)$, of this Markovian probability model, the following differential equations expressed in matrix form

$$\frac{d}{dt}\begin{bmatrix} p_1(t) \\ p_2(t) \\ p_3(t) \\ p_4(t) \end{bmatrix} = \beta \begin{bmatrix} -3 & 0 & 0 & 0 \\ 3 & -4 & 0 & 0 \\ 0 & 4 & -3 & 0 \\ 0 & 0 & 3 & 0 \end{bmatrix} \begin{bmatrix} p_1(t) \\ p_2(t) \\ p_3(t) \\ p_4(t) \end{bmatrix}.$$

Solving these in the standard manner, subject to the initial conditions $p_1(0) = 1$, $p_2(0) = p_3(0) = p_4(0) = 0$, we can obtain

$$p_1(t) = e^{-3\beta t}$$
$$p_2(t) = -3e^{-4\beta t} + 3e^{-3\beta t}$$
$$p_3(t) = 12(\beta t e^{-3\beta t} - e^{-3\beta t} + e^{-4\beta t})$$
$$p_4(t) = 1 - p_1(t) - p_2(t) - p_3(t).$$

One quantity we may evaluate if we are required to predict the course of the epidemic is the mean number of infectives at time t. This is given by the formula

$$m(t) = 4 - 3p_1(t) - 2p_2(t) - p_3(t).$$
$$= 4 + 3e^{-3\beta t} - 6e^{-4\beta t} - 12\beta t e^{-3\beta t};$$

it describes the average number of infections to be expected by time t, and may serve as a useful estimate of the number of people in the family who are expected to become ill. As $t \to \infty$, after a very long time, $m \to 4$ so that everyone will have had the illness.

Similar epidemic models have been used to describe a variety of diseases, among them the common cold, measles and malaria. A complete account of the present state of epidemic theory can be found in a recent review paper of Dietz [14]. Such probabilistic models arise frequently in the description of scientific phenomena which involve an element of randomness: in population studies, in quantum theory, in chemical processes, in the description of cancer cell multiplication, in queueing problems. For those interested in models of this kind the books of Bartlett [15] and Karlin [16] may prove useful.

We have now examined four different examples of model building, in psychological, social, mathematical (deterministic) and probabilistic contexts. To stress the recurrence of conceptual models in other fields of human endeavour would be to belabour the point. Let us turn rather to the problem of whether model-building, at least in its mathematical form, can be taught.

8.6. CAN MODEL-BUILDING BE TAUGHT?

The fact that conceptual models arise in so many of our activities makes it appear almost irrelevant to inquire if model-building *can* be taught. It seems rather more to the point to ask if this partly subconscious creative activity can be brought under intelligent control, or if basic elements in the art of model-building can be effectively imparted to students. The capacity for conceptual (and possibly mathematical) model-building lies dormant in all men; how can its useful development best be encouraged?

Let me discuss first a method which is already in use. In the U.K., the teaching of Applied Mathematics has an accepted place in the school curriculum. Students are taught the basic principles of Statics and Dynamics, with some elements of model-building illustrated in a variety of simple problems. In these, numerous spheres are rolled down inclines, elastic balls collide, rudimentary vehicles drive around curves; students are taught to construct simplified models of these which lead to satisfactory mathematical answers.

The main components of this curriculum are of ancient vintage. But I must confess for my own part, that when I worked at these exercises, I rarely felt them to reflect the realities I knew. What seemed lacking in the pre-rocket era was the element of relevance. It was never made quite clear, for example, what the 'coefficients of restitution' in the collision of two elastic balls stood for conceptually. Was it a convenient assumption, or a law based on experimental results? What I think I missed most was an understanding of the historical development of the subject matter. Even Newton's Laws of Motion were accepted as articles of faith rather than presented as the final results of a long chain of observation and reasoning.

Yet these courses in Applied Mathematics have their strengths. To improve them, my minimal suggestion would be to supplement the formalised examples with some elements of the experimental and philosophical history of the subject. More particularly, the concepts involved in the building of the model should be carefully discussed. In the case of the elastic collisions for example, my curiosity would have been satisfied if it had been explained that for billiard balls, experimental results had led to the simple hypothesis that speed of separation was some fraction of speed of approach.

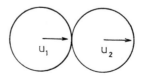

Fig. 8.7. Collision of 2 billiard balls.

Thus

$$u_2' - u_1' = e(u_1 - u_2)$$

where u_1, u_2 (u_1', u_2') are the velocities of the two balls before (after) collision, and e is the constant coefficient of restitution for these balls.

But even this modest additional information would not have been quite adequate. In Applied Mathematics, classical models are constructed which are often remote from the areas of one's own direct experience. I would have enjoyed far more models of economic input and output, discussions of elementary linear programming problems, elementary models in mathematical genetics, simple applications of graph theory. This is very much the area which Kemeny and Snell have made theirs in their enlightening and stimulating texts [17], [18]. Thus I would support every attempt to widen the scope of classical Applied Mathematics to include the creation of models for almost all of our practical daily experiences, much as has happened in Operations Research.

And, I would above all, stress the concept of relevance and economy of thought in the creation of such models. This is indeed a tall order, and I should hardly expect that we could move towards such an aim rapidly. Perhaps I could provide a short example of a situation, frequent in my own family, for which a model can be constructed. That is the optimal allocation of financial resources. To simplify the problem, let us assume that we have a family of 2 only: a husband (H) who is willing to provide a maximum of \$250 for Christmas presents, and a wife (W) who does the shopping. Each has made a list of presents which are ranked in order of preference; their costs are

	H	W
1st choice:	\$150	\$200
2nd choice:	100	125
3rd choice:	75	90

Neither wishes to spend more than twice on his or her present than the other, and it is agreed between them that the optimum choice will be the one for which the cost of the husband's present plus one and a half times the cost of the wife's is maximized. If h is the price of the husband's present and w the wife's, then we could construct a conceptual model of the situation which would lead to the three inequalities

$$h + w \leqslant 250$$

$$h \leqslant 2w \quad \text{and} \quad w \leqslant 2h$$

and subject to these, the maximization of $h + 1.5w$. Translating these into their graphical equivalents, we obtain the permissible triangular purchasing

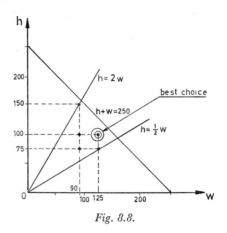

Fig. 8.8.

region in Figure 8.8. Clearly the choice of $h = 100$, $w = 125$ would be one of the five which are possible; one might guess that it would satisfy each partner most since it ranks fairly high on both their lists. It is, in fact, the one which maximizes $h + 1.5w$ to the value of 287.5. The example is frivolous, but other more classical applications of linear programming can doubtless be found to suit more serious occasions.

I hope you will have been convinced that the art of model-building has an interesting history; it has, I believe, a place in school instruction, possibly as an extension of the topics covered in Applied Mathematics. If my paper has convinced even a few of you of the desirability of teaching model-building as a subject part experiment, part history of science, part logic, and part unconscious inventiveness, or "sleepwalking" in Koestler's terminology, I shall have achieved my intention.

REFERENCES

Section 8.2

1. Piaget, Jean (1937), La Construction du Réel chez l'Enfant. Delachaux et Niestlé, Neuchatel.
2. Piaget, Jean (1952), The Child's Conception of Number. Routledge and Kegan Paul, London.
3. Isaacs, Nathan (1960), New Light on Children's Ideas of Number. Ward Lock, London.
4. Isaacs, Nathan (1961), The Growth of Understanding in the Young Child. Ward Lock, London.

Section 8.3

5. Malinowski, Bronislaw (1960), "A woman-centered family system" in Exploring the Ways of Mankind. Holt, Rinehart & Winston, New York.
6. Schusky, E. L. (1965), Manual for Kinship Analysis. Holt, Rinehart & Winston, New York.

Section 8.4

7. Koestler, Arthur (1959), The Sleepwalkers. Macmillan, New York.
8. Toulmin, S. and Goodfield, June (1961), The Fabric of the Heavens. Pelican Books, London.
9. Synge, J. L. and Griffith, B. A. (1942), Principles of Mechanics. McGraw Hill, New York.
10. Butterfield, H. (1957), The Origins of Modern Science (2nd edition). Bell, London.
11. Whitehead, A. N. (1926), Science and the Modern World. Cambridge University Press.
12. Whitehead, A. N. (1933), Adventures of Ideas. Pelican Books, London.

Section 8.5

13. Bailey, N. T. J. (1957), The Mathematical Theory of Epidemics. Griffin, London.
14. Dietz, K. (1967), Epidemics and rumours: a survey. J. R. Statist. Soc. A, 130, 505–528.
15. Bartlett, M. S. (1960), Stochastic Population Models. Methuen, London.
16. Karlin, S. (1966), A First Course in Stochastic Processes. Academic Press, New York.

Section 8.6

17. Kemeny, J. G., Snell, J. Laurie, and Thompson, G. L. (1957), Introduction to Finite Mathematics. Prentice-Hall, Englewood Cliffs, N.J.
18. Kemeny, J. G. and Snell, J. Laurie (1962), Mathematical Models in the Social Sciences. Blaisdell, New York.

9. Probability and pre-calculus analysis

Samuel Goldberg

Oberlin College
Oberlin, Ohio, U.S.A.

Teachers of mathematics in American secondary schools have experimented with a variety of courses for college-bound twelfth-grade students. Many such students take a full year of differential and integral calculus and increasing numbers are able to receive college credit for this work by satisfactory performance on the Advanced Placement Examinations in Mathematics offered each year by the College Entrance Examination Board. Other students are offered a semester course in probability and statistics, often modeled on the course developed by Professor Mosteller for the Continental Classroom television series. It is safe to say, however, that most college-bound students are studying neither calculus nor probability, but rather some algebra, analytic geometry, and the elementary functions in a pre-calculus analysis course. Secondary school (and college) teachers believe such a course serves well to strengthen the student's background in analytic skills and techniques and thus is good preparation for a course in calculus to be elected in college.

Previous speakers at this Conference have given many excellent reasons in support of a pre-college course in probability and statistics. The point I wish to make is that one need not offer a course in analytic geometry and elementary functions in order to develop the student's background in analysis. I wish to show by some examples that a probability course can serve this important purpose as well and thus should be seriously considered by secondary school teachers who may prefer to develop the student's maturity in pre-calculus analysis in the context of an interesting, important, and new subject for the student.

I turn now to three problems that serve to illustrate how an interest in analysis can be combined with material in a probability course. The first two problems are so well-known that only an outline of their solutions is given. The third problem, although not new, is less well known to teachers of probability and a detailed exposition is included here.

Problem 1.—An unknown number, say N, of animals inhabit a certain region. To get some information about the size of the animal population, the following experiment is performed. First, M of the animals are caught, marked in some way, and then released. After waiting for these marked animals to disperse throughout the region, a sample of n animals is then drawn (without replacement) from the entire population. It is observed that exactly m of these n animals are marked. The problem is to estimate N (the unknown population size) from the known numbers M (the total number of marked animals in the population), n (the sample size), and m (the number of marked animals in the sample).

Of the $\binom{N}{n}$ possible samples, there are $\binom{M}{m}\binom{N-M}{n-m}$ that contain exactly m marked and $(n-m)$ unmarked animals. Hence, if X denotes the number of marked animals in the sample,

$$P(X=m) = \frac{\binom{M}{m}\binom{N-M}{n-m}}{\binom{N}{n}} = p(N), \text{ say.}$$

(The functional notation $p(N)$ makes explicit the fact that this probability depends on the unknown population size N and leaves implicit the dependence on the other parameters M, n, and m.) The probability $p(N)$ is called the *likelihood* of the observed event (m marked animals found in the sample of n animals.) A value of N, denoted by $\hat{N}$, that maximizes the likelihood $p(N)$ is a so-called *maximum-likelihood estimate* of N. My experience with beginning students is that of two estimates of N, they find it intuitively reasonable to put more faith in the one for which the probability of getting the actually observed experimental outcome is larger. Thus they readily accept the principle of maximum-likelihood estimation and the problem is reduced to one in analysis: find N to maximize $p(N)$.

To determine $\hat{N}$, we study the ratio $p(N)/p(N-1)$. For, considered as a function of N, $p(N)$ increases as long as this ratio is larger than 1 and decreases when the ratio is less than 1. The ratio therefore gives us information about where the graph of $p(N)$ rises and where it falls and so enables us to find the value of N where it is highest.

Using the definition of binomial coefficients and simplifying, one easily finds that

$$\frac{p(N)}{p(N-1)} = \frac{(N-M)(N-n)}{N(N-M-n+m)}.$$

This ratio is greater than, equal to, or less than 1 according as N is less than, equal to, or greater than nM/m. We thus conclude that $\hat{N}$, the maximum-likelihood estimate of the unknown population size N, can be taken as the largest integer not exceeding nM/m.

A student working through the solution to this problem has not only some useful practice in algebraic manipulations, but more important, sees an example of *incremental analysis*: seeking to maximize an output quantity (here the likelihood $p(N)$) that depends upon an integer-valued input variable (here N) by studying the effect on the output of a unit change in the input variable. Understanding how this analysis locates the relative position of neighboring points of the graph of the output quantity (and hence the maximum point) is a lesson well worth emphasizing in the classroom.

Problem 2.—The demand for a certain product is an integer-valued random variable D with probability mass function f and cumulative distribution function F, i.e., $f(d) = P(D=d)$ and $F(x) = P(D \leqslant x)$. A unit costs $\$c$ to stock and is sold for $\$s$. Assuming no loss associated with an inability to satisfy customer demand and that unsold items are worthless, determine the number of items to be stocked in order to maximize the expected profit.

I mention this problem because here too an incremental analysis is appropriate. It is easy to see that the expected profit when n items are stocked, say $y(n)$, is given by

$$y(n) = \sum_{d=0}^{n} (sd - cn) f(d) + \sum_{d=n+1}^{\infty} (s-c) nf(d).$$

Although the *ratio* of successive terms proved useful in the preceding problem, students soon see that the *difference*

$$y(n) - y(n-1) = s - c - sF(n-1)$$

is more useful here. Since expected profit is increasing as long as this difference is greater than zero, it is a simple matter to conclude that the stock needed to maximize expected profit is the largest integer n such that

$$F(n-1) < (s-c)/s.$$

A student solving this problem obtains practice simplifying algebraic expressions involving summation signs and must also, as in Problem 1, see the relation between the sign of the difference $y(n) - y(n-1)$ on the one hand and the rising and falling of points of the graph of the expected profit function y on the other. (Although this Conference is devoted to pre-college courses, I cannot resist mentioning that college students also should be exposed to maximizing problems of the kind we have been talking about. Calculus students are too often brainwashed into the reflex reaction "take the derivative and set it equal to zero" when they are confronted with a maximum or a minimum problem. Optimization problems requiring only an incremental analysis are useful antidotes to this reflex.)

Problem 3.—Consider an event E that can occur when an experiment is performed. If someone announces to us that E did indeed occur, we express a certain degree of "surprise" at this news. For example, if two dice are rolled and we are told that the sum of the numbers showing on the dice is less than 15, we are not surprised at all since we were sure this would be the case before being told. The news that the sum is less than seven evokes some measure of surprise and that the sum is less than three even more surprise. Our problem is to develop this intuitive idea of "surprise" and to make it a precise and useful concept.

Twelfth-graders to whom I have presented only this brief introduction have been able (with some guidance) to proceed in the classroom toward this goal. They quickly agree that the "surprise" one feels upon hearing that an event E has occurred depends on only the probability of E. Let us then denote by $S(p)$ *the surprise evoked by the occurrence of an event with probability p.* Our procedure is first to agree on a number of reasonable conditions that this surprise function S should satisfy and then, assuming our conditions are consistent, that is, that there exist functions satisfying all the agreed-upon conditions, to characterize these surprise functions by determining their functional form. We assume throughout that S is defined for $0 < p \leqslant 1$ so that the surprise function we seek is meaningful for all events with positive probability, but is undefined for impossible events having probability zero.

Our first condition stems from the intuitive feeling that there is no surprise at all if we are told an event sure to occur actually did occur.

Axiom 1. $S(1) = 0$, i.e., the surprise associated with the occurrence of a sure event (having probability one) is zero.

Our second condition expresses the fact that of two events, the occurrence of the one with greater probability produces a lesser surprise than the occurrence of the other. For example, the news that an event with probability 0.9 has occurred evokes less surprise than the news that another event with probability 0.2 has occurred. When stated formally, this leads to the second requirement to be satisfied by the function S.

Axiom 2. S is a decreasing function, i.e., if $x > y$, then $S(x) < S(y)$.

Intuitively, we expect that a small change in the probability of an event will correspond to a small change in the surprise evoked by the event. Although we do not assume twelfth-graders have studied the precise definition of continuity, the rough notion of a "smooth" graph is adequate here.

188

Axiom 3. S is a continuous function.

Consider now two independent events E and F with $P(E) = x$ and $P(F) = y$. Since $P(E \cap F) = xy$, the surprise evoked by the occurrence of both E and F is $S(xy)$. If we are first told only that event E occurred, then the surprise we feel upon hearing this news is $S(x)$ and thus the difference $S(xy) - S(x)$ represents the surprise remaining to be evoked when we learn that event F also occurred. Since E and F are independent, the knowledge that E occurred does not change the probability of F and so this remaining surprise is still $S(y)$. This reasoning suggests the following condition.

Axiom 4. $S(xy) = S(x) + S(y)$ for $0 < x \leqslant 1, 0 < y \leqslant 1$.

At this point only a little prodding gets a class to guess that the logarithm function may be making an appearance. We can then actually prove the following result.

Theorem. If the surprise function S satisfies Axioms 1–4, then

$$S(p) = -C \log p$$

where C is an arbitrary positive number and the logarithm base is any number greater than 1.

The proof uses Axiom 4 to establish first that $S(p^x) = xS(p)$ for all positive integer exponents x, then for all rational exponents x, and finally, by the continuity guaranteed by Axiom 3, for all positive real exponents x. The extension to $x = 0$ follows from Axiom 1. Now choose any $b > 1$ and let $x = -\log_b p$. Then $p = b^{-x}$ and

$$S(p) = S((1/b)^x) = xS(1/b) = -C \log_b p$$

where $C = S(1/b) > 0$ since $1/b < 1$ and $S(1/b) > S(1) = 0$ by Axioms 2 and 1.

Let us from now on follow the custom adopted in information theory of choosing $C = 1$ and taking logarithms to the base 2. Then the surprise S is expressed in units called *bits* (a contraction of binary digits).

If instead of one event, we consider an experiment $\mathcal{E}$ whose sample space is partitioned into the n events $E_1, E_2, \ldots, E_n$ with positive probabilities $p_1, p_2, \ldots, p_n$, then we can compute the average or mean surprise at the experimental outcome. This mean surprise will be a weighted average in which the surprise of each event is multiplied by the probability with which this surprise is evoked. That is, if we denote by $H_n(p_1, \ldots, p_n)$ the mean surprise associated with experiment $\mathcal{E}$, then

$$H_n(p_1, \ldots, p_n) = -\sum_{j=1}^{n} p_j \log p_j.$$

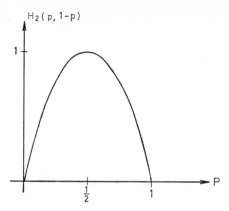

Fig. 9.1. *The entropy of a coin-tossing experiment.*

The quantity H_n is known in information theory as the *entropy* of the experiment

$$\mathcal{E} = \{E_1, E_2, \ldots, E_n\}.$$

(Let us also agree to extend the definition to include the possibility that one or more of the probabilities p_j are zero. We keep the above definition of the entropy H_n but agree that any expression of the form $0 \log 0$ is defined to be zero.)

As an example, let $\mathcal{E}$ be the toss of a coin and suppose p is the probability of a head. Then

$$H_2(p, 1-p) = -p \log p - (1-p) \log (1-p).$$

The graph of this function is given in Figure 9.1 and we observe that the toss of a fair coin has an entropy of 1 bit, that the entropy is greatest when $p = \frac{1}{2}$ and decreases as the coin becomes more biased, becoming zero when we are sure that the coin will fall heads ($p = 1$) or fall tails ($p = 0$).

Information theory supplies another useful interpretation of the entropy measure H_n. Suppose an experiment $\mathcal{E}$ can result in exactly one of the five events E_1, E_2, E_3, E_4, E_5 with probabilities 0.15, 0.35, 0.20, 0.25, 0.05, respectively. The result of $\mathcal{E}$ is to be determined by a sequence of questions, each of which must be answered either "yes" or "no". A sample of such questions is outlined in Figure 9.2. We ask first if E_2 or E_4 occurred. If, let us suppose, E_1 actually occurred, we receive a "no" answer and proceed to ask if E_3 occurred. Another "no" response follows, and then the question "Did E_1 occur?" receives a "yes" answer and we are finished.

Also indicated in Figure 9.2 is a way to assign a *binary code word* to each of the five possible events $E_1, \ldots, E_5$. The sequence of "yes" or "no" answer identifying each event is transformed into the binary code word for the

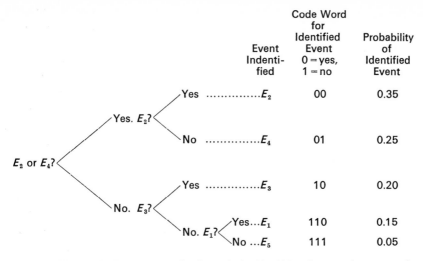

		Event Indenti- fied	Code Word for Identified Event 0 = yes, 1 = no	Probability of Identified Event
Yes. E_2?	Yes ....E_2		00	0.35
	No ....E_4		01	0.25
No. E_3?	Yes ....E_3		10	0.20
No. E_1?	Yes...E_1		110	0.15
	No ...E_5		111	0.05

Fig. 9.2. *"Yes" or "no" questions and code words for identifying the event that occurs when an experiment is performed.*

event by making a "yes" answer correspond to a zero in the code word and a "no" answer to a one.

Now let L denote the random variable that is the number of "yes" or "no" questions required to identify the result of the experiment. As we have seen, L can also be interpreted as the length of the binary code word for the resulting event, i.e., the number of binary digits making up the code word. In our illustrative example, we note that $L=2$ whenever $\mathcal{E}$ results in E_2, E_3, or E_4, and $L=3$ whenever $\mathcal{E}$ results in E_1 and E_5. Hence, the expectation of L is given by

$$E(L) = 2(0.35 + 0.25 + 0.20) + 3(0.15 + 0.05) = 2.20.$$

The "noiseless coding theorem," one of the fundamenta lresults in information theory, asserts that $E(L)$ cannot be made to fall below $H_n(p_1, ..., p_n)$. In our example,

$$H_5(0.15, 0.35, 0.20, 0.25, 0.05) = -0.15 \log 0.15 - 0.35 \log 0.35$$
$$-0.20 \log 0.20 - 0.25 \log 0.25 - 0.05 \log 0.05,$$

and one computes an entropy of 2.12 to two decimal accuracy. In general, it is possible to interpret the entropy H_n of an experiment $\mathcal{E}$ as the greatest lower bound of the number of "yes" or "no" questions (or equivalently, of the expected lengths of binary code words) required to identify the event resulting from one performance of $\mathcal{E}$.

191

Although much more can be said about each of the three problems I have presented (see References), I turn now to some general remarks about the teaching of probability in the twelfth grade.

1. Our first aim, of course, should be to present problems which cause students to think about important and central topics in probability. The three problems discussed here involve a selection of such topics: combinatorial techniques, random variables, expectation, the relation between a probability mass function and the cumulative distribution function, independence of events, etc.

2. We should ask students to spend more time and thought on "word" problems. Here I applaud the examples in the papers of Professors Engel, Holm, and Kruskal and strongly agree with the suggestion in Professor Gani's paper that building simple models of real-world phenomena has a place in the schools. But there is need for students to understand that axiom systems can be thought of as models within mathematics itself. One has an intuitive idea (like "surprise" in Problem 3) and writes down axioms that will hopefully have interesting mathematical consequences. A great many important topics in game theory, utility theory, statistical decision theory (see Luce and Raiffa) and elsewhere in mathematics are developed in this way and it is well for students to realize this as early as possible in their studies.

3. It is possible and desirable to present problems in a twelfth-grade probability course that will make students learn or review some pre-calculus analysis. The three problems we have discussed involve the following topics in analysis in addition to those of a purely probabilistic nature: mathematical induction, summation notation, analytic geometry and the graphs of functions, incremental analysis, rational and real numbers, logarithms to various bases, and the inverse relation between the logarithm and exponential functions. Such topics in analysis are more interesting to students and hence are often better-learned when they are presented not as ends in themselves, but rather in the context of problems which have separate and independent interest and which require the analytic techniques as means toward arriving at solutions.

4. It is well to indicate to students that there are always more things to learn. Our problems allow a teacher to mention limits and continuity, functional equations, and axiomatics as more advanced topics to which twelfth-graders can look forward.

5. At the same time, a probability course can and should serve to open the eyes of young students to applications of mathematics that are relatively new and less well-known than they should be. Let students know that prob-

ability is used a great deal in ecology, genetics, epidemiology, and other areas of biology, in learning theory in psychology, in inventory theory and generally in the management sciences or operations research, in information and communication theory, etc.

The three problems I have briefly discussed illustrate these general remarks. I believe we would do well to develop more such illustrative examples in a form suitable for twelfth-graders and to make room in our courses for discussion of these problems and their solutions.

REFERENCES

1. Ash, R. Information Theory, John Wiley and Sons, Inc., New York, 1965.
2. Blackwell, D. "Information Theory" in Modern Mathematics for the Engineer, Second Series, E. F. Beckenbach (Ed.), McGraw-Hill Book Co., New York, 1961.
3. Brillouin, L. Science and Information Theory, second edition, Academic Press, New York, 1962.
4. Hillier, F. S. and G. L. Lieberman, Introduction to Operations Research, Holden-Day, Inc., San Francisco, 1967.
5. Luce, R. D. and H. Raiffa, Games and Decisions, John Wiley and Sons, Inc., New York, 1957.
6. Quastler, H. (Ed.), Information Theory in Biology, Univ. of Illinois Press, Urbana, Ill., 1953.
7. Reza, F. M., An Introduction to Information Theory, McGraw-Hill Book Co., New York, 1961.
8. Shannon, C. E. and W. Weaver, The Mathematical Theory of Communication, University of Illinois Press, Urbana, Ill., 1949.

10. Statistical examples for use in high school

William Kruskal

University of Chicago
Chicago, Illinois, U.S.A.

10.1. INTRODUCTION

My talk today is a double one. First, I shall in part substitute for Frederick Mosteller, who is unable to attend, but who had been planning to tell you about a joint committee of the American Statistical Association (ASA) and the National Council of Teachers of Mathematics (NCTM) to deal with probability and statistics at the secondary school level. Second, I shall discuss two or three statistical examples that have been suggested towards one publication planned by the ASA–NCTM committee.

A few years ago, Professor Mosteller, who was then President of the American Statistical Association, spoke at a meeting of the NCTM. Out of that meeting came suggestions for the joint committee, and something over a year ago the committee was formed. Its initial members were

For ASA: Frederick Mosteller, Harvard University, Chairman
Richard Link, Louis Harris Associates
William Kruskal, University of Chicago
For NCTM: Julius Hlavaty, then President of NCTM
Gerald Rising, University of Buffalo.

Since then, Mr. Hlavaty has resigned because of the pressure of his presidential duties; he asked Richard Pieters (Phillips Andover Academy) to replace him, and Mr. Pieters has kindly agreed.

The committee has had three meetings and a great deal of correspondence. One of our first conclusions was that secondary school probability as such is a topic for which many authors have been preparing teaching materials at an increasing pace. Probability is a branch of mathematics, and it is not unreasonable that secondary school mathematics teachers be able to present it fairly readily, given good textbook and other teaching materials.

Statistics, on the other hand, has important non-mathematical aspects, aspects that are relevant to secondary school courses in the natural sciences, the social sciences, and of course in laboratory work. It is probably inevitable that most secondary school statistics will be taught by mathematics instructors, yet it is important that the *non*-mathematical aspects of statistics be presented, along with the mathematical ones.

Quite aside from this, there seems to be a considerable shortage of interesting and authoritative high school level teaching material in statistics proper. Much of what is available suffers from one of two difficulties. Some of it is limited and dull, so that the student comes away thinking that all statistics is what we would call elementary descriptive statistics: means, medians, modes, quartiles, and so on. On the other hand, there are some excellent treatments intended for high school students that turn out simply to be over-difficult.

Hence our committee's first project is preparation of a book of examples of statistics, many of them with real data, and with discussion of both mathematical and non-mathematical aspects of statistics. The format will probably be question and answer, with rather complete treatments for most of the examples. We want to find instructive and fascinating examples, from many context areas and at a variety of levels of difficulty. I suppose that our median target user is a bright high school junior or senior who is doing an advanced unit in statistics, but I hope that most of the examples will be useful for a wider audience. The NCTM members of our committee will, among other functions, help us to keep our material at an appropriate level.

We hope to publish the resulting volume, and we hope that it will be used, not only by teachers, but also by textbook authors as new books come out. The second part of this talk will be about three proposed examples for the volume; these examples are by no means in final form.

At present we have 15 or so examples at various draft stages, and we are working on an outline of themes and topics, to be sure that the content areas and statistical developments are varied and balanced. We hope to enlist the aid of a number of colleagues not on the committee.

Our second projected publication is at an earlier stage. We have in mind a book of about 50 short articles, at a very non-technical level, that will discuss specific applications of statistics. The anticipated audience will be that of people in charge of secondary school curricula, teachers, and perhaps the general educated public. We do not intend to teach any technical statistics, but rather to describe fields like quality control to improve ball bearings, sampling to find the unemployment rate, queuing theory to help solve traffic problems.

To be quite frank, we are not absolutely sure that the job can be done. There is little mathematical or quasi-mathematical exposition that is sufficiently non-technical and sufficiently interesting to reach those we have in mind. But we think there is an excellent chance that the goal can be substantially accomplished. We have received a grant from the Alfred P. Sloan foundation to facilitate preparation of the second publication.

Before turning to the three draft examples for the first publication, I want to raise a problem that troubles me. Most, perhaps nearly all, of the materials I have seen for dealing with probability and statistics at the pre-college level are pointed towards the superior student, perhaps the upper ten per cent in terms of high school students in this country. What about the larger group of average students, say those within one standard deviation of the mean? There are many reasonably intelligent students who have a great deal of trouble with high school mathematics and leave it with a devout wish never to have any more to do with that subject.

Yet there are parts of probability and statistics that are important for any citizen: the notions of natural variation, measurement error, and distributions; the more frequent statistical fallacies; some experience with tables and graphs. I don't know whether it is possible or practicable, but it might be worth working towards statistical teaching materials that are truly accessible to the upper 80 % of high school students, that are interesting, and that will directly help towards critical and clear statistical thinking. It is my hope that some of the examples in our examples book will be of this kind.

I turn now to the three draft examples, roughly in order of complexity. Each will be stated in its current draft form and then followed by commentary. The first begins with a magazine advertisement. The second example is centered about a quotation from Thomas Paine. The third example is taken from the book by Bush and Mosteller on learning theory.[1] This example illustrates the kind of empirical data that we plan to have in many examples.

10.2. MILLER HIGH LIFE EXAMPLE (William Kruskal)[2]

An advertisement in *The New Yorker* for 22 April 1967 began as follows:

WILL THE REAL MILLER HIGH LIFE
DRAFT BEER PLEASE STEP FORWARD

We've tried our famous Miller High Life taste test on many a "beer expert"; pouring three classes, one from the tap, one from the can, and one from the bottle. And then we've asked which is which.
Result? No one, up to now, has identified the three correctly. Why?
All three glasses have the same distinctive Miller High Life flavor.

---

[1] R. R. Bush and F. Mosteller, Stochastic Models for Learning, Wiley, New York, 1955.
[2] Second draft, March 1969.

197

Think about this advertisement critically and ask yourself whether the claim is plausible.

Discussion

Something strange was brewed by the Miller High Life advertising agency. Suppose that the three ways of packaging the beer lead to indistinguishable glasses. There are six ways of saying which is which, as follows.

Glass 1	Glass 2	Glass 3
T	C	B
T	B	C
C	T	B
C	B	T
B	T	C
B	C	T

Here T, C, and B stand for Tap, Can and Bottle respectively. If the three kinds of beer are indistinguishable, even by an expert, then any one of the six ways of assigning labels is equally likely, and the chance of being wrong is 5/6. The chance that two experts are both wrong would be $(5/6) \cdot (5/6)$, assuming that they do not consult each other. Similarly, the chance that n experts are all wrong is $(5/6)^n$. How big is n? It depends on what the ad writer mean by "many a". Here's a little table.

n	Chance that n "experts" are all wrong (2 sig. figures)
1	$5/6 = 0.83$
2	$25/36 = 0.69$
5	0.40
10	0.16
20	0.026
30	0.0042
40	0.00068
50	0.00011

If "many a 'beer expert'" means 10 people, then there are about 4 chances out of 25 that none make correct assignments if the three kinds of packaging lead to indistinguishable beer. That is not so improbable. But if there were 30 experts, the chance goes down to less than 5 out of 1000, quite a small probability. And if there were 50 experts, the chance is only a bit more than one out of ten thousand.

So an initial reaction is that there were not very many "experts" after all. Other explanations, however, are possible. For example, it might be that

198

the three kinds of beer *are* distinguishable, but in a way that leads to systematically wrong assignments. It might be that the canned beer tastes to "experts" like bottled beer, the bottled like tap, and tap like canned.

Again, it might have been the case that the glasses of the three kinds of beer were systematically labelled in what was thought to be a neutral way; for example, the bottled beer glasses might have been labelled "A", the canned beer glasses "B", and the tap beer glasses "C". Then the tasters might have been given slips to fill out like this.

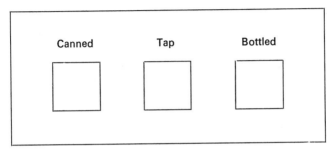

Canned   Tap   Bottled

Fig. 10.1.

The tasters are given instructions to put the appropriate letter in each box. Suppose that the order A, B, C is psychologically preferred because of our familiarity with the alphabet. To be specific, suppose that the (wrong) ordering A, B, C has probability 0.5, while each of the other orderings has probability 0.1. Then the probability that all n tasters are wrong is $(1-0.1)^n = (9/10)^n$, and this of course is larger than $(5/6)^n$. This troublesome possibility would have been avoided if the labelling scheme varied, perhaps best by randomly choosing the labels for each trial.

One might also conjecture that, by the time the testing was well under way, everyone would be under the influence and unable to keep count.

There is also the possibility that the "experts" chattered among themselves so that there were effectively only a few independent ones. Such alternatives could be discussed further if we know details of how the testing was done, and if we know how many times each assignment was made by the tasters. But an advertisement in *The New Yorker* is not a scientific article. Even some scientific articles omit important details like these.

You might wish to try a class experiment. Take three presumably identical bottles of a soft drink and label them T, C, and B. Ask your class-mates to try little glasses from the three bottles and to suppose that one comes from a soda-fountain tap, another from a can, and the third from a bottle. Of course you will keep the labels on the bottles hidden, or else use a secret code instead of the letters T, C, and B. It would be wise to keep changing the code.

After each of 20 or 30 class-mates makes his considered assignments, tabulate the results and see how many have them all correct. You might go further, and tabulate how many had none correct, exactly one correct, and exactly two correct. Try to compute the corresponding probabilities under the randomness assumption; first think about the probability of having exactly two correct ... the answer is zero.

By way of contrast, you might want to try blindfold tests on three soft drinks that really are different, but not grossly so. For example, take three competitive cola drinks. Compare the numbers of tasters with none right, exactly one right, and all three right for the two situations.

Commentary

I regard this example as pointing several morals: the difficulty of coming to reasonable conclusions even from simple data, the existence of many explanatory theories, the need for detail in trying to choose between theories. On the technical side, the example requires only the simplest combinatorics. The suggested class-room experiments are relatively easy to carry out, but they do require organization and planning.

There are a number of ways in which this example's discussion could readily be extended. Some are

1. How to compute, and how to approximate, $(1 - \frac{1}{6})^n$.
2. The importance of taste trials for food manufacturers, institutional buying of food products (e.g., Army coffee), etc.
3. How might the Miller Company have planned the trials carefully had the experiment been serious? How many experts? Operational definition of an expert? Are expert taste testers appropriate? Watching out for artifacts, perhaps color. What is the operating characteristic of the procedure for interesting alternatives?
4. On the analytic side, don't we lose information by just attending to the number of tasters who get at least one wrong? Perhaps one should look at the number who get all wrong. Full information presumably would be the numbers of tasters who guess

All wrong	(2/6)
T correct, but others wrong	(1/6)
C correct, but others wrong	(1/6)
B correct, but others wrong	(1/6)
All correct	(1/6)

So that we have a 5-nomial situation; the fractions in parentheses are the cell probabilities under the randomness hypothesis. It might be reasonable to combine the three middle cells, depending on envisaged alternatives. One could discuss how to evaluate the randomness hypothesis in the light of a set of data.

Presumably it would not be worthwhile proliferating in some directions. It is not clear to me at present how extensive the discussions should be.

10.3. TOM PAINE AND SOCIAL SECURITY, A STATISTICAL EXAMPLE (William Kruskal)[1]

The following paragraphs[2] are from Thomas Paine's *Rights of Man* (Part II, Chapter V, p. 249 of the Everyman edition):

At fifty, though the mental faculties of man are in full vigour, and his judgment better than at any preceding date, the bodily powers for laborious life are on the decline. He cannot bear the same quantity of fatigue as at an earlier period. He begins to earn less, and is less capable of enduring wind and weather; and in those retired employments where much sight is required, he fails apace, and sees himself, like an old horse, beginning to be turned adrift.

At sixty his labour ought to be over, at least from direct necessity. It is painful to see old age working itself to death, in what are called civilized countries, for daily bread.

To form some judgment of the number of those above fifty years of age, I have several times counted the persons I met in the streets of London, men, women, and children, and have generally found that the average is about one in sixteen or seventeen. If it be said that aged persons do not come much in the streets, so neither do infants; and a great proportion of grown children are in schools and in workshops as apprentices. Taking, then, sixteen for a divisor, the whole number of persons in England of fifty years and upwards, of both sexes, rich and poor, will be four hundred and twenty thousand.

Discussion

Rights of Man was published in 1791 and 1792 as a defense of the French Revolution and its principles. It was regarded as inflammatory and seditious by the ruling groups of England, and Paine fled from England to France in order to avoid a trial. *Rights of Man*, especially in Chapter V, presents a quantitative appeal for aid to the poor, education for all, financial help to the aged, and other such revolutionary themes.

In the quoted passage, Paine is tripped by what may seem a plausible argument into an interesting mistake. There is, of course, the problem of telling whether a person is 50 or over from a glance on the street, the dif-

[1] Second draft, March 1969.
[2] Professor Robert Streeter, University of Chicago, kindly brought this example to my attention.

ficulty that the streets of London in which Paine walked might not be typical, and the doubtful assumption that aged persons stay off the streets as much as infants and grown children. But even if such objections are put to one side, Paine's argument is fallacious. Here is an analysis.

Suppose there are three classes of people,

1. Those over 50,
2. Infants and 'grown children',
3. Others.

Suppose the proportion of class i in the population is p_i $(p_1+p_2+p_3=1)$. Paine wants to estimate p_1.

Suppose further that α_i is the probability that a person from class i will be in the street. That is, α_i is the average fraction of time that a person of class i spends in the street.

Paine's method gives him an estimate of

$$\frac{\alpha_1 p_1}{\alpha_1 p_1 + \alpha_2 p_2 + \alpha_3 p_3}.$$

This comes from a familiar probability calculation that is often called Bayes' Theorem. Briefly, $P(\text{class } i)=p_i$ and $P(\text{in street}\,|\,\text{class } i)=\alpha_i$. Hence $P(\text{class } i \text{ and in street}) = \alpha_i p_i$ and $P(\text{in street}) = \Sigma\alpha_i p_i$. Finally,

$$P(\text{class 1}\,|\,\text{in street})$$

is given by the above expression.

Paine appears to claim that this is satisfactory since $\alpha_1 = \alpha_2$. Assume that $\alpha_1 = \alpha_2$; then (since $p_1+p_2=1-p_3$) Paine is estimating

$$\frac{p_1}{p_1+p_2+(\alpha_3/\alpha_1)\,p_3} = \frac{p_1}{1+((\alpha_3/\alpha_1)-1)\,p_3},$$

which will not be p_1 unless $\alpha_1 = \alpha_3$ or $p_3 = 0$. For example, suppose $\alpha_3/\alpha_1 = 3$ and $p_3 = 3/4$. The denominator above is $5/2$.

It is a worthwhile exercise to show that for the equality

$$\frac{\alpha_1 p_1}{\alpha_1 p_1 + \alpha_2 p_2 + \alpha_3 p_3} = p_1$$

to hold for all p_1, p_2, p_3 satisfying $p_1+p_2+p_3=1$, it is necessary and sufficient that the α_i have a common (non-zero) value, that is, that the probabilities of being in the street must be the same for all three classes.

There are other questions about the quotation from Paine. For example, it may surprise some that there did not then exist explicit census information about the age distribution in England. In fact, the first real census in

Great Britain did not take place until 1801. It gave about nine million as the population for England, Scotland, and Wales together, but it did not provide information about ages. Not until the census of 1841 was a comprehensive age break-down available.

Of course Paine did use an estimate of the total population (of England alone.) His figure of 420,000 for those 50 or older was obtained by dividing 16 into the total population; hence the total Paine used must have been about 6,720,000. (A few pages earlier he used 7,000,000.) I do not know where these numbers came from, but there must have been a variety of estimates based on fragmentary evidence. In fact, both the population of England and the distribution of ages had been estimated almost a hundred years before *Rights of Man*; an introduction to this history is given in Chapter IV of Harold Westergard's *Contributions to the History of Statistics*.

Commentary

This example introduces sample survey notions, especially non-sampling errors, Bayes' Theorem in a context free from philosophical controversy, the application of a bit of elementary algebra, and some sense of the history of demography.

Here are some ways in which the example's discussions could be extended.

1. It might be conjectured that, even though assuming $\alpha_1 = \alpha_2$ doesn't guarantee unbiasedness (or consistency), one is still better off if $\alpha_1 = \alpha_2$ than if $\alpha_1 \neq \alpha_2$. A direct algebraic analysis shows, however, that, in general, some $\alpha_1^* \neq \alpha_2^*$ will provide a smaller bias than a given $\alpha_1 = \alpha_2$. To go further in Paine's context would require some guesses about the actual magnitudes of the parameters.

2. The Bayes' Theorem application could be accompanied—or even replaced—by a verbal argument or by a numerical one in detail.

3. What would be a sensible underlying sample space here?

4. Current censuses give detailed age distributions, but we still have problems, for example, serious under-representation of some minority groups at particular age brackets.

5. There could be a brief exposition of sample survey ideas, including stratification and clustering.

6. Try a small sample survey at school: the proportion of students wearing blue jeans, the proportion expressing this or that opinion. Problems of introducing randomness. Biases via interviewer effect (boy vs. girl) and via question wording.

7. The demographic history could be extended.

10.4. ESCAPE-AVOIDANCE EXPERIMENT EXAMPLE
(Frederick Mosteller)[1]

The psychologists Solomon and Wynne performed an experiment in which dogs in response to a light and a rising panel could avoid a shock by jumping over a barrier adjusted to shoulder height or escape the shock by jumping after the electricity was turned on. Prior to the first shock trial, the dogs almost never jumped the barrier voluntarily. In the attached data (see table on page 206) S stands for shock and a blank for an avoidance. The trials are numbered 0 to 24 and 30 dogs participated.

(*a*) Describe the rate at which the dogs learned.

(*b*) In some experiments learning is insightful so that animals suddenly learn. Is this experiment like this?

(*c*) Do shock trials or avoidance trials make the dogs more likely to avoid?

(*d*) Supposing shock trials and avoidance trials are all equally effective at improving the chance of avoidance, is it reasonable that the animals all have the same rate of learning and some are just luckier than others?

Possible answers.

(*a*) The trial numbers of last observed shock were 5, 13, 16, 13, 7, |13, 11, 10, 24, 11, |16, 11, 8, 8, 7, |6, 13, 7, 9, 13, |8, 16, 6, 18, 14, |10, 5, 12, 17, 12.

Frequency distribution.

x	f	x	f	x	f
5	2	10	2	15	—
6	2	11	3	16	3
7	3	12	2	17	1
8	3	13	5	18	1
9	1	14	1	24	1
					30

Half the dogs had their last shock by trial 11, 90 % by trial 16. We could compute the mean trial and show a graph of percentage avoiding trial by trial.

(*b*) No, only a few dogs get shocked until they start avoiding and then are never shocked again, (Dogs 21, 43, 52). If we allow one avoidance before the last shock we add dogs 16, 29, 67. So only 20 % of the dogs have data that follow the "insight" model closely. Even adding dog 34 doesn't raise the percentage much.

[1] First draft, January 1968.

204

(c) Let's go a little way and see. We'll look at outcome on trial 6 after various numbers of shocks on 0–5.

Previous numbers of shocks	Outcome on trial No. 6	Proportion Avoidances
6	SSASSŜSA	2/9
5	ASSSAAAAA	6/9
4	AAASSASSA	5/9
3	AAA	3/3

It looks as if having more shocks tends to reduce the chance of avoidance and so maybe learning proceeds faster owing to avoidance trials.

(d) We need a model. One such model would say that at each trial the probability of shock is p^n where n is the trial number and p is the probability of shock on the second trial (the trial numbered $n=1$).

As estimates we have for the first 5 trials

Trial No.	Observed	Calculated with $p=.9$ (casual choice)
0	$p^0 = 1 = \dfrac{\overset{\frown}{30}}{30} = 1.0$	$(.9)^0$
1	$p^1 = p = \dfrac{\overset{\frown}{27}}{30} = .90$	.90
2	$p^2 \quad = \dfrac{\overset{\frown}{26}}{30} = .87$	.81
3	$p^3 \quad = \dfrac{\overset{\frown}{25}}{30} = .83$	.73
4	$p^4 \quad = \dfrac{\overset{\frown}{18}}{30} = .60$	.66

Looks like (by trial) an estimate of p of about .9 would be pretty good. If $p=0.9$, then

$$1 + p + p^2 + \dots = \sum_{i=0}^{\infty} p^i = \frac{1}{1-p}$$

and for $p=.9$ this is 10. This is the expected number of shocks when animals are all alike. Observed average is 11.6, not too bad. We could have estimated p by setting $1/(1-p)=11.6$ and solving for p.

We observed one dog whose final shock is at trial 5. What is the chance of this? It's hard to compute $(1-p^6)(1-p^7)\dots = .029$ (I had a helpful

205

Record of shocks for the first 25 trials on each of 30 dogs in the Solomon–Wynne experiment. Occurrence of shock is indicated by S, non-occurence by a blank. (The number assignments to the dogs were made by Solomon and Wynne and do not imply that a selection has been made.)

Dog	Trials																								
	0	1	2	3	4	5	6	7	8	9	10	11	12	13	14	15	16	17	18	19	20	21	22	23	24
13	S	S		S		S																			
16	S	S	S	S	S	S	S		S	S	S	S	S	S											
17	S	S	S	S	S			S			S	S			S		S								
18	S			S	S				S		S		S												
21	S	S	S	S	S	S	S	S																	
27	S	S	S	S	S	S					S	S		S											
29	S	S	S	S	S		S	S	S	S	S	S													
30	S	S	S	S	S	S	S			S	S														
32	S	S	S	S	S		S		S		S			S	S	S						S			S
33	S	S	S	S		S	S		S		S														
34	S	S	S	S	S	S	S	S	S	S						S									
36	S	S	S	S	S						S	S													
37	S	S	S			S		S	S																
41	S	S	S	S			S			S															
42	S	S	S		S			S																	
43	S	S	S	S	S	S	S																		
45	S		S			S	S	S				S													
47	S	S	S	S			S		S																
48	S		S	S	S	S			S	S	S														
46	S	S	S	S			S		S			S		S											
49	S	S	S					S																	
50	S	S		S		S											S	S							
52	S	S	S	S	S	S	S																		
54	S	S	S	S	S	S	S	S				S		S	S	S			S						
57	S	S	S	S	S	S		S					S		S										
59	S	S		S				S			S														
67	S	S	S	S		S																			
66	S	S	S		S		S				S		S												
69	S	S	S	S			S	S				S		S		S		S							
71	S	S	S	S							S		S												
Total	30	27	26	25	18	18	14	12	10	7	9	11	4	8	4	3	3	2	1	0	0	1	0	0	1

table). This is about 3 %, and 3 % of 30 dogs is about 1 dog, which is what we observed. What is the expected number of shocks from trial 24 on?

$$p^{24}+p^{25}+\ldots = \frac{p^{24}}{1-p} = \frac{.9^{24}}{.1} = 10(.9)^{24} = 0.8.$$

So, it is not at all unreasonable that at least one out of 30 dogs has a shock trial this late. This analysis doesn't provide much evidence against the dogs being equivalent—some lucky, some unlucky. Naturally, we *believe* the dogs differ in ability to learn, but we haven't presented strong *evidence* for it yet.

Commentary

To my thinking, this example illustrates some aspects of describing a moderately sized set of data, some initial steps towards the framing of explanatory summaries, and an initial try at a mathematical model. To go much more deeply into mathematical modelling would probably get to a mathematical level that is too deep for high school students.

Some directions of expansion are indicated in the text of the draft example. A few other possibilities are:

1. There are many ways of summarizing the data beyond that in the text: trial of first avoidance, trial of second shock from the last, etc. One could bunch trials in groups of four and get at the rate of learning via the groupings.

2. The discussion for part *d* might be extended to variances. The use of indicator variables could be made explicit.

3. One might investigate Poisson-ness for the number of S's after, say, trial 10.

11. A non-frequentist view of probability and statistics

D. V. Lindley

University College
London, England

Most approaches to probability used in teaching today are based on some form of frequency concept such as the proportion of successes in a long sequence of trials. The degree of sophistication will vary with the type of student: at the most elementary level it will be phrased in terms of tosses of a coin, throws of a die or drawings from an urn; for the more advanced student the concepts of measure theory will be invoked and probability will be expressed as a normed measure with the notion of independence described through product measures. The purpose of the present paper is to discuss how probability might be taught when it is based on the occurrence of an event on a single occasion and reflects one's conviction about the likely outcome. Without repetitions the coins and the dice do not loom so large in the elementary approach, and although measure theory plays an important role at a more sophisticated level, its importance is not as great as in the frequency-based idea. No attempt is made in this paper to defend the 'single occasion' approach; we merely wish to explore its pedagogical consequences. However it will be seen that if it is adopted then it could (and I would say, should) have desirable consequences outside the immediate field of probability as a mathematical discipline, and this aspect will loom large in the discussion.

The customary account of probability begins with an event, A, and a number associated with it, $p(A)$, termed the probability of A. Thus if A refers to the event of an ace when throwing a poker die then $p(A) = 1/6$ if the die is fair: if it is not then $p(A)$ is some other number equal to the long-run relative frequency of aces in repeated throws of the die. In any case $p(A)$ describes a property of the die and is reasonably termed 'objective'. The probability $p(A)$ then satisfies the basic axiom that if $A_1, A_2, \ldots, A_n$ are exclusive events, the probability of their union is the sum of the separate probabilities. It is this fact that enables probability to be described as a measure and the elegant and useful results of that branch of mathematics to be employed: this approach is due to Kolmogorov [5].

If we are interested in the occurrence of an event on a single occasion without reference to long-run properties, then it is no longer sensible to speak of the probability of the event but we must remember to introduce as well the circumstances surrounding the isolated occasion. We may illustrate again with the die. Let A be the event that on the next throw the ace will be uppermost. Then if Peter contemplates the possibility, having little acquaintance with the die beyond a cursory inspection which suggests it is typical, and therefore probably a fair one, he will assign a probability of $1/6$ to the event. But if Paul, who knows it is a specially rigged die which only comes down ace high about one time in ten, does the same he will come up with 0.1. It is not a case that one of them is right and one wrong. In the view presented here both are right and they disagree because Peter has different information from Paul, information affecting the conviction that an ace will occur. This has to be reflected in our formal description and is accomplished by introducing a second event, B, being a description of the circumstances under which A is being contemplated. Then probability is a function both of A and B; we write $p(A|B)$ and read it as the conditional probability of A given B. In our example, if B_1 and B_2 describe the knowledge possessed by Peter and Paul respectively, then $p(A|B_1) = 1/6$ and $p(A|B_2) = 0.1$: A is common to both, but B_1 and B_2 differ. For us, probability is essentially a function of *two* arguments, not one. Notice that neither $p(A|B_1)$, nor $p(A|B_2)$, need agree with the frequentists' $p(A)$. The last is an objective property of the die whose value can be approximately assessed by repeated throws: the other quantities are individual assessments made by Peter and Paul. The manner of the assessment will be discussed later in the paper.

With probability described in the form $p(A|B)$ it still remains true that, as a function of its first argument, it is a measure: that is, the probability of the union of a number of exclusive events, given B, is the sum of the separate probabilities, given B. But it is clear that this cannot be the whole of the story since this result merely describes how probability changes as a function of its first argument: we have still to describe how the second affects it. This is accomplished by means of the result that

$$p(AB|C) = p(A|C)\,p(B|AC). \tag{1}$$

In words, the chance of two events, A and B, both happening is the product of the chance of the first and the chance of the second given the first, all probabilities (or chances) being considered, given C.

To summarize: in this approach probability is a function of two arguments and obeys two basic rules, sometimes called the addition and multiplication rules respectively.

Of course, the multiplication law, equation (1), does occur in the frequentist approach; but there it arises through the definition of conditional probability $p(A|B)$ as $p(AB)/p(B)$. This seems to me to be pedagogically unsound because it introduces a basic idea, namely the relevance of the conditioning event, as an afterthought and not as an essential ingredient of the whole notion of probability. There is no such thing as probability, only conditional probability. Many of the paradoxes of probability come about because this fact is forgotten: consider, for example the 'surprise' paradox. You are told that one working day next week there is to be a surprise fire practice. Now the practice cannot be held on Friday, for if so one would know on Thursday evening that, since it had not happened already, it was going to happen tomorrow and therefore would not be a surprise. Similarly it cannot happen on Thursday, because Friday having been ruled out, it would be known by Wednesday evening that it was going to take place on the morrow. And so on; we cannot have a surprise fire practice. There have been many attempts to solve this paradox. To my mind there is no difficulty since the various probabilities being discussed implicitly are considered under different conditioning events. If A_i is the event that the practice occurs on day i $(1 \leqslant i \leqslant 5)$ then initially $p(A_i|B) = 0.2$, where B refers to the previous week's information. Under any reasonable definition of surprise[1] any event A_i occurring would occasion surprise. On Monday evening, however, the practice not having occurred, we are dealing with $p(A_i|\bar{A}_1B) = 0.25$ $(2 \leqslant i \leqslant 5)$ and the surprise element has diminished. On Thursday evening we are down to $p(A_5|A_1A_2A_3A_4B) = 1.0$ and the element of surprise has disappeared.

To emphasize the lowly role that the multiplication law, at least in its full generality of equation (1), plays in much frequentist probability, we cite the fact that it is possible to study several branches of probability theory without using it. For example, the book by Gnedenko and Kolmogorov [4] mentions conditional probability on p. 21 but never seems to use the idea. (This is not intended as a criticism of this excellent book, but merely as an illustration of the specialization that is possible.) The reason for being able to dispense with the notion is that the authors are dealing with the special case of independence where (1) reduces to

$$p(AB|C) = p(A|C)\,p(B|C)$$

so that everything can be expressed in terms of a *fixed* conditioning event C and consequently reference to it is conveniently forgotten. Then $p(AB) = p(A)\,p(B)$ and we are dealing with product measures. In passing may I remark that although this last equation is typically taken as the definition

[1] For example, using the surprise index Σp_i^2 for a distribution $(p_1, p_2, \ldots, p_n)$.

of independence, it is surely better teaching practice to use the form

$$p(B|AC) = p(B|C)$$

which more clearly demonstrates the irrelevance of A to the probability of B, given C.

It is not only in the special case of independent random variables that the conditioning event is often omitted. Less sensibly it is often mislaid when discussing Markov processes. Many is the paper that appears with a statement such as "the chance that an event occurs in $(t, t+\delta t)$ is $\lambda \delta t + o(\delta t)$" without any mention that this is independent of the whole history of the process prior to t and of other events that might occur in the small interval under consideration.

Whilst it is true to say that almost all the results we have outside the more elementary parts of probability hinge on this fundamental concept of independence, it is also true to say that independence is such an unusual and subtle phenomenon that one cannot really be said to understand probability until one is familiar with non-independent events and the methods of handling them. Statistics provides a good testing ground for these ideas, for it is in that subject that the conditioning event plays such a vital role.

Consider the familiar n tosses of a coin, the tosses being carried out under similar conditions and in such a way that the tosses are unconnected one with another. In such a situation it is customary to say that the tosses are independent—or more precisely, the occurrence of heads on a toss form independent events. But looked at statistically this cannot possibly be so, for knowing the results of the first $(n-1)$ tosses would typically affect one's judgement of the likely result of the final toss, so that the last toss depends on the earlier ones in some sense. Indeed, if it did not, one could not make any inferences about future experiences on the basis of the past. Students often have considerable difficulty in understanding this apparent contradiction between the unconnectedness of the tosses and the relations between the inferences.

The paradox is again easily resolved by remembering the conditioning event. If it is known that the coin is a fair one, and we summarize this knowledge together with the previous information about the tosses by the symbol H, then it is certainly true that $p(A_i A_j | H) = p(A_i | H) p(A_j | H)$ for $i \neq j$, where A_i refers to the event of heads on the ith toss. But if we are not informed about the fairness of the coin and denote our weaker information by H', then it is no longer true that, given H', A_i and A_j, $i \neq j$, are independent. All that H' is likely to say is that the events $\{A_i\}$ are exchangeable. If so, de Finetti's elegant result [2] says that there exists a number θ, $0 \leqslant \theta \leqslant 1$ and a distribution function $F(\theta)$ such that

$$p(A_i A_j | H') = \int \theta^2 dF(\theta)$$

and generally for more complicated events. Given H' and θ, the $\{A_i\}$ are independent. If θ is known (as when the coin is known to be fair) then truly the events are independent, but not otherwise. When as statisticians we say they are not independent and that inferences can be made about future tosses on the basis of past experience, θ is unknown to us, and, indeed, inferences may be made via inferences on θ.

The concept of independence is even more elusive when three or more events are being considered. Let us consider three events, A, B, and C, under a fixed set of conditions, reference to which will be omitted in the notation: thus $p(B)$ really means $p(B|\text{conditions})$ and $p(A|B)$ means $p(A|B')$ when B' includes B and the conditions. Then independence of these events requires not only $p(ABC) = p(A)\,p(B)\,p(C)$ but also that each pair be independent, thus $p(AB) = p(A)\,p(B)$ with two similar relations. These are necessary because the natural concept of independence that we are trying to formalize requires that whatever information we are given about the other events does not affect the probability of the event under consideration. Thus we require $p(A|B) = p(A)$ and $p(A|BC) = p(A)$; and equally $p(AB|C) = p(AB)$. All these results follow from the four basic requirements just mentioned. Of course strictly we should not speak of independence, but only of independence given the conditions. Weaker forms are possible: thus $p(AB|C) = p(A|C)\,p(B|C)$ means that A and B are independent, given C and the conditions, which does not imply that A and B are independent given merely the conditions. Another important way of expressing this last requirement is to say $p(A|BC) = p(A|C)$. This is essentially the Markov property, for if C refers to the present state of a stochastic process and A and B respectively to the future and past, it says that, given the present, the future development of the process is uninfluenced by the past. A proper understanding of independence is important in many aspects of life, a point we will return to below.

The general multiplication law, equation (1), is therefore of fundamental importance in the sort of probability teaching that we are envisaging. It is an easy deduction from (1), obtained by interchanging the roles of A and B, that

$$p(A|C)\,p(B|AC) = p(B|C)\,p(A|BC)$$

and that therefore

$$p(B|AC) = p(A|BC)\,p(B|C)/p(A|C). \tag{2}$$

This famous result, Bayes' theorem, is so important in our use of probability, especially in statistics, that the attitude is often described as Bayesian. Equation (2) describes how $p(B|AC)$ is related to $p(A|BC)$ in which the roles of A and B are reversed. With A a particular event and B a general hypothesis, Bayes' theorem describes how we can pass from the particular to the general and is the basis for inductive behaviour.

We now consider the problem of how this single occasion, subjective, Bayesian probability could be taught. Firstly it seems reasonable to conjecture that no serious attempt should be made to do this until the child has reached a degree of sophistication that enables him to have some hope of appreciating the concept of measuring such an apparently unmeasurable thing as belief. It takes a child a long time before he can handle the simpler spatial relations and, rather from a position of ignorance, I would suggest that it is not until about the age of fourteen that an attempt should be made with probability. As a function of *two* arguments obeying *two* basic rules, it is much harder to understand than the concepts of length, mass, temperature, etc. Another relevant factor to be remembered is that this type of probability is intimately related to decision making, and as a child is not involved in this activity in his earlier years it is perhaps best to leave the subject until he has the motivation to help him.

It may be rather important to motivate the student adequately: a possible way of doing this is by means of the type of experiment originally suggested by Edwards [1]. Imagine that you have in front of you two urns. The urns are outwardly identical and both of them contain a very large number of balls, identical except for colour. One of the urns, to be called the red urn, contains two-thirds red balls and one-third black. In the other, black, urn the proportions are reversed, with one-third red and two-thirds black. Now suppose that you select one of the urns. Since they are outwardly identical you do not know whether it is the red or the black urn that you have chosen, and the chance that it is one is $1/2$. Next suppose a number of balls are drawn at random from the selected urn, how ought your beliefs about which urn it is that was chosen change? To be specific, suppose 33 are drawn and 20 are found to be red and 13 black, what are the odds in favour of the urn being the one with predominantly red balls? (The reader of this paper may like to stop at this point and try to assess his own odds without using probability calculations.) The sort of figure usually quoted is around 10–1, and people have been known to give odds of 1–2, that is against its being red, on the grounds that life is usually contrary for them! I have, on numerous experiments with first-year undergraduates, never had an answer greater than 20–1. In fact the true odds are over[1]

[1] Precisely $2^7 - 1$, or $128 - 1$.

100–1. This example serves to show that people need some advice on calculating odds.

The introduction of the two basic rules of probability to a student naturally ought to take place in the context of simple situations, and for this reason one is led, like the frequentist, to consider dice, coins and similar tools of elementary teaching. But the emphasis ought to be on the two aspects equally and not predominantly on the additive property. For example, there is far too much emphasis in some current teaching on calculations, usually involving permutations and combinations, leading to the number of favourable cases. Instead one might consider simple finite populations and the consequences of sampling therefrom. For example, let a population of $n_{..}$ items contain n_{11} having properties A and B; n_{10} having A, but not B; n_{01} having B, but not A; and n_{00} having neither. Then if a member is drawn at random (an important part of the conditioning event, C) $p(AB|C) = = n_{11}/n_{..}$; etc. and the rules naturally follow. This leads to discrete probabilities but it should be possible at an early stage to bring in continuity by considering, for example, the fall of a point at random in a unit square. Quite elementary geometrical considerations lead again to the two basic rules, since, in this context, probability can be identified with area. Thus the addition rule for exclusive events follows immediately since the areas of non-overlapping regions are additive. The product rule is only a little harder to derive.

In this elementary teaching it needs continually to be emphasized what the probability concept means, and, in particular that it refers to a single occasion. Thus with the illustration of drawing a member at random from a finite population of the constitution just described, to say that it is at random means that we judge any one member to be just as likely to be selected as any other. Specifically, if we were to be awarded a prize (or given a penalty) if one of five selected members were drawn, then we should not mind if the rules for the prize were to be changed so that they similarly depended on five other members. This judgement is irrespective of the magnitude of the prize, or penalty. If this attitude is adopted consistently then I expect that the student will have less difficulty than otherwise when he passes from elementary problems to others involving less obvious quantitative statements of belief.

Finite populations also provide a convenient vehicle for the discussion of the important idea of independence. With three descriptions, A, B and C, instead of just two, one can discuss various types of dependence from grand overall independence to partial types like the Markov property already mentioned, or the almost classic example where they are independent in pairs but not as a triplet. Consider also the example due to Simpson [7]:

	Male		Female	
	Untreated	Treated	Untreated	Treated
Alive	4	8	2	12
Dead	3	5	3	15

Ignoring sex the situation looks like this

	Untreated	Treated
Alive	6	20
Dead	6	20

Here treatment and death are independent, but they are not independent given sex: for both sexes the treatment has a beneficial effect. I believe that similar paradoxes lie at the heart of many failures with multiple regression analyses.

In dealing with simple examples of a finite population the students' need for judgement is minimal. When we pass to other examples, or to finite population illustrations where the constitution of the population is unknown, the subjects' judgement is increasingly invoked. At this point it hardly seems possible or desirable to separate the probability assessments and calculations from decision-making, for the purpose of judgement is to reach a decision. But in decision-making the probability assessment is only part of the mechanism: it is also necessary to introduce utility and the important concept of expectation. It is easy to discuss this last idea in the frequency context by considering what will happen over a long sequence of identical and disconnected trials. For the Bayesian the idea needs more careful nurture. Essentially utility is a measure of the desirability of a consequence expressed on a scale which makes expected utility the relevant criterion to be used in decision making: namely to choose that action of highest expected utility.

Again the motivation is important and it becomes necessary to convince the student that he needs some rules to help him to become a decision-maker. A possible type of experiment is one in which the student is invited to consider several bets. The bets will each involve two out of a set of say six monetary values: for example, $-10, -1, 0, +1, +10, +50$ dollars, though larger sums may be appropriate depending on the affluence of the audience. Having the concept of probability fairly clear in his mind, he is asked to consider the least probability for a win that would make him accept each of several bets. For example, what is the least probability of winning 10 $(+10)$ dollars that would lead you to accept a bet in which you stand to lose 1 dollar (-1)? With the answers to four suitably chosen bets it is possible to determine the student's utility function for money. With five or more it becomes possible to search for and exhibit inconsistencies between the various bets. In this way the student can be made to appreciate the need for some guide to the way in which he should select bets.

With the concepts of probability and utility available the student can make progress in elementary decision-making. A point now arises that seems to me to be of great importance. Every adult citizen is actively engaged in decision-making either at the personal level in connexion with his everyday affairs or, in a democratic society, in social matters where he is invited to choose the individuals who will make the major decisions. It is surely essential therefore that everyone receives some training in this vital activity. Consequently when we contemplate teaching a program of probability along the lines suggested in this paper, it must be remembered that this is not a program for specialists in any sense (say, mathematical or scientific) but for everyone who claims in any sense to be educated.

Let me try to indicate some of the valuable lessons that might come out of a course on probability and decision-making along these lines. Such a course would demonstrate that any selection of an action must involve consideration of the alternatives available at the time of the choice: one cannot decide whether to go to the theatre tonight, one must decide between the theatre, the cinema, TV, etc. How often does one find a course of action condemned because of some unpleasant features, without the alternatives also being investigated for flaws. An action is not selected because it is good but because it is better than the other options that are open. This leads naturally to a second lesson to be learned from Bayesian decision making: namely that any selected action has to balance up all the pros and cons and cannot consider merely some of them. In maximizing expected utility every possible consequence is described quantitatively by its utility, and every possibility by its chance of arising. The operations of expectation and maximization take every aspect into account. Other decision making processes do not do this. For example, I recently heard a military strategist advocate planning for the most likely contingency: such a strategy would be unfortunate if the unlikely event had serious consequences when the proposed strategy was used. A minimax strategy in guarding against the worst is open to the same objection, namely that it does not consider all the possibilities.

In a democratic society an exposure to the theory of decision-making might almost be described as a necessity. Many of us, I am sure, despise the way in which the democratic process works in modern society, in the way, for instance, in which politicians have to resort to baby-kissing and other equally ridiculous activities. Yet the democratic process has many advantages, principally perhaps in the airing of alternative views. It therefore seems worth while trying to improve the process as best we can. An appreciation of elementary decision-making might make a contribution in this regard. It may be a while before a presidential candidate publicly announces his party's probabilities and utilities, but part of the democratic process consists in the public's saying what utility function should be used. NASA or race relations in the U.S.; East of Suez or a healthy economy in the U.K.; these are alternatives whose choice is partly dictated by the society's utility function.

So far I have suggested that a course should refer to rather simple situations, such as finite populations and monetary outcomes. In problems of this type the numerical aspect is reasonably clear-cut. But inevitably there must come a point where the student passes from such situations to those where most of them will need pretty firm convincing of the appropriateness or possibility of quantitative descriptions of the concepts involved. What, for example, is your probability that the 38th president of the U.S. will be Spiro Agnew? Many will deny that probability statements can be made about such a unique, future event. Yet all of us have feelings about it: for example, that it is more probable than the event that Shirley Temple will hold the same office. The real difficulty is the assignment of a number; the quantification of the concept.

I must confess that I do not see how such a step is to be made. For myself, I find convincing the argument that as a minimal requirement I want my decision-making to be coherent in the sense that separate decisions shall fit together and not contradict one another. A coherency condition can be proved to imply the quantification of opinions about future events (through probabilities) and of consequences (through utilities), but it appears unlikely that this rather sophisticated argument would appeal to school children of any age. Perhaps I do not do it very well but in my experience even graduate students are resistant to the idea. However a relevant factor here is that the graduate audiences have been exposed to frequency concepts of probability; perhaps a less inhibited group would not have the same difficulty. We need more psychological knowledge than we appear to possess at the moment about people's attitudes towards quantification.

Some useful suggestions have been made and they need more testing in class than they would seem to have had up till now. The simplest and obvious one, already mentioned, is the idea of getting the student to place bets. In the examples already cited the probabilities were to be determined by reference to standard situations, like throws of a fair die. In the bets now being suggested the future uncertain events replace such reference sets. The utility function for money having been determined, the acceptance or rejection of a bet will at least determine bounds on the probability of the event. This idea may work rather better in the U.K. where the community spends a large proportion of its resources in the gambling industry and where it is possible to get odds quoted on almost anything—even Spiro Agnew. For example, if the utility of money is linear then a bet to win 10 dollars if he becomes the 38th President for a 1 dollar stake, if accepted, implies a probability of at least $1/11$ of his attaining that office. The idea can be improved on by offering a selection of bets from which one must be chosen, the choice determining the probability reasonably accurately rather than merely giving a bound for it. A simple way to do this is to choose awards which are quadratic in a variable describing the bet: thus let bet $x(0 \leqslant x \leqslant 1)$ result in an award of $x(2-x)$ if the event occurs and a loss of $2x^2$ if it does not. If p is your probability that the event will occur, then it is easy to see that the best bet is that with $x = p/(2-p)$. Consequently from the selection of the bet it is possible to infer your probability for the event by the formula $p = 2x/(1+x)$. There is some evidence to suggest that the answer depends upon the way the question is put: thus a request for odds may yield a different response from one for a probability assessment: see Winkler [8], and [9].

This question of quantification of beliefs is related to an idea explored by de Finetti (3) and others of alternative methods of responding to examinations consisting of multiple choice questions. Instead of the subject simply selecting one of the choices—a procedure which is perfectly satisfactory if he knows the answer—he might be asked to indicate the probabilities he has for each of the suggested answers being correct. This would allow the candidate to reveal that he thinks the answer is A but it might reasonably be B: it is certainly not C or D. It also distinguishes between a correct answer from someone who really knew his facts, and a lucky correct answer that resulted from a guess; for the guesser would, under a suitable scoring scheme, spread his probabilities over the choices.

It does seem to me to be likely that if the population had some training in this sort of quantitative thinking in their formative years, then it might be better able to conduct its affairs when the individuals are in positions of responsibility. All of us, every day of our lives, are making crude probability assessments and few, if any, of us make them coherently. This is particularly true of very small probabilities: most of us have very little appreciation of probabilities near zero or one. In driving our cars we perform risky acts with a small chance of leading to disaster, yet cumulatively over the years these small values will amount to a substantial probability of our being seriously hurt in a road accident. The U.K. government has found that its premium bonds (a form of investment in which the interest is paid out by randomly chosen prizes) attract more money if a few of the prizes are very big: it scarcely matters how small the chance is of winning. Other lottery promoters have similarly found that it is the big prizes that should be advertised. The result is that people gamble on a prize of 10^6 for a unit stake, when the chance of the prize is only 10^{-12}.

Of course such considerations involve not only probability; utility is also of vital importance. But as has already been explained utility is essentially a measure on a probability scale, thereby enabling expectations to be invoked. This is perhaps most clearly brought out by the approach suggested by Raiffa, Schlaifer and Pratt [6]. Given a set of consequences they select the worst and the best, and then compare any other consequence with a gamble that has chance p of the best and $(1-p)$ of the worst. Under mild assumptions it is not hard to see that there must exist a unique value of p that equates the gamble and the consequence: this unique value is the utility of the consequence on a scale which assigns a utility of 0 to the worst and 1 to the best consequence. It is then reasonable to expect most people's utility functions for money to be bounded, increasing and concave at least. Again training in such ideas seems important for future citizens of a democratic society.

Little has been said so far about statistics. In the approach here adopted there is no real distinction between the science of statistics (that is, the singular noun) and probability: for statistics is the science that studies our appreciation of data and how inferences should be drawn from them, a procedure that is carried out using the multiplication rule in the form of Bayes' theorem. (In addition there is the important and neglected topic of descriptive statistics (in the plural) dealing with the presentation of data.) The differences between probability and statistics are therefore primarily questions of emphasis. Probability, for example, in stochastic processes, studies the way in which the data should behave granted certain assumptions; statistics studies our reaction to the assumptions given the data. We have already discussed one example in the independence or otherwise of simple events like coin tossing. Let us explore it in more detail.

Suppose that a coin or similar object has been tossed n times with a result that will be denoted by X. (Note that X does not just consist of a knowledge of the number of heads: it also says on which tosses those heads occurred.) Suppose we wish to infer the likely result of the next toss. If H_{n+1} denotes the event of heads, then we require $p(H_{n+1}|XC)$. (Here C denotes the general conditions of the situation, including, for example, the lack of physical connection between the tosses.) This probability is equal to the ratio $p(XH_{n+1}|C)/p(X|C)$. Now we saw that if the conditions C implied exchangeability of the events on the various tosses, these two probabilities could be easily calculated since they both refer to the chance of a particular sequence of outcomes. Thus the denominator may be written

$$p(X|C) = \int p(X|\theta C)\, dF(\theta|C)$$

$$= \int \theta^r (1-\theta)^{n-r} dF(\theta|C)$$

where r is the number of heads in X and θ is a parameter describing the coin. The numerator is a similar expression with θ^r replaced by θ^{r+1}. Myron Tribus has rather delightfully termed this idea, extending the conversation, from the sequence of tosses to include θ. In many inferential situations it is similarly necessary to extend the conversation. By the extension we are on the familiar ground of the binomial type of density and the prior distribution $F(\theta|C)$. It is convenient to suppose the latter to be of the family conjugate to the binomial, namely the beta-family. Then $dF(\theta|C)$ is proportional to $\theta^{a-1}(1-\theta)^{b-1}d\theta$ with a, $b > 0$ and the appropriate inferences easily made. There are considerable difficulties in presenting statistical ideas at the school level—at least so U.K. experience suggests. It may be that this rather more natural transition from the rules of the probability calculus to an inferential analysis will prove easier to handle.

Of course, there is another aspect of statistics that must not be forgotten. Variously named, a popular description at the moment is data analysis. This subject does not have the formal apparatus associated with that aspect we have been discussing, but should not be ignored or despised because of that. I doubt whether data analysis should be taught until the student is faced with a problem that really needs it, for otherwise he finds it hard to understand what the subject is about. To bring this successfully into a program appears to need the active cooperation of teachers in those subjects that generate data, particularly scientific disciplines. I do not know how it is in the U.S., but in Britain practical work in scientific subjects at the school level is seriously deficient because the student is never made aware of the possibility of variability either in his material or in his technique. Without this there is little need for sophisticated data analysis. But in the real world, practical data is highly variable. This aspect should be present in the most elementary laboratory teaching.

I have tried in this brief account to present what I see as the more important aspects of probability and to say how I see they should be incorporated into a program for general teaching (as distinct from the teaching of probability specialists). Essentially my case is a plea for more instruction in numeracy: not merely in connexion with those aspects of life which already have an appreciable degree of quantification, but also in those which are not normally associated with measurement. Not everything is numbers, but numbers can contribute to everything, and without that contribution we are innumerate. Let us look forward to the day when innumeracy is as distasteful as illiteracy. A significant appreciation of such ideas can be gained by an application of 'single occasion' probability ideas to elementary situations in inference and decision.

REFERENCES

1. Edwards, Ward and Phillips, Lawrence D., "Man as Transducer for Probabilities in Bayesian Command and Control Systems", in Maynard W. Shelley and Glenn L. Bryan, Eds., Human Judgment and Optimality. New York: Wiley, 1964, 360–401.
2. De Finetti, Bruno, "Foresight: Its Logical Laws, Its Subjective Sources", translated by Henry E. Kyburg, Jr., in Henry E. Kyburg, Jr. and Howard E. Smokler, Eds., Studies in Subjective Probability. New York: Wiley, 1964, 93–158.
3. De Finetti, Bruno, Methods for Discriminating Levels of Partial Knowledge Concerning a Test Item. Brit. J. Math. and Statist. Psychol., 1965, 18, 87–123.
4. Gnedenko, B. V. and Kolmogorov, A. N., Limit Distributions for Sums of Random Variables. Reading: Addison-Wesley, 1954. (Translation from 1949 Soviet edition.)
5. Kolmogorov, A. N., Foundations of the Theory of Probability. New York: Chelsea, 1956. (Translation from 1933 German edition.)
6. Pratt, John W. Raiffa, Howard and Schlaifer, Robert, The Foundations of Decision Under Uncertainty: an Elementary Exposition. J. Amer. Stat. Ass. 1964, 59, 353–375.
7. Simpson, E. H., The Interpretation of Interaction in Contingency Tables. J. Roy. Statist. Soc. B, 1951, 13, 238–241.
8. Winkler, Robert L., The Assessment of Prior Distributions in Bayesian Analysis. J. Amer. Statist. Ass., 1967, 62, 776–800.
9. Winkler, Robert L., The Quantification of Judgment: Some Methodological Suggestions. J. Amer. Statist. Ass., 1967, 62, 1105–1120.

12. Elementary Teaching of Probability and Statistics with Indeterminism in Science as a Background

Jerzy Neyman

University of California
Berkeley, California, U.S.A.

12.1. INTRODUCTION

This paper was prepared for, and delivered at the International Conference on The Teaching of Probability and Statistics at The Pre-College Level, organized by The Comprehensive School Mathematics Program of The Central Midwestern Regional Educational Laboratory Inc. and Southern Illinois University, held in Carbondale, Illinois, March 18–27, 1969. The paper reflects the ideas that underlie a book I have been trying to write for the Harper and Row Company over a number of years now. On many points of principle these ideas agree with those in the material prepared for the Conference by its organizers, Professors Burt Kaufman and Lennart Råde. Such differences as exist are due to the fact that Kaufman and Råde contemplate very exceptionally gifted students while I am concerned with a broader class of gifted youngsters. The material described below is limited to what I expect to be digestible to pre-calculus students of this category and to what I think would be useful to them in their future lives as members of the general intellectual community, irrespective of their particular interests and irrespective of their field of work.

The program of instruction that I visualize is composed of three interconnected parts.

(i) The development by the students of awareness of what might be roughly called chance variation in the various phenomena. This would be combined with manipulations of data, leading to a few simple concepts of descriptive statistics.

(ii) Elements of the theory of probability, conceived as an idealization of the phenomena relating to relative frequencies.

(iii) Several basic concepts of mathematical statistics, treated as the theory of decision functions. Here, an important part of the program of instruction constitute examples illustrating two points. One is that, in many situations of modern life, it is unavoidable to make decisions based on ob-

Table 12.1. Stature Correlation of Father and Son. (K. Pearson and Alice Lee, Biometrica, 1905, 2).

Son's Stature	Father's Stature																	Totals
	58.5–59.5	59.5–60.5	60.5–61.5	61.5–62.5	62.5–63.5	63.5–64.5	64.5–65.5	65.5–66.5	66.5–67.5	67.5–68.5	68.5–69.5	69.5–70.5	70.5–71.5	71.5–72.5	72.5–73.5	73.5–74.5	74.5–75.5	
59.5–60.5	—	—	—	—	0.5	0.5	1	—	—	—	—	—	—	—	—	—	—	2
60.5–61.5	—	—	—	—	0.5	—	—	—	1	—	—	—	—	—	—	—	—	1.5
61.5–62.5	—	0.25	0.25	—	0.5	1	0.25	0.25	0.5	0.5	—	—	0.25	—	—	—	—	3.5
62.5–63.5	—	0.25	0.25	2.25	2.25	2	4	5	2.75	1.25	—	—	1.25	—	—	—	—	20.5
63.5–64.5	1	0.1	1.5	3.75	3	4.25	8	9.25	3	1.25	1.5	0.25	—	—	—	—	—	38.5
64.5–65.5	2	0.5	0.5	2	3.25	9.5	13.5	10.75	7.5	5.5	3.5	0.75	2.5	—	—	—	—	61.5
65.5–66.5	—	1.5	1	2.25	5.25	9.5	10	16.75	17.5	16	5.25	2.5	3.25	—	—	—	—	89.5
66.5–67.5	—	—	2	4.75	3.5	13.75	19.75	26.5	25.75	19.5	12.5	2	8.5	1	1	—	—	148.0
67.5–68.5	—	—	1.5	2	7.5	10	10.25	24.25	31.5	23.5	29.5	13.75	10	0.5	—	—	—	173.5
68.5–69.5	—	—	1	—	5.25	5	12.75	18.25	16	24	29	13.25	14.5	9.5	2.25	1	1	149.5
69.5–70.5	—	—	—	—	1	2.5	5.75	18.75	11.75	19.5	22.5	21.5	10.75	3.5	3.5	—	1	128.0
70.5–71.5	—	—	—	—	—	3.25	5	8.75	10.75	19	14.75	19.5	10	6.25	5	0.5	—	108.0
71.5–72.5	—	—	—	—	—	0.25	3	1.25	7	7.75	10.75	20.75	7.5	8	2.75	0.5	—	63.0
72.5–73.5	—	—	—	—	1	—	0.75	0.75	2.5	7.5	6.5	11.25	6.5	6.25	3.25	0.5	0.5	42.0
73.5–74.5	—	—	—	—	—	—	1.5	1.5	—	—	2.25	6	2.5	3.25	3.25	—	2	29.0
74.5–75.5	—	—	—	—	—	—	—	—	—	—	2	2.5	0.5	0.75	1.75	—	—	8.5
75.5–76.5	—	—	—	—	—	—	—	—	—	1.25	0.25	—	—	—	1	—	—	4.0
76.5–77.5	—	—	—	—	—	—	—	—	—	1.25	0.25	1	—	1	1.5	—	—	4.0
77.5–78.5	—	—	—	—	—	—	—	—	—	—	1	1	—	0.25	0.75	—	—	3.0
78.5–79.5	—	—	—	—	—	—	—	—	—	—	—	—	—	0.25	0.25	—	—	0.5
Totals	3	3.5	8	17	33.5	61.5	95.5	142	137.5	154	141.5	116	78	49	28.5	4	5.5	1078

Table 12.2. Stature Correlation of two Brothers. (K. Pearson and Alice Lee, Biometrica, 1905, 2).

Younger Brother	Elder Brother																	
	62–63	63–64	64–65	65–66	66–67	67–68	68–69	69–70	70–71	71–72	72–73	73–74	74–75	75–76	76–77	77–78	78–79	Totals
60–61	—	—	—	—	0.5	—	—	—	—	—	—	—	—	—	—	—	—	0.5
61–62	—	—	—	—	1.5	—	—	—	—	—	—	—	—	—	—	—	—	1.5
62–63	1	—	—	2	—	—	—	—	—	—	—	—	—	—	—	—	—	3.5
63–64	—	1	1.25	1.25	—	1.25	0.25	0.75	—	—	—	—	—	—	—	—	—	5.5
64–65	—	1	1.25	3.75	4	3	1.75	—	—	0.5	—	—	—	—	—	—	—	14.5
65–66	—	1	0.25	0.75	6.25	4	1.25	0.25	—	—	—	—	—	—	—	—	—	12.5
66–67	0.5	—	5.25	4.25	2.25	7.5	6	2.25	1	—	—	—	—	—	—	—	—	38.5
67–68	0.5	1.5	1	5	7	9.5	10.75	6.5	2.75	1.25	1	—	—	—	0.25	0.25	—	44.5
68–69	—	1.5	2.5	3	0.75	12.25	9.25	6.5	5	2.25	1.75	2	—	—	0.25	0.25	—	62.5
69–70	0.25	0.25	1.5	1	3	4.5	6.25	6.25	11.5	5.75	1.25	2.75	—	—	—	—	—	36.5
70–71	0.25	0.75	0.5	1.5	1	6.5	5.5	5.5	6.5	4.25	1.5	2.5	—	—	—	—	—	47.5
71–72	—	—	—	0.5	—	0.5	3	3	3.25	6	2	1.5	1.25	1.25	0.25	—	—	23
72–73	—	—	—	0.5	1.5	—	0.75	4.5	7.75	4.25	0.5	1.5	1.25	1.25	0.25	—	—	15
73–74	—	—	—	—	—	—	0.75	2.75	1.75	1.5	1.5	0.5	1.5	0.75	1.5	—	—	10.5
74–75	—	—	—	—	—	—	0.25	0.25	1.5	1	1.25	—	1.5	0.25	—	—	—	4.5
75–76	—	—	—	—	—	—	0.25	0.25	0.5	0.5	—	0.75	—	0.25	—	—	—	3
76–77	—	—	—	—	—	0.25	—	—	—	1	—	—	—	—	—	—	—	2.5
77–78	—	—	—	—	0.25	0.25	0.25	—	—	—	—	—	—	—	—	—	—	0.5
78–79	—	—	—	—	—	—	0.25	—	—	—	—	—	—	—	—	0.5	0.5	0.5
79–80	—	—	—	—	—	—	—	—	—	—	—	—	—	—	—	—	—	1
Totals	2.5	6	13.5	24	31.5	50.5	55	38	41.5	30	14.5	13.5	5	1	0.5	0.5	0.5	328

servations subject to chance variation. The other point is that the possible decision rules differ in their efficiency and that the choice among them may make a good deal of difference.

12.2. DETERMINISM VS. INDETERMINISM IN SCIENCE

All studies of the empirical world are reducible to observations of groups of variables, say $X_1 X_2, ..., X_s, Y$, and to efforts to establish some relations among them. Here two different approaches are distinguishable and the understanding of the difference between the two is likely to be useful to high school students.

If I ask about the values of Y that are associated with any given systems of values of $X_1, X_2, ..., X_s$, so that Y is contemplated as a function of X's, then, by definition, my approach to the given phenomenon is deterministic. On the other hand, if I ask *how frequently* does Y assume the value, say, of unity, when $X_1, X_2, ..., X_s$ have certain given values, *then my approach* to the phenomenon studied is *indeterministic*.

I think that it is useful to emphasize that the descriptions "deterministic" and "indeterministic" apply to the approach to a given phenomenon and not to the phenomenon itself. Also, it is useful to be clear that, on occasion, a given phenomenon can be, and actually is, studied both deterministically and indeterministically. For example, the relationship between volume, temperature and pressure of a quantity of gas, embodied in the Boyle-Mariotte law, is the result of a deterministic study. This is contrasted with an indeterministic approach involved in the consideration of gas as an assembly of molecules, each with a different velocity, etc.

The students should be made aware of the fact that, on occasion, indeterministic studies are more fruitful than those which are deterministic. One example is the phenomenon of heredity. The class attending the course may be shown a correlation table of stature of sons and fathers, or of two brothers, as exemplified in Tables 12.1 and 12.2. Also, the students could be encouraged to collect the relevant data on their own relatives and/ or friends, which then could be compiled in class into a table similar to that exhibited at an earlier lecture. The moral to be deduced from these and similar exercises is that, if X and Y stand for the height measurements of father and of adult son, respectively, then it is idle to try to consider Y as a function of X; on the other hand, the contemplation of the correlation table, or of the corresponding scatter diagram, would indicate that tall sons occur *more frequently* in families with tall fathers than in those with short fathers, etc. As an extension of the exercise, the students should be encouraged to calculate the mean stature of sons that correspond to varying statures of fathers.

The general conclusion would be that, in a number of natural phenomena where one or more observables $X_1, X_2, \ldots, X_s$ do not determine uniquely the value of an interesting Y, the frequencies of various particular values of Y are determined by the values of the X's and are of some interest.

I need not emphasize that the recent decades are distinctly marked with a strong trend to indeterminism in all sciences.

12.3. AWARENESS OF STABILITY OF CERTAIN RELATIVE FREQUENCIES

The establishment of the awareness that certain relative frequencies are "stable" in the empirical world is a very important stage of the elementary instruction program. The point of this is to create among the students an appropriate motivation for studies of probability and of statistics. The awareness of differences in numbers or in spatial relations comes to children more or less automatically. This is not so with stability of frequencies and, as emphasized by Professors Kaufman and Råde, a special effort in school is strongly indicated.

Naturally, personal experience is the best teacher and the instructor in the course will be well advised to prepare several illustrations that would be sure to suceed. One rather safe possibility is to require that the students go to the library and examine a certain number of issues of the local paper for a total of about 100. Each student should write down the dates, the number of recorded births and the number of male births per day. Subsequently, in class, these records could be combined to illustrate two things: (i) the relative stability of the frequency of male births, slightly more than 50 per cent, from one group of 100 consecutive births to the next, and (ii) the considerable variability of this percentage from one group of about 10 consecutive births to the next.

A few similar examples are likely to convince the students of the existence of "experiments", each with several possible outcomes, such that, while it appears impracticable to predict the outcome of any single one of them, the relative frequencies in reasonably long sequences of trials are stable and predictable. (The instructor should be warned that actual experiments of the above kind are tricky and that, for example, the use of coin tossing in class or the use of dice, may prove embarrassing. The point is that the outcome of a die depends very much on apparently insignificant details of the method of throwing, including the dependence of the next throw on the outcome of the one before, which may foul up the experiment. In Berkeley,

227

we once made a special effort to prepare experiments that could easily demonstrate that the frequency with which a die falls with a given side up is this die's measurable property just as is its weight, etc. We were not successful, even though we tried to load dice. It is true that at a certain shop in San Francisco we could buy, at a price of some $150, pairs of very effectively loaded dice showing frequencies of aces sharply different from 1/6, but we did not like the price. With ordinary dice thrown in turns by several different individuals, the frequency of aces in 100 throws varied from one individual to the next in a manner that forced us to abandon this particular illustration. It is the difficulties of this kind that led to the construction of tables of "random numbers". This particular circumstance deserves the attention of the high school students, but not at the moment when they are being introduced to the phenomenon of stability of relative frequencies.)

At this moment, when the students become accustomed to the phenomenon of stability of frequencies, one is logically brought to the concept of a "random event" or "random mechanism" or "random experiment". Unfortunately, if one wants to be dissociated from anything metaphysical, the concept is quite delicate and I am not sure about the ease with which it can be digested by teenagers.

Strictly speaking, the term "random mechanism" describes not so much the mechanism in question as the attitude of the individual who contemplates the working of the mechanism. If I give up any effort to predict (say at the time of conception) the sex of a child to be born, but am aware of the stability of relative frequencies involved, then, for me, the mechanism of sex determination is a random mechanism, quite irrespective of what is going on in the reproductive cells, etc. In other words "chance mechanism" is already an abstraction idealizing happenings in the empirical world, in the same sense as a "plane" is an abstraction idealizing the polished surface of a table, etc. Presumably, one can begin with the definition more or less as follows: if it is impossible to predict which of the several possible outcomes of an experiment will occur in any given case, then we say that the given experiment is "random". This is not a satisfactory definition but it, or some similar version, is probably unavoidable with very young students.

12.4. ELEMENTS OF DESCRIPTIVE STATISTICS

The next logical step in the program of instruction (and here again I am in full agreement with Professors Kaufman and Råde) is to acquaint the students with several types of distributions encountered in the empirical world, with histograms and with bivariate frequency tables as the elementary methods of their description, and with the phenomenon of stability. For some phenomena, the typical distribution is symmetrical bell shaped (for example stature of adult persons of a particular sex). For other phenomena (24 hour rainfall, income of inhabitants of a given country) the typical distribution is J shaped, etc. The distribution of the number of accidents per year per person (possible to establish in school) would resemble the negative binomial, etc.

It is to be hoped that, after constructing several histograms relating to the same phenomenon but in different conditions, the students will notice that, with a degree of change, a given phenomenon is ordinarily characterized by a histogram of a particular shape. One "safe" example is the phenomenon of the distribution of income (Pareto Law) in different countries or, even, in different parts of the same country. The distribution of income (or of wealth) in rural Louisiana is not the same as in the state of New York, but the histograms constructed (say from publications of the Internal Revenue Service) will have a certain outstanding feature in common: high frequency of small, and low frequency of relatively large incomes.

When the students notice that each of the several phenomena studied in class has a particular type of distribution of its chosen characteristic, this will be the time to suggest to them the existence of particular chance mechanisms governing these phenomena, and the desirability of discovering what these mechanisms are. Also, this will be the time to tell them of the existence of a special mathematical discipline, called theory of probability (most unfortunate term!) that deals with chance mechanisms and is oriented to answer the question: *how frequently will this or that outcome be produced by a chance mechanism of a specified structure.*

12.5. ELEMENTS OF PROBABILITY THEORY

As will be clear from the closing paragraph of the preceding section, my personal approach to probability, and also to statistics, is strictly "frequentist". Here I try to combine the views of R. von Mises (1) on the relationship between probability and statistics with the empirical world, on the one hand, and A. Kolmogorov's approach (2) to the mathematical theory on the other. Naturally, for high school students, Kolmogorov's approach requires simplification. My own version, reflected in an elementary text (3), is limited to finite outcome spaces and to the number of elements in a subset serving as a measure.

Because of this restriction, the basic concept of the theory is what Kolmogorov calls "Grundmenge" and what I translate as the fundamental probability set (F.P.S.). In order to have a well specified problem of probability, one has to define an F.P.S., a finite nonempty set of arbitrary elements, say A. Whatever be the attribute B, each element A may possess this attribute or not. Let $N(AB)$ stand for the number of those elements A that possess the attribute B and $N(A)$ the number of all elements of F.P.S. Then, by definition, the probability of B in the given F.P.S. (or the "probability of B given A") is simply the fraction:

$$P(B|A) = N(AB)/N(A). \tag{1}$$

Obviously, if $N(AB) > 0$, and C denotes another attribute, then the (conditional) probability of C given AB is given by the same definition

$$P(C|AB) = N(ABC)/N(AB), \tag{2}$$

and all the customary concepts and properties of probability follow at once. In particular, C is independent of B if,

$$P(C|AB) = P(C|A). \tag{3}$$

When in a problem one deals constantly with the same F.P.S. of elements A, then the latter A may be omitted from the above formulas.

The advantage of this approach is the direct relation of what one calls probability with the relative frequency that one wants to study. The disadvantage of the approach is that probability problems, as customarily formulated, have to be translated into terms consistent with the above beginnings. I must say that this particular difficulty is experienced not so much by the beginning students as by the others who already learned probability from another point of view.

Particularly after the experience with constructing histograms relating to some particular phenomenon (say income) observed in different conditions (say in rural Louisiana and rural New York), the students would have become accustomed to the idea that the same trait, say being a millionaire, may have different frequencies of occurrence depending upon where it is observed. Thus, the dependence of the probability of a given attribute B on the F.P.S. is, ordinarily, easily accepted. As to the necessity of "translation", the following example will illustrate what I mean.

Example 1.—We consider a bag B and two urns U_1 and U_2. It is given that B contains 3 balls, one marked with the numeral 1 and each of the other two with the numeral 2. Urn U_1 contains 5 balls, one red and four white. Urn U_2 contains 3 balls, two red and one white.

An experiment E is to be performed consisting in drawing a ball from B and then a ball from either U_1 (if the ball drawn from B bears the numeral 1) or from U_2 (in the contrary case). The problem consists in calculating the probability that the ultimately drawn ball will be red.

The problem can be solved easily by using the addition and the multiplication theorems. (Yes, theorems, in the present system!) However, there is an advantage in teaching the students to obtain the answer through what may be called direct enumeration of elements of the relevant F.P.S. The first question that must be asked and answered is what are the elements of the F.P.S. contemplated in the problem.

An immediate answer might be: the red and white balls in urns U_1 and U_2. However, if that be so, what would have been the purpose of mentioning bag B in the conditions of the problem? A little deliberation will convince the student that the description of the problem is a little "picturesque" and that the F.P.S. considered is meant to be composed of hypothetical "pairs of draws", a certain number N of them. Each of these pairs of draws, say A, one draw out of B and the other either from U_1 or from U_2, would end with the second ball being either R or W and our problem is of computing

$$P(R|A) = N(AR)/N. \tag{4}$$

What is the meaning of the description of bag B? Easy contemplation will lead to the conclusion that this description means

$$P(1|A) = N(A1)/N = 1/3, \quad \text{or} \quad N(A1) = N/3, \tag{5}$$

$$P(2|A) = N(A2)/N = 2/3, \quad \text{or} \quad N(A2) = 2N/3.$$

Similarly, the interpretation of the urns implies

$$P(R|A1) = N(RA1)/N(A1) = 1/5, \quad \text{or} \quad N(RA1) = N(A1)/5 = N/15 \tag{6}$$

$$P(R|A2) = N(RA2)/N(A2) = 2/3, \quad \text{or} \quad N(RA2) = 2N(A2)/3 = 4N/9.$$

However,

$$N(R) = N(R1) + N(R2) = N(\tfrac{1}{15} + \tfrac{4}{9}) \tag{7}$$

and it follows

$$P(R) = \tfrac{1}{15} + \tfrac{4}{9} = \tfrac{1}{3} \cdot \tfrac{1}{5} + \tfrac{2}{3} \cdot \tfrac{2}{3}, \tag{8}$$

which could have been obtained through the application of the addition and multiplication rules.

In my own teaching I found it useful to insist on a clear cut description of the F.P.S. and it is a pleasure to find that some other probabilists have a similar attitude. For example, in the writings of Fréchet I remember the emphasis on "probabilité dans un système d'expériences déterminé". In my parlance this would correspond to "probability with respect to a specified F.P.S.".

The usefulness of the above emphasis may be illustrated by the following example.

231

Example 2.—The addition theorem asserts that, if B_1 and B_2 are disjoint (or incompatible) in the F.P.S. of elements A, then

$$P(B_1 \cup B_2 | A) = P(B_1 | A) + P(B_2 | A). \tag{9}$$

Now consider the following problem. A reconnaissance plane is sent to take photographs over two targets A and B in turn. Previous experience indicates that the probability of being shot down over A is $P_1 = .63$ and that of being shot down over B is $P_2 = .57$. What is the probability P_0 of the plane being lost when it attempts to photograph both targets?

Being lost over A and being lost over B are exclusive events. Thus, the immediate answer, obtained through the application of the addition theorem, might be the absurdity $P_0 = P_1 + P_2 = 1.2$. If the student is accustomed to think of the fundamental probability sets, then this, and also some other similar mistakes, will be avoided.

12.6. EXTENT OF PROBABILITY MATERIAL ACCESSIBLE TO HIGH SCHOOL STUDENTS

The amount of probability material that may be made accessible to youngsters depends very much on the talent of the teacher. I, personally, am very slow indeed. On the other hand, having once sneaked into a classroom where a colleague taught an elementary course on probability, I was amazed at the speed with which he proceeded solving with the students a very substantial number of combinatorial problems while, as far as I could judge, none of some 30–40 students was "lost" and all of them seemed fascinated.

A substantial number of interesting problems on computing probabilities appears a necessity. My own preference are problems relating to population genetics, such as the elegant results of G. H. Hardy on stabilization of gene frequencies under panmixia, the probability that a progeny of a brother-sister mating will be an undesirable recessive, etc.

Quite apart from the so to speak substantive interest that the students show in solving such problems, they are attractive in offering an opportunity for the discussion of the fundamental probability sets to which the particular probabilities refer.

While these and some other similar problems are important, enough time must be saved in the course to cover concepts of random variables, expectations including the very useful formula $E(Y) = E[E(Y|X)]$, variance and the two inequalities, one of Markov and the other of Bienaymé–Chebyschev, leading to the simplest form of the Weak Law of Large Numbers. Some colleagues appear successful in teaching, heuristically, the Central Limit Theorem. My own attempts were not very successful, except perhaps when I limited myself to the statement of the theorem and then to illustrations by the Monte Carlo method.

In connection with some discussion at the Carbondale Conference, I must be specific on the question whether Bayes' Theorem should be included in the elementary course on probability. My answer is in the affirmative, subject to the condition of a class discussion of the F.P.S. to which the *a posteriori* probability refers. In other words, the *a posteriori* probability should be given a frequency interpretation, preferably accompanied by a Monte Carlo illustration.

12.7. SOME PARTICULAR CHANCE MECHANISMS

In my opinion, it is particularly important to study with the students, perhaps through Monte Carlo methods, a few chance mechanisms that might be thought to generate the distributions which the students have studied empirically in the premathematical phase. Also, familiarity with certain mechanisms involved in the reduction of data which often lead to misinterpretations is rather important.

With reference to the first category, I find it interesting and important to use the Mendelian Law and the assumption that human stature is a sum of contributions of a relatively large number of unlinked genes, in order to generate, through Monte Carlo methods, a sample of statures of father and son. After just a little preparation, with each student using a convenient table of random numbers to produce half-a-dozen pairs of "synthetic" fathers and sons, a reasonable sample might be obtained exhibiting a distinct similarity to real data.

With reference to misinterpretations of statistical data due to mishandling, it is useful to bring to the attention of the students a method frequently used in economic and social studies, which is likely to lead to unfounded conclusions. While actual examples are many, in order to avoid controversies it is advisable to deal with a hypothetical situation somewhat as follows.

We consider the assertion that, as a rule, or "on the average", an increase in alcohol consumption in a community is accompanied by an increase in crime. In order to document the assertion, a reasonably large number of communities, perhaps towns, are being investigated with regard to three variables: X = number of inhabitants, Y = number of bars and Z = number of crimes committed during a given calendar year.

Obviously, the population X in the communities considered will not be the same and, in fact, will vary within broad limits. Also naturally, the larger

Table 12.3. Do storks bring babies? — Raw data.

County no.	Women in 10,000s	Storks	Babies born	County no.	Women in 10,000s	Storks	Babies born
1	1	2	10	28	4	6	25
2	1	2	15	29	4	6	30
3	1	2	20	30	4	6	35
4	1	3	10	31	4	7	25
5	1	3	15	32	4	7	30
6	1	3	20	33	4	7	35
7	1	4	10	34	4	8	25
8	1	4	15	35	4	8	30
9	1	4	20	36	4	8	35
10	2	4	15	37	5	7	30
11	2	4	20	38	5	7	35
12	2	4	25	30	5	7	40
13	2	5	15	40	5	8	30
14	2	5	20	41	5	8	35
15	2	5	25	42	5	8	40
16	2	6	15	43	5	9	30
17	2	6	20	44	5	9	35
18	2	6	25	45	5	9	40
19	3	5	20	46	6	8	35
20	3	5	25	47	6	8	40
21	3	5	30	48	6	8	45
22	3	6	20	49	6	9	35
23	3	6	25	50	6	9	40
24	3	6	30	51	6	9	45
25	3	7	20	52	6	10	35
26	3	7	25	53	6	10	40
27	3	7	30	54	6	10	45

the town the more bars it will have and the more crimes are likely to be committed. Thus, it is argued, a direct comparison of numbers Y and Z would not provide an unbiased answer to the question as to whether, all other things being equal, the increase in the number of bars leads to an increase in crimes. In order to obtain such an unbiased answer, one should compute the quotients, say

$$u = 1000 \ Y/X \quad \text{and} \quad v = 1000 \ Z/X, \tag{10}$$

giving both bars and crimes per a convenient standard unit of population.

When the towns are classified according to values of u, the corresponding values of v will vary in a somewhat irregular manner, indicating a not-unexpected variability in social phenomena. However, if the values of v corresponding to fixed values of u are averaged to obtain, say $v(u)$, lo and

Table 12.4. Do storks bring babies? — Analytical presentation.

Density of storks per 10,000 women	Number of counties	Average birth rate	Class average
1.33	3	6.67	7.12
1.40	3	7.00	
1.50	6	7.08	
1.60	3	7.00	
1.67	6	7.50	
1.75	3	7.50	9.22
1.80	3	7.00	
2.00	12	10.21	
2.33	3	8.33	11.67
2.50	3	10.00	
3.00	6	12.50	
4.00	3	15.00	

behold an unmistakable tendency is discovered of $v(u)$ being an increasing function of u! The conclusion is obvious: even though there is a substantial amount of variation, an increase in the number of bars per unit of population leads, on the average, to an increase in the frequency of crimes.

The students should be taught that the real subject of study is the conditional correlation of Y and Z given fixed values of X, while it is admitted that both Y and Z are likely to be positively correlated with X. Simple calculations will then show that, even if Y and Z are conditionally independent given X, that is even if the variation in the number of bars in communities of fixed size has no relation to crimes, ordinarily the quotients will be correlated and, under conditions that are easily established, that this correlation will be positive. In other words, the assertion about crimes and alcohol may be true or may be false, but the frequently used method of proving it is faulty.

With young audiences, and also with a category of adults, arithmetic calculations are occasionally more convincing than algebra. For the benefit of such audiences I once produced (4) a hypothetical set of data purporting to support the assertion that storks bring babies or, at any rate, that an increase in the number of storks in a community somehow stimulates the birth rate. The relevant set of "raw" data is given in Table 12.3, their "analytical presentation" in Table 12.4. Table 12.3 is so constructed as to emphasize that, for a fixed number of women in a community, the number of births and the number of storks are independent. On the other hand, as shown in Table 12.4, the annual birth rate and the "density of storks" per 10,000 women are positively correlated.

Naturally, the consideration of quotients u and v is just one example of spurious methods of studying chance mechanisms. Recently I saw a modern study of the mechanism of interaction of two neurons. Here the conclusion that this interaction exists is based on the empirically established correlation between two functions $u(X_1, X_2)$ and $v(X_1, X_2)$, each of two arguments X_1 and X_2, with X_i representing a measurement relating to the ith neuron. Obviously, u and v may be correlated even though X_1 and X_2 are independent. Obviously, this fact is within easy reach of young students. An effort to acquaint them with it is likely to have most desirable consequences not only for their own future research activity, if any, but also for the development of an intelligent attitude towards articles published in the daily press and elsewhere.

12.8. PROGRAM OF INSTRUCTION IN MATHEMATICAL STATISTICS

Ordinarily, in an elementary course in mathematical statistics an effort is made to teach the students a few concepts of descriptive statistics (histograms, measures of central tendency, measures of dispersion, etc.) and then a set of rules of numerical manipulations involved in the application of several tests, perhaps of the analysis of variance, etc. Particularly for youngsters in the high school, of whom only an insignificant fraction will be involved in any kind of statistical work, I am inclined to de-emphasize the calculations and, instead, make a strong effort to implant in the students a few basic concepts of the modern theory. The purpose is, of course, to see to it that, when in the future the students hear the term mathematical statistics, they know "what does one eat it with".

For many of my colleagues, mathematical statistics is a section of probability theory. I, personally, like to make a distinction emphasizing the making of decisions based on observations of random variables and, particularly, the problem of optimality of statistical decision rules.

In my opinion, the teaching of mathematical statistics in the high school should have the following three main objectives:

(i) to make the students understand the general nature of the subject of study,

(ii) to document the importance of some problems of contemporary life that depend on the correct statistical treatment, and

(iii) to illustrate the fact that the choice among several alternative statistical methods can make a good deal of difference.

All these three objectives are conceptual rather than manipulative. One way of pursuing them is as follows.

I find it convenient to begin with the term "inductive behavior" describing the psychological phenomenon which humans share with many animals. This consists (*a*) in our minds recording frequency relations of various more or less indifferent phenomena with certain favorable and unfavorable occurrences and (*b*) in adjusting our behavior so as to increase the frequency of pleasant experiences and so as to decrease the frequency of those unpleasant. Already in childhood humans notice that, *frequently*, the appearance of heavy clouds is followed by rain. Thus, with heavy clouds in the sky, our children and also many animals "behave inductively" and try to take cover.

While illustrating the concept of inductive behavior, the clouds-and-rain example cannot be used as a motivation for the development of a special mathematical discipline: the consequences of errors in the decision, viz. perhaps unnecessarily missing a swim, in one case, and being drenched with rain, in the other, are relatively mild. Thus, the students' attention must be drawn to problems of inductive behavior in which the penalty for a wrong decision is heavy. The following examples might be considered.

Example 3.—It is common knowledge that polio is a terrible illness, frequently resulting in death or in incurable paralysis. A few years ago, certain doctors claimed that the vaccine they learned to prepare will save children from polio, perhaps not all of them, but many. Also, the claim was that the administration of the vaccine had no undesirable effects, perhaps not universally, but overwhelmingly. The prospect was attractive and public health authorities contemplated a heavy expenditure on vaccine and on its mass application.

However, how does one know whether the relevant doctors are right? What if they are mistaken? What are the means of checking whether the doctors are justified in their claims or not? Experiments, of course, first with animals and then, possibly, with humans willing to take the risk of being vaccinated and then intentionally infected. How many of these volunteers could there be? Not very many and here the students can be easily introduced to the fact that, in the above situation, the public health authorities are faced with an unavoidable necessity of making an important decision based on experiments subject to chance variation. In fact, these authorities can do only one of two things: either institute a substantial vaccination campaign or not. If they do, they may find that the vaccination is not followed by a decrease in cases of polio, which would mean waste of the funds for the vaccination campaign. However, in addition to the uselessness of the expenditures, the authorities may find that the vaccine is poisonous and kills children! These are dangers connected with one of the two possible actions; they may suggest that the other action namely "do nothing", is the safer one. However, it should be pointed out to the students that the decision to do nothing is, in fact, a particular "action" for which there may be a terrible penalty. It may happen that the doctors are right in their claims and that a mass vaccination campaign could save thousands of children from polio. In this case, the apparently safe decision to do nothing would amount to the condemnation of thousands of youngsters to unnecessary suffering and even death.

The children should be taught that, as long as the decision is to be based on experiments subject to chance variation, there can be no definite proof of the harmlessness or otherwise of a new medicine and that, ultimately, the decision would have to be taken by the administrator in accordance with his confidence as to which of the two alternative action is the safer one. Here his subjective feelings, combined with the sense of responsibility, must play an important role. Experiments and their statistical treatment are the foundation on which to base the development of confidence and the choice of action.

The situation just described, or some similar one, could serve to introduce the students to a host of the basic concepts of statistical theory, such as the concept of a statistical hypothesis, the concepts of statistical test and of the two kinds of error, and of the power of a test. The latter is very important and need not be difficult. For example, one might discuss the following situation.

Suppose that a consignment of medicine is to be tested for the presence of toxic impurities. Suppose it is agreed that, if the toxicity of the medicine can produce a long run 10 per cent (or higher) mortality among mice, then it would be unsafe for humans. Finally suppose that the suggested test consists in giving the medicine to $N = 10$ experimental mice and in accepting the medicine for use on humans only if none of the ten mice dies. The students should be asked to express their opinion whether this test is adequate. Thereafter they should be required to calculate the probability that the consignment of the drug will pass the test even if the probability of a mouse dying is $p = 0.1$, or $p = 0.2$, etc. Some of the students are likely to change their original opinion of the adequacy of the test and here the teacher will have a precious opportunity to discuss with the students a variety of important questions. One such question is about the number N of mice to be used in the same test so as to make it adequate.

The toughness of the decision involved in Example 3 (whether to institute a mass vaccination campaign or not) to be taken using the outcome of experiments subject to chance, and also the possibility of introducing the students to the basic concepts of the theory of testing statistical hypotheses,

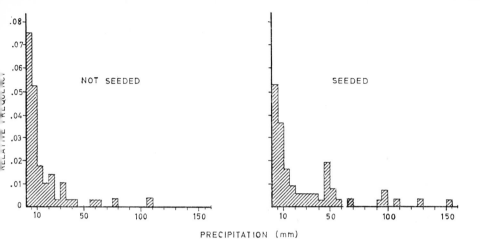

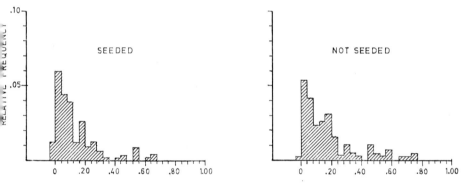

Figure 12.1. Histograms of average daily precipitation amounts

is the advantage of the polio vaccine illustration. Its disadvantage is that, if one deals only with the probability of becoming ill with polio, the decision problem may appear too simple. It is obvious that the proper criterion to use is the proportion of experimental animals that do fall ill. Thus, in order to bring out the motivation for a mathematical study of the decision problem, another example is necessary, also with important consequences of errors, in which, however, the choice of the test criterion is not obvious. The following example might be useful.

Example 4.—Since about the end of World War II claims have been made repeatedly that, in cases of insufficient rainfall, precipitation from clouds (composed of supercooled water droplets) might be increased by so-called "cloud seeding" (spreading of silver iodide smoke). The assertion is ordinarily accompanied by another, that "overseeding", resulting in a decrease in rain, is a practical impossibility. Currently, special legislation is under consideration which would make it the policy of the Federal Government to finance extensive cloud seeding operations wherever there is need for more rain. Some 25 experiments to test the above contentions have been performed in several countries and Figure 12.1 gives histograms of the 24 hour rainfall amounts, seeded and not seeded, as observed in two such experiments, the Swiss experiment Grossversuch III (1957–1963) and the American experiment labeled Whitetop (1960–1964). The two experiments, performed in very different conditions, indicated opposite effects of seeding (5). In the presence of the so-called stability layers, the average seeded rain in the central part of Grossversuch III target (Zone 3) was almost double that without seeding. Averaged over the whole target, some 1500 square miles, the apparent increase in rain was about 60 per cent. Contrary to this, in the so-called Missouri Plume of the Whitetop trial, the seeded precipitation was about one-half that without seeding. Also the seeded precipitation averaged over 100,000 square miles was less than that without seeding by the 20 per cent.

The students must be told that the two experiments were conducted using a special device called "randomization" ensuring that the observable differences in the rainfall can be due to chance variation or to seeding, but to nothing else. Thus, the question is whether the differences in the distribution of the rainfall illustrated in Figure 12.1 could be reasonably ascribed to chance variation. How does one do that? Obviously, in cases of insufficient rain, the average amount is the important quantity. Does this mean that in order to decide in favor or against the proposed governmental policy, all that one should do is to calculate the means for seeded and not seeded days and to consider the sign of the difference? A glance at the histograms will convince the students of the great variability of the rainfall, whether seeded or not, and that something more than the average rainfall would be needed for the decision. But what?

The importance of the decision problem, perhaps not as great as that in the polio vaccine case, should be brought to the students by indicating that the data on Whitetop experiment refer to average rainfall over a very vast area, slightly more than 100,000 square miles, exceeding that of England, Scotland and Wales combined. Also, according to authorities in such matters, the rainfall in the Whitetop area is critical for agriculture and increases of some 5 to 10 per cent were considered as something desirable.

240

Hopefully this and perhaps some other examples will bring to the minds of students the consciousness of the following two basic ideas:

(i) In a great variety of cases, modern life creates the necessity for decision with important consequences, and that these decisions must be taken on the basis of experiments that are subject to chance variation.

(ii) In many cases the method of making such decisions is not obvious and the gravity of consequences of possible errors justifies an effort to develop a methodology whereby the relative frequency of important errors could be reduced to an acceptable calculable level.

After this "pre-mathematical" preparation it is appropriate to give the definition of mathematical statistics, including the sample space, say W, the decision space, say D, the state of nature say N, the loss function defined on $N \times D$ and the decision function from W to D. The definition of mathematical statistics will be: a mathematical discipline concerned with decision functions, with the properties of such functions and, in particular, with the determination of those that have some specified properties of optimality.

Naturally, the degree of generality and of abstraction of the definition will have to be adjusted to the level of sophistication of the students concerned. One possibility is to restrict the presentation to two separate categories of the general decision problem, to tests of statistical hypotheses and to estimation. However, in any case it appears advisable to indicate to the students a simple criterion to distinguish between a problem in probability theory and a problem of statistics: (i) If in a given problem, the question to answer is *how frequently* something happens in specified conditions, then this problem is one of probability theory; (ii) On the other hand, if the problem consists in determining a rule of inductive behavior satisfying certain conditions (usually specified in terms of probabilities), then we deal with a problem of statistics. More specifically, the calculation of probability of eventual ruin when gambling in a specified way, is a problem of probability. On the other hand, the answer to the question "How to gamble, if you must?" (6) belongs to statistics.

The third element of elementary instruction program deserving emphasis is as follows. After realizing that the problem of a decision function does not necessarily have an obvious solution (as in the cloud seeding example), the students should become convinced that, in some cases at least, the choice of the decision function can make a great deal of difference. The following example is likely to be convincing.

12.9. EXAMPLE ILLUSTRATING A DIFFERENCE IN PERFORMANCE OF TWO ALTERNATIVE DECISION FUNCTIONS

It would be most satisfactory if the difference in the performance of some two alternative decision functions could be illustrated on an example taken from real life, as is the case with the polio and the cloud seeding examples above. Unfortunately, such real life examples that I could think of involve complicated substantive details and the effort to digest these details is likely to distract students' attention. For these reasons the suggested illustration is a "bookish" one.

We visualize a bag filled with an unknown number θ of balls, numbered consecutively $1, 2, \ldots, \theta$. It is required to estimate this number θ using a sample of n, say $n = 10$, balls randomly drawn from the bag, with replacement. Let $X = (X_1, X_2, \ldots, X_n)$ be the numbers written on the balls drawn, let $\overline{X}$ denote their arithmetic mean and $X^* = \max(X_1, X_2, \ldots, X_n)$.

Two confidence intervals are suggested for the estimation of θ, both corresponding, approximately, to the same confidence coefficient $\alpha = .9$. The first is given by the formulas, depending upon $\overline{X}$ only:

$$I_1(X) = \begin{cases} \Phi_1(\overline{X}) = 1.54\,\overline{X} & (11) \\ \Phi_2(\overline{X}) = 2.86\,\overline{X} & (12) \end{cases}$$

The second confidence interval depends solely upon X^*:

$$I_2(X) = \begin{cases} \theta_1(X^*) = X^* & (13) \\ \theta_2(X^*) = 1.26X^* & (14) \end{cases}$$

For convenience of the exercise, the two pairs of straight lines corresponding to (11) and (12) and to (13) and (14) are drawn in Figure 12.2. The suggested exercise consists in empirical verification that the relative frequency of cases where the intervals I_1 and I_2 cover the true value of θ is approximately the same, about 9 in 10, but that the precision of the estimate, measured by the length of the interval, is very different indeed. The exercise gains in interest if one asks the students to guess which of the two intervals is the better one.

Drawing of balls out of a bag is a lengthy procedure and, in addition, unless elaborate precautions are made, the mutual independence of consecutive draws may be difficult to achieve. In these circumstances, a sheet of random numbers out of a reliable table will be useful. Each student participating in the exercise should be given such a sheet and be invited to do the following.

First fix a number θ arbitrarily between the limits say 50 and 200. Next, simulate 10 independent drawings from the bag containing the chosen

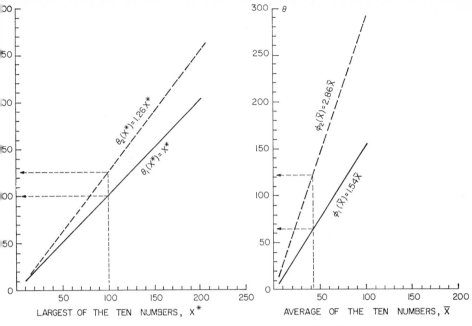

Figure 12.2. Graphs facilitating the construction of confidence intervals for θ.

number θ of numbered balls. This is done simply by reading from the provided table ten groups of the appropriate number of digits in some preassigned order, subject to the condition that the group determine an integer not exceeding the chosen θ. For example, if the chosen $\theta = 135$, it will be necessary to read groups of three digits and retain only those that form an integer not exceeding 135. When the sample of 10 integers so formed is accumulated, the student should calculate $\bar{X}$ and determine X^*. Next the confidence limits are approximately read from Figure 12.2, both for I_1 and I_2. Finally, the student should record whether these intervals cover his chosen "true" value of θ or not and determine the lengths of I_1 and I_2.

The expected length of I_1 is almost 3 times that of I_2 and to create the conviction that the "precision" of I_2 is vastly superior to that of I_1, a half dozen samples are likely to be sufficient. On the other hand, in order that the students acquire the intuitive feeling that the long run frequency of I_1 covering the true value of θ is the same as that for I_2, some 200 independent samples would be required.

Here are a few pitfalls that on occasion may ruin the experiment. First, the computations of the mean $\bar{X}$ may be faulty. Second, in some cases in my experience, the students, advised of the arbitrary order in which they should read the table of random numbers, understand this to mean that

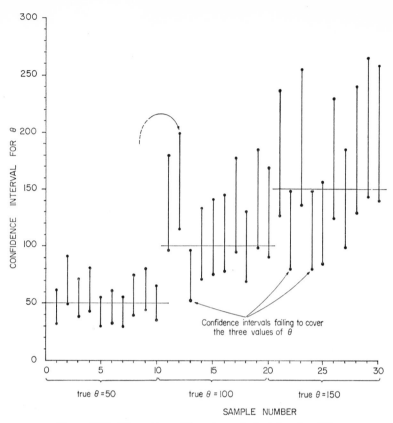

Figure 12.3. 30 sample confidence intervals for θ based on X*

they are at liberty to select out of the table those numbers not exceeding θ that they like better than others. Naturally, liberty of this kind can ruin the experiment as easily as faulty calculations of mean $\bar{X}$. Thus, in order to ensure the success of the experiment, it is advisable to compile a few samples on the blackboard with an active participation of one or two back benchers and with the whole class watching the procedure.

The approximate character of the two pairs of confidence limits is due to considering the numbers X_i as uniformly distributed between zero and the unknown θ and to using the normal approximation to the distribution of $\bar{X}$. With $θ \geqslant 50$ and $n = 10$, the two approximations work satisfactorily. The upper bound for the "true" $θ = \leqslant 200$ is imposed merely for convenience in using Figure 12.2.

One particular point in the above exercise deserves emphasis. That is that it is desirable to arrange that each of the several students participating select for his own work the "true" value of θ different from those of the

244

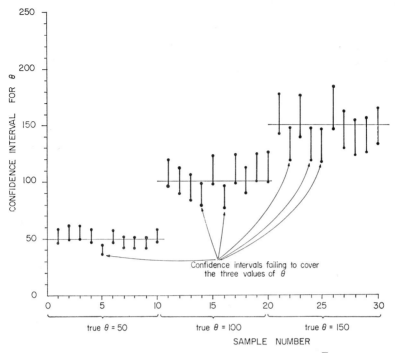

Figure 12.4. 30 sample confidence intervals for θ based on X̄.

others. This precaution would discourage the formation of the idea that the frequency of success in estimation by confidence intervals somehow depends on *sampling from the same population*. Strange as it may seem, this idea appears to be popular in certain statistical circles even today.

The final outcome of the exercise, combining the results of all the participating students, might be in the form of two graphs exemplified in Figures 12.3 and 12.4. Here, the vertical axis is that of θ. Each of the vertical lines exhibited represents the sample confidence interval obtained in the manner described. There are 30 such intervals in each figure, 10 each for three selected values of $\theta = 50$, 100 and 150. The difference in the length of intervals in the two figures is striking and there would be no difficulty in convincing students that the confidence intervals based on X^* are vastly superior to those based on $\bar{X}$. However, Figure 12.3 and 12.4 exhibit another detail which is likely to require explanations. This is that, in both figures, the relative frequency of the confidence intervals covering θ is less than the anticipated 90 per cent. Also, the shorter intervals based on X^* appear less successful in covering θ than the broader intervals based on $\bar{X}$. Finally, the two figures exhibit something like an increase in the frequency of errors as θ is increased.

245

Vagaries of this kind are unavoidable. In occasional lectures accompanied by the exercise now discussed I had to deal with a variety of cases in which the actual frequencies of coverage of the true θ did not appear consistent with the confidence coefficient $\alpha = 0.9$. In particular, in some cases the true θ was covered by all the confidence intervals calculated by the class. The suggestion is that, prior to performing the experiment in class, the instructor should perform it himself taking a reasonable number of samples and thereby acquiring a realistic feeling of the results to be anticipated. With this experience he should be able to prepare his audience and avoid embarrassment. The very desirable consequence of some untoward result, such as that exhibited in Figures 12.3 and 12.4, might be that some of the youngsters decide to check on the instructor and use the available sheet of random digits in order to take more samples of their own initiative.

Exercises with actual sampling, similar to the one just described, are useful from a point of view more general than that of their immediate purpose, for example to illustrate that the confidence interval I_2 is preferable to I_1. This more general idea is that theorems of mathematical statistics are "verifiable" empirically in terms of frequencies in exactly the same sense as that theorems of plane geometry can be "verified" in terms of measurements on a sheet of paper. In particular, a false assertion in the domain of statistics and probability can be contradicted by a sampling experiment.

REFERENCES

1. R. V. Mises, "Probability, Statistics and Truth". Second Revised English Edition prepared by Hilda Geiringer. MacMillan, New York, 1957.
2. A. N. Kolmogorov, "Grundbegriffe der Wahrscheinlichkeitsrechnung". Springer, Berlin, 1933.
3. J. Neyman, "First Course on Probability and Statistics". Henry Holt and Co., New York, 1950.
4. J. Neyman, "Lectures and Conferences on Mathematical Statistics and Probability". Graduate School, U.S. Department of Agriculture, Washington, D.C., 1952.
5. J. Neyman and E. L. Scott, "Statistics in Meteorology". Bull. Inst. Intern. Statistique.
6. L. E. Dubins and L. J. Savage, "How to Gamble if You Must". McGraw-Hill, New York, 1965.

REMARKS ON PROFESSOR J. NEYMAN'S PAPER

D. V. Lindley

I have much enjoyed reading and listening to Professor Neyman's paper: in particular, the examples which so strikingly illuminate the text. I should like to discuss one of these, namely the last one that appears in the paper. In the text this is discussed in the context of balls from a bag, but in his oral presentation today he used the analogy of automobiles in a city numbered consecutively from 1 to θ: the distinction is an important one as we shall see. My purpose in discussing this example is to demonstrate that the differences between the Bayesian point of view and that adopted by Neyman are not just philosophical differences but result in techniques that are operationally quite distinct: in the example the two approaches could lead to quite different answers.

Let us begin with the example set in the context of balls drawn from a bag. In § 5 the importance of the fundamental probability set (fps) is emphasized. Unfortunately we are not told what the fps is in the example. But we can guess, and a few simple calculations confirm that it is the space of all samples of size 10 drawn from the bag. The usual confidence interval calculations produce the interval given by equations (13) and (14) of the text. The point I want to emphasize that this interval is based on the assumption that the fps is as stated: without such an assumption the calculations are impossible.

Now in his presentation this morning, Neyman made the story a little more romantic. He was sitting in a café watching automobiles go by. This sounds interesting, so let us join him with his coffee and suppose we sit there for 20 minutes counting the registration numbers of the automobiles: the time we stay being dictated by the time we had to kill before our appointment in the office next to the café. Suppose further that we too observe 10 automobiles, the same 10 noted by Neyman and thereby obtain the same sufficient statistic X^*. What is our fps now? By what rationale can it continue to be the space of all samples of size 10; for 10 was a random variable, the number of cars that happen to pass during our sojourn in the café? Repeat the procedure on another day and we may only obtain 5 results in our 20-minute stay. I do not know what fps to use but the one that springs naturally to mind is the space of all 20-minute visits to the café, for 20 minutes was the fixed value I had in mind before beginning the observations, just as 10 was the number of balls it was intended to draw from the bag. If this is so, then the fps is quite different from the fps with the bag—in particular 10 is now a random variable—and the confidence interval calculations proceed quite differently. Let us follow them through.

It seems reasonable to suppose n, the number of automobiles recorded, to have a Poisson distribution. Let us further suppose that the mean, μ, of this distribution is known. (This simplifies the calculations and also eliminates the difficulties that arise with nuisance parameters when constructing a confidence interval.) Since estimation is impossible within the Neyman approach when $n=0$, it will be supposed that the zero class is missing. Then

$$P(n|\mu) = \frac{\mu^n}{n!} \frac{1}{e^\mu - 1}$$

and simple calculations show that

$$P(X^* = y | \mu, \theta) = \frac{\mu}{\theta} \frac{e^{\mu y/\theta}}{e^\mu - 1}.$$

(Here the discrete distribution on $1, 2, \ldots, \theta$ has been replaced by the uniform distribution in the interval $(0, \theta)$ for ease in the analysis.) With the single sufficient statistic X^* for the single unknown parameter θ it is a simple matter to find an interval of the form of equations (13) and (14) by calculating

$$P(X^* \leqslant \lambda\theta | \mu, \theta) = (e^{\mu\lambda} - 1)/(e^\mu - 1).$$

With a 90 % level of confidence, and supposing μ not too small (which in any case is rather necessary in order to avoid the zero class) we obtain the interval extending from X^* to

$$X^*/(1 - \mu^{-1} \log_e 10).$$

(Of course, this interval is not necessarily the best—but it is a confidence interval.) It is clear that, in general, this interval will be entirely different from that based on a fixed sample of size 10. In other words what I am saying is that the fps is of vital importance in the calculation of a confidence interval.

This is quite distinct from the Bayesian approach. Here the likelihood principle obtains and inferences should be based on the likelihood function alone: in this case, θ^{-10}, for $\theta \geqslant X^*$. This does not depend on whether the observer sets out to count 10 automobiles or to sit in the café for 20 minutes, as does the confidence interval argument. Consequently there is a major *operational* difference between the two approaches.

My sympathy lies with the likelihood approach, so now let me say a few words in its favour by recounting a simple experiment that I carry out with some students. They are asked to take part in an estimation problem and I report on the results of an experiment involving the spinning of a thumbtack, saying, for example, that it was spun 16 times and came down with the point uppermost on 7 of them. They are then asked to estimate

248

the chance that it will fall uppermost on a further throw. Of course, at first they are timid and will not answer—presumably because 7/16 is such an obvious value and they suspect a catch. So then I ask them if they need any further information. Then there is usually some response; for example, they want to know if the spinning was random, occasionally they even ask for the order of the results. Several students have asked for the consequences of the estimation: they have heard about loss functions and appreciate that it could be that overestimation, for example, is more serious than underestimation. The discussion may go on for quite a while, but the main point I want to make is that I have never yet encountered a student who wanted to know where the number 16 came from. No one has ever said: "Did you decide on 16 spins, or did you decide to spin until 7 landed with their points uppermost, or did you stop when your coffee was drunk?" They never ask me what the fps was; they seem content with the likelihood function. Of course, if they were bothered, they should come up with 7/16 if the 16 was fixed, and 6/15 if the 7 was fixed, assuming unbiased estimation. This seems some evidence that the reference to an fps is not a natural one. I wonder whether in his analysis of experimental results, Professor Neyman enquires about the fps: I suspect not.

The distinction between the type of argument that uses a confidence interval and that based on the likelihood principle is that the former cannot proceed without embedding the observed result in a sequence of other results; that is, without an fps. The latter can. Consequently, there is a real operational difference between the two approaches and, for example, in instruction from a Bayesian viewpoint the notion of a confidence interval in Neyman's sense would not appear.

REPLY TO PROFESSOR D. LINDLEY

J. Neyman

I am grateful to Professor Lindley for his interesting remarks regarding my paper. Yes, it would be nice if the material to be offered to students in their pre-college years could be expanded, and the inclusion of the Poisson distribution is certainly most attractive. However, if one tries to do so, one is forced to explain what the base of natural logarithms is and also to convince the students of the validity of the formula for the expansion of e^x, etc., which is likely to take up a prohibitive amount of time. I agree with Professor Lindley's suggestion that the idea of the F.P.S. is not something that the youngsters are born with and that it requires some effort to teach. However, I find that this effort is rewarding.

13. A multidisciplinary approach for teaching statistics and probability

C. Radhakrishna Rao

Indian Statistical Institute
Calcutta, India

13.1. STATISTICS—A NEW TECHNOLOGY

A few years ago, the Indian Statistical Institute introduced a 4-year course leading to B. Stat. (Bachelor of Statistics) degree, for students with high school education. The object of the course is "to offer a comprehensive instruction in the theory and practice of statistics and provide at the same time a general education together with the necessary background knowledge in the basic natural and social sciences expected of a professional statistician". The broad guide lines for the course were formulated by the late R. A. Fisher, the late J. B. S. Haldane and Professor P. C. Mahalanobis, all of whom shared some common views on the scope of statistics. Speaking on "Statistics as a Key Technology" at the 125th Anniversary of the American Statistical Association, Mahalanobis (1965) described the broad scope of statistics and the role of a statistician as follows:

> The time has come to introduce educational programs appropriate for statistics as a fully developed technology which calls for the utilization of a wide range of scientific knowledge to help in solving scientific or practical problems. As Fisher has pointed out, *a professional statistician, as a technologist, must talk the language of both theoreticians and practitioners.* The education of a statistician like that of other technologists, must have a broad base.

Thus the object of the new course is not to teach statistics as a separate discipline with a well defined area of study like physics, chemistry or biology, but introduce it as a body of techniques for application in research problems of various disciplines. Or, in other words, teaching has to be problem oriented with emphasis on collection of live data, their analysis and interpretation rather than drilling the boys in the use of known statistical techniques on what Fisher calls "mock up data for the use of students only". The training of a statistician should be on the same lines as that of an engineer or a medical practitioner with emphasis on professional aspects.

In the course that is being currently given, mathematics, statistics and economics constitute the main subjects of study. In addition, courses are given in a number of science subjects, but here the emphasis is not so much on the content of knowledge as on methods, with more of practical exercises involving experimentation and collection of data. Besides physics, chemistry and biology, which are taught during the first two years of the course, lectures are given on selected topics in sociology and psychology during the third year, with emphasis on quantitative approach.

The mathematical content of the high school curriculum in India is not very high. Students admitted to the B. Stat. course would not know calculus or would not have studied it in a rigorous way. The first task was to work out courses in modern mathematics spread over the first three years of study. There was difficulty in the beginning in formulating the syllabii for other subjects such as economics, physics, chemistry, psychology and sociology as only selected topics in these areas were intended to be covered. But during the period of last eight years the Institute has gathered considerable experience, and an integrated syllabus was evolved for mathematics and different branches of social and natural sciences with statistics as a central discipline providing a common bond between subjects. Along with the syllabus, certain methods were developed to teach statistics and to instill in the students a spirit of true intellectual inquiry. In my lecture today, I shall try to cover both these aspects: the syllabus for an introductory (first year after high school) course in statistics and probability and some methods of teaching statistical techniques.

13.2. POPULATION PROJECTION—A FIRST PROJECT

The first batch of students for the B. Stat. course was admitted to the Institute in September 1960. That was the time when hectic preparations were going on in the country for conducting the decennial census in January 1961. Population or demography seemed to be an appropriate and timely topic to introduce to the students for discussion. It is also a subject with a long history and of great current interest. Further, demography has contributed in a significant way to the early development and study of statistics. Thus an early discussion of population problems would also provide the students with an opportunity to look into the history of statistics.

The first problem set to the class was how to anticipate the Registrar General and predict the population in 1961 in advance of the census. This was a crucial and at the same time a dangerous exercise. The predicted figure would be subject to test a few months later when the census count would be available. If the agreement was good it would inspire some confidence in the students in learning techniques of "counting chickens before

252

they are hatched", which are novel to their way of thinking[1]. On the contrary, the effect could be depressing both for the students as well as the teacher. However, the investigation was worth undertaking. I shall describe how the problem was approached and what the students had learned, more by experience than by direct teaching, during the process.

Contact with official statistics

The problem gave the students their first introduction to what are called official statistical publications. Population Census volumes had to be consulted to obtain the previous figures which might give some idea of the trend of growth. They had to hunt up for current publications giving annual figures of births, deaths, migration and immigration during the decade 1950–60, which, if available, would reduce the problem of prediction to a simple exercise in arithmetic.

What is a population census? How is it conducted and what are the difficulties in making a complete enumeration at a national level? What are the likely inaccuracies in the published census figures? These are some of the questions which had to be discussed to make the students familiar with the data they had to deal with.

How are the data on current births and deaths recorded and published? How accurate can they be? If both are underregistered, to what extent can the difference, births–deaths, which is the net addition to population (apart from emigration–migration) be correct? These constituted another series of questions which have led the students into the realm of reality and exercised their thought. Is there any method of checking the accuracy of published figures and making suitable corrections? The students were already placed in the thick of the problem and they had to think their way out.

Preparation of schedules

The class had an assignment to prepare the census schedule (questionnaire or data sheet). They had to examine the previous schedules and discuss *what fresh questions* could be added and for what purpose. The designing of a schedule is itself an art and each student produced his own version, which gave an opportunity for discussing some general principles to be followed in such cases.

[1] It is unfortunate that at a young age we are exposed to stories to drive home the moral, *Do not count the chickens before the are hatched*. Nothing can be more devastating and demoralising than this on the young mind which realises the need for foreseeing the future in order to make any progress.

Stratification

Any method chosen for prediction based on previous census figures could be directly applied on population figures for the country as a whole, or applied separately on different regions and the regional projections added up to get the national figure. It is easy to demonstrate that the two procedures lead to different results unless the rate of growth is the same for all the regions, and more accurate results are obtained by the latter procedure. This discussion led to construction of indices of growth for different regions and methods of comparing them.

Performance test

When different methods are available, there arises the problem of choosing a method appropriate for a given situation. One way of doing this is to try out different methods in cases where the accuracy of the predicted value can be ascertained by comparison with known figures and to choose the one with the best performance. In the present problem, the different techniques suggested were applied on census figures prior to 1951 to predict the figure for 1951, which was known. By comparing the predicted with the known figure, it was found that two methods gave equally good results compared to a third method. The two methods were then used to predict the 1961 population. The need for testing the performance of a suggested method, before application in a new situation, was stressed.

Growth model and fitting of constants

The most difficult part of the project was a discussion of the methods employed for prediction. What is a model as distinct from a function which gives the relationship between population and time? This is a difficult concept and some time had to be spent in stressing the importance of an equation such as observed value at time $t = M(t) + \text{error}$, where $M(t)$ is a function of t, representing the model. The error term was introduced as a deviation of the observed from the model value and its nature discussed through appropriate examples.

For population projection, a polynomial of a suitable degree or a logistic function may be suggested as a model and simple methods of fitting such functions discussed. By applying these methods, the population for 1961 was estimated to be 420 millions. There was good agreement with the census figure of 439 millions which was available a few months later, the error being less than 5 per cent considering the simplicity of the method used and enumeration errors in the cencus figure itself. The exercise was worth undertaking in a number of other ways.

Population figures provide good material for teaching descriptive statistics. For instance the age pyramid which is the histogram of age of individuals in a population, gives an interesting characterization of a population in terms of the relative frequencies of the young and old. Comparisons of age pyramids between sexes, between states or countries and over time (for instance before and after a great war) and writing reports on such studies are excellent exercises for a beginner in statistics. Summarisation of data in terms of measures of location such as mean, median and mode and their comparison, and measures of variation such as inter-quartile range and standard deviation can also be illustrated with age frequency distributions.

The concepts, construction and uses of birth, death and net reproduction rates and life tables could also be discussed in connection with population projection.

The problem of estimating annual population between the census years leads to a discussion of interpolation formulae, which should be a part of the first year course in statistics.

Thus, a single project led to a detailed study of topics, wider in content than those generally listed under the syllabus for a first year course in statistics.

13.3. GENETICS OF SEX DETERMINATION— A SECOND PROJECT

While throwing of dice, drawing of cards and sampling of beads of different colours from a bag are useful devices in demonstrating and understanding the results of simple chance mechanisms, the knowledge so experienced will remain abstract if its application to the study of *natural events* is not emphasized. In fact, it would be more interesting to begin with observed sequences of natural events and then examine whether they could be *mimicked* by mechanical chance devices. The problem chosen for investigation was the process of sex determination of children.

The students were sent to a maternity hospital to obtain information on the sex of successive children born, during certain periods of the day over a number of months. A record of over thousand observations is shown in Table 13.1, where M stands for a male and F for a female child. The students had no knowledge of probability. They were aware that the sex of an unborn child could not be predicted and that roughly half the children born were male. With such background knowledge there was no way of interpreting the observed sequence of random events. But before the discussion on the observed sequence started, the students were asked to carry out a

Table 13.1. Data on sex of successive children delivered in an Indian Hospital observed during certain periods in some months in 1956.

January

```
F M M F F    M M M M F    M F M F M    M M F F M    F F M F F
F M F M M    M M M M F    M M M M M    F F F F M    M F M M M
M M M M M    M M F M F    M M F F F    M M F M M    F F F M F
F M F M M    M F M M M    F F M M F    M F F M M    F M F M M
F F M F M    M F M F F    F M M F F    M F M F F    F M M M F
F F M F M    F M M M M    M F M F F    M F M F M    M F M M F
F F F F F    F F F M M    F M M M F    M M M M F    F M F F F
F M F M M    M M F F F    F M F F F    M M M M M
```

February

```
                                                    F F M F F
F F M M M    F F F F M    F F F M F    F M F F M    F F M F F
M M M F M    M F M F M    F F M F M    M F M F M    M M F M M
F M M F F    F M M M F    F F F F M    M M F F F    M M F F M
M F M F M    F M M M M    F F M M F    F M M F M    F M M F M
F F
```

March

```
      M F F    F M M M M    M M M F M    F F F F F    M M M F M
M F M F F    M F M F F    F F F M M    F M F F M    F M M F M
M F F F F    F M M F M    F M M F F    M M M M M    M M F F M
M M F F M    M M M F M    F F M F M
```

April

```
                                        F M F F M    F F M M M
F F M F M    M F F F M    F M M F F    M F F F M    M F F M F
F M F M M    M M M F M    M M M M M    F F M M M    F M F M F
M M F M M    M M F F M    F M M M M    M M M M F    F M M F M
F M F F M    M F M F F    M M F M F    M F M F M    F F M F M
F F F F M    F M M M F    F M F F F    M M F F F    M M M F F
F F M F F    F M M M F    F M F M F    M F M F M    M M F M F
M F M M F    F M M F F    F M M F M    M M M M M    F M M F F
```

July

```
F M M M M    F M M M M    F F M F F    F F M M F    F M F M M
F F F M M    F M F F F    F M F M M    F M F M M    M M M M M
M F M F F    M M M M M    F M F M M    M F M M F    F M F M F
M F M M F    F F M M M    M M M F M    M M F F M    M M M F F
F M F F M    M F M F F    F F F F F    M M M M F    F F F M M
F F M M M    M M M M F    M M M M F    F M M F F    F F F M M
F
```

October

```
      M M M F    F F F M F    F M M F M    M F M M F    M M M M M
M F M F M    F F F F M    F M F F F    F M F M M    M F F F M
M F M M F    M M F F F    F F M F F    F M M M M    M F M M F
F M M F F    M F M M F    F F M F F    M M F F M    F F F M F
F M M F F    M M F M M    F M M F F    F M F F M    M F M F M
F F M M F    F F F M F    M M M M F    F F M F M    F F M F F
M M F M M    F F F M F    M F F M F    M M M F F    F F F F F
M F M F M    M M F F F    M F F M F    M M F M F    M M M F M
M F M M F    M M F F F    F F M F M    F F F M M    M F M M M
M F F F M    M F M F F    M F F F M    M M F F M    M F M M M
M F M M F    F M M M F    F F M M F    F F F F F    F F F M F
M M F M M    M F M F F
```

256

Table 13.2. Data on colour of successive beads drawn from a bag containing equal numbers of white and black beads.

```
B W W B W    B W W B B    B B B W B    B B W W B    W W W B B
B W B B B    B B W W B    W B W W W    B B W W W    W W W W B
W W B W W    W B B W B    W W W B B    B B B W W    B W B W W
B W W W W    B B W B B    W W B B W    B W W B B    W B B W B
W B W B W    B W B B W    B B B B W    B B B B B    B B W B W
W B W B B    W B W B B    W B W B W    B W B B B    W W B B B
B W W B B    B W W B W    B W B B W    B W B B B    W B W B W
B B B W W    W W W B W    W B W W W    W W W B B    B B W W B
B B B W W    B W W W B    B B W W W    W W B B W    B B B W W
W W B B W    W W B W B    B B W B W    B W W W W    W B W B W

B W B B B    W W W B W    B W B B B    W B B W W    W B W B B
W B W B W    W W B W B    W W B W W    B W W W B    B B B W B
W W W W B    B B W W W    W W W W W    B B B B W    W W B B W
B W B W B    B B B W W    B W W W W    B W B B W    W B B B B
B B W B B    B B W W W    B W B W W    B W B W W    B B B W B
W W W B W    B W W W W    W W W W B    B B W B W    W W W B B
W W B W B    W W W B B    B B B W W    B W B W W    W W W B W
B B B W B    B W W W B    B W W B B    B B W B W    B B B B B
W W B W B    W B W W W    W B B B W    B B W B B    W B W W B
B W B W B    B B W B B    B B B B B    B B W B W    W W W W B

B W W W B    W W B W B    W B W W B    B B B W B    B W W W B
B W B W B    W W B B B    B B W W B    B W B W B    W W B B B
W W W B W    W B B B B    W W W W B    B W W W B    B B B B B
W B B W W    B B B W B    W W B B B    W W B W W    W W B B B
B B B B W    W B W B B    W W B W W    B B B W W    B W B W W
W W B W B    W B W B W    W B W W B    W B W B W    B B B W W
B W B W B    W W W W W    B W W W B    B B W B W    B W B W W
B B B B W    W B W W B    W W B B W    B W W W W    B B B W B
W B W B B    W B W W W    W W B W B    W W W B B    B B B W W
W B W B B    B B B W W    W B B W W    W B W B W    B W W B B

W B W W W    B B B B W    W B B B W    B W W W W    W B B W B
W B W B B    W B B W W    W W W W W    W B B W B    B B W W B
W B B W W    B B B B B    B W W B B    B W W W B    W B B W W
W W B B W    W W W B B    W W W B W    B B W B W    B W B B W
W B W B W    W B W B W    W B B B B    W B W W W    B W B B W
B W W B B    W B B B B    W W W W B    B W W W W    B W B W W
B W B W B    B W B B W    W B W B W    B W W W W    W B B W B
B B W B W    W B W B B    W W W B B    B W B B B    W B W B W
B B W W W    B W W B W    W W W B B    B B B W W    B W B W W
W W W B W    B B W B B    B W B B W    B W W W W    W W W W W
```

mechanical experiment of drawing beads from a bag containing black and white beads in equal numbers and noting down the colour of the bead drawn each time after thorough mixing. The observed sequence of black and white beads in 1000 draws is given in Table 13.2.

How does one recognize from an observed series of events such as the occurrence of white and black beads (Table 13.2) the nature of the chance mechanism that has produced it (such as drawing at random from a bag containing equal numbers of white and black beads)? How does one com-

Table 13.3. Frequency distributions of different sets of events.

	Artificial series					Real series			
Set type	First 166 sets	Second 166 sets	Total	Expected value	Total	Second 166 sets	First 166 sets	Set type	
B B B	17	20	37	41.5	46	23	23	M M M	
B B W	20	26	46	41.5	36	20	16	M M F	
B W B	23	25	48	41.5	49	20	29	M F M	
B W W	27	24	51	41.5	50	27	23	M F F	
W B B	18	15	33	41.5	37	16	21	F M M	
W B W	27	18	45	41.5	37	16	21	F M F	
W W B	15	17	32	41.5	43	23	20	F F M	
W W W	19	21	40	41.5	34	21	13	F F F	
Total	166	166	332	332	332	166	166	Total	

pare two series of events and infer that underlying chance mechanisms are similar or not? Answers to these questions may enable us to infer on the mechanism producing a sequence of events genuinely occurring in nature such as the sex of children of successive births by comparison with a sequence of artificially produced events such as the occurrence of white and black beads in successive draws. We shall refer to the data on children as the real series and the data on the beads as the artificial series.

We shall first carry out the same type of analysis on both the series (of Tables 13.1 and 13.2) in an attempt to find differences in their behaviour. An inference of the type that the underlying chance mechanisms for both the series are the same will be a consequence of our inability to distinguish between them by appropriate analysis. In such a situation, since the mechanism for the artificial series is known, the same chance mechanism can be postulated for the real series.

Bernoulli Distribution

If we consider a set of three events each of which has two alternatives such as M and F or W and B, then there are 8 possible sets. The frequency distributions of these 8 possible sets in the first 166 sets, in the second 166 sets and for the total of 332 sets are obtained for the artificial and the real series. The results are as shown in Table 13.3. Both the distributions are compared with what may be called "theoretical expectation according to Bernoullian hypothesis", under which all possible sets are equally likely.

It is interesting to note the following:

(i) In either series, the frequencies for the first and second 166 sets are similar showing that parallel sets of data from the *same* mechanism conform to a certain pattern although they differ in individual frequencies.

Table 13.4. Frequency distribution of the number of events of one kind in sets of three.

Artificial series			Real series	
No. of beads	frequency	Expected value	frequency	no. of males
0	37	41.5	34	0
1	127	124.5	130	1
2	128	124.5	122	2
3	40	41.5	46	3
Total	332	332	332	Total

(ii) The pattern is as indicated by the Bernoullian hypothesis of equal frequency.

(iii) There is considerable similarity between the artificial and real series in the behaviour of frequencies.

It would indeed be difficult to say as to which analysis relates to artificial data and which to real data, when the labels attached to Tables 13.1 and 13.2 are unknown (or withheld).

Binomial distribution

We have made one kind of analysis of the sequences of binary data, which may not always be possible to carry out. For instance we may not have the actual series of events but we may know the number of black beads or the number of males in a set of three events. In such a case we can obtain the frequency distributions of the number of events of one kind. The results are given in Table 13.4.

The expected values of Table 13.4 are obtained from those of Table 13.3 by adding over the combinations containing the same number of events of one kind. Thus the expected frequency for 2 black beads is the sum of the expected values for the combinations B B W, B W B, and W B B. Again the similarity between the artificial and real data is brought to light by the analysis given in Table 13.4.

At this stage the derivation of the binomial distribution under the Bernoullian hypothesis could be demonstrated, first in the case of equal probabilities for the two kinds of events.

Let us consider sets of n events instead of 3 chosen in the example. There are 2^n possible sets all of which are equally likely. Thus in N sets, the theoretical frequency of each kind is $N/2^n$. To find the frequency of r events of one kind, we have to add up the frequencies over sets containing r events of one kind. There are precisely $\binom{n}{r}$ such sets, which is the number of com-

Table 13.5. Frequency distributions in sets of 5.

Artificial data							Real data					
No. of W's	1st 50	2nd 50	3rd 50	4th 50	all sets	Expected value	all sets	4th 50	3rd 50	2nd 50	1st 50	No. of M's
0	1	2	1	1	5	6.25	5	2	1	1	1	0
1	6	10	6	5	27	31.25	27	8	7	3	9	1
2	19	11	17	17	64	62.50	64	20	12	19	13	2
3	17	16	19	16	68	62.50	64	12	20	17	15	3
4	7	10	6	9	32	31.25	31	8	6	8	9	4
5	0	1·	1	2	4	6.25	9	0	4	2	3	5

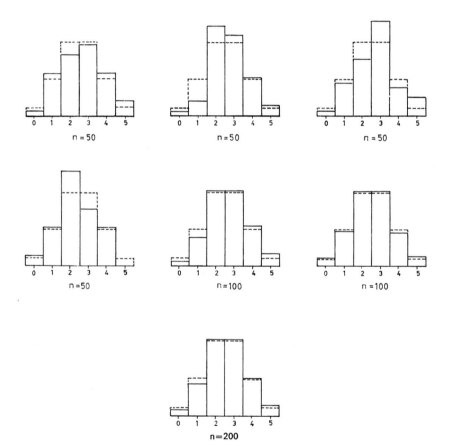

Figure 13.1. Histograms for number of male children in sets of 5 births (n denotes the number of sets)

260

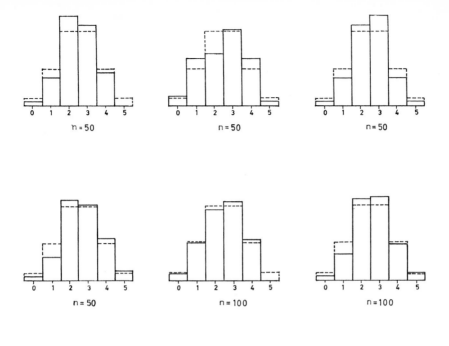

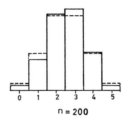

Figure 13.2. Histograms for number of white beads in sets of 5 draws (n denotes the number of sets)

binations of r positions out of n. Hence the required frequency is $N \binom{n}{r}/2^n$, giving the relative frequencies for $r=0, 1, ..., n$ as

$$\binom{n}{0}\frac{1}{2^n}, \ \binom{n}{1}\frac{1}{2^n}, \ \cdots, \ \binom{n}{n}\frac{1}{2^n},$$

which is called a binomial distribution with probability $1/2$ for one kind of event.

We shall now examine the frequency distribution of the number of events of one kind in sets of $n=5$ using the derived theoretical formulae for the expected values. The results are given in Table 13.5.

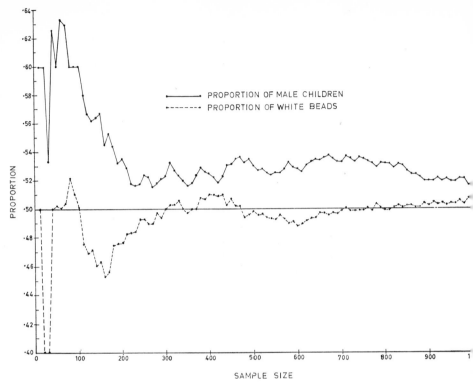

Figure 13.3. The relative frequencies of white beads and male children for different sample sizes

Histograms are drawn for 4 different sets of 50, 2 different sets of 100 obtained by pooling the first two and the last two sets of 50 each, and for all the 200 sets both for the real and artificial data (see figures 13.1 and 13.2). The following comments can be made.

(i) The histograms for $n=50$ and 100 of parallel sets of observations although produced by the same mechanism are not the same but are similar in shape.

(ii) The variation in shape between parallel sets is small when the number of observations is increased.

(iii) The situation is the same for the real as well as the artificial data.

(iv) In all cases the shape of the observed histogram conforms closely to the theoretical or expected one and the agreement gets closer as the number of observations increases.

The limiting frequency
We shall analyse the two series in a slightly different way. From the first n terms of the series, the ratio $r_n = m_n/n$, where m_n is the total number of

262

Table 13.6. Frequency distributions of number of white beads.

No. of white beads	Frequency			
	1st 50 sets	2nd 50 sets	all 100 sets	expected value
0	9	13	22	23.730
1	23	20	43	39.551
2	11	9	20	26.367
3	6	8	14	8.789
4	1	0	1	1.465
5	0	0	0	0.098

events of one kind, is computed for $n = 10, 20, \ldots$. The graphs of r_n against n for the natural events (ratio of males) and for the artificial events (ratio of white beads) are shown in Figure 13.3. It is seen that in either case, the graph is characterised by large variations for small values of n, moderate variations for medium values of n and a tendency to be constant with minor variations for large values of n. Another feature of interest is the tendency of the graph for artificial data to approach 1/2, suggesting a relationship between the limiting value and the proportion of white beads in the bag. Such a phenomenon could be demonstrated by altering the proportion of white beads in the bag and repeating the experiment. The limiting relative frequency in such case is expected to be the chosen proportion of white beads in the bag.

The graph for real data, while exhibiting the same general features as that for artificial data, tends to a limiting proportion slightly over half demonstrating the possibility of an excess of male over female children at birth.

Distinguishability between chance mechanisms

What kind of sequences would result if the proportion of white beads in the bag had been 1/4 instead of 1/2. A sequence of 500 observations was generated from such a mechanism and frequency distributions were obtained for the number of white beads in sets of 5 events separately for the first 50 sets and the second 50 sets. The results were as shown in Table 13.6.

Histograms were drawn in a similar way for parallel sets of 50 each and for all the 100 sets. They are compared with the theoretical histograms which are shown by dotted line in figure 13.4. It is interesting to observe that histograms from parallel samples behave in a similar way and the general pattern is according to the theoretical expressions for a binomial distribution with probabilities 1/4 and 3/4 for the two kinds of events deduced below. The histograms in figure 13.4 are clearly different in shape

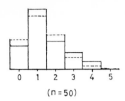 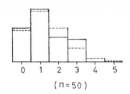 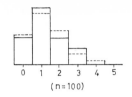

0 1 2 3 4 5	0 1 2 3 4 5	0 1 2 3 4 5
(n = 50)	(n = 50)	(n = 100)

Figure 13.4. Histograms of number of white beads in sets of 5 draws when the proportion of white beads is one-fourth (n = number of bets of 5 draws).

from those in figure 13.2, which are based on equal proportions of black and white beads. Thus we could distinguish between chance mechanisms by differences in shapes of histograms based on observed data and also identify a chance mechanism by comparing the observed histogram with the expected shape.

How do we define the theoretical histogram in the last experiment when the proportion of white beads is $1/4$? This could be easily done by imagining that the bag contains beads of four colours in equal numbers and one colour is designated as black and rest as white. It is reasonable to make the hypothesis that any given sequence of colours in a set of 5 is equally likely to occur. Then a simple computation shows that the hypothetical frequencies are

$$\binom{5}{r}\left(\frac{1}{4}\right)^{r}\left(\frac{3}{4}\right)^{5-r}, \quad r = 0, 1, ..., 5,$$

which is the binomial distribution when the proportion of black beads is $1/4$.

Inference on the mechanism of sex determination

The analyses of real and artificial data (of Tables 13.1 and 13.2) indicate a common underlying structure, and since the mechanism of the latter is known it is reasonable to postulate a *similar* mechanism for the former, i.e., sex of a child is determined by a chance mechanism with equal probabilities for male and female.

It may also be noted that when the chance mechanism is known it is possible to work out the theoretical expectations to which observed events conform. So in practice, if an inference has to be drawn on an unknown mechanism of observed events, it is enough to examine to which theoretical expectations they show closest agreement, instead of producing a number of artificial series for comparison.

Speculative theory of sex determination

At this stage, one could speculate on the physical model for sex determination, which produces a sequence of male and female children, analogous

264

Table 13.7. Three possible hypotheses about parental reproductive cells.

	Hypothesis 1 ♂	Hypothesis 1 ♀	Hypothesis 2 ♂	Hypothesis 2 ♀	CASTLES HYPOTHESIS ♂	CASTLES HYPOTHESIS ♀
PARENTS	M* / M*	M / F	M* / F*	F / F	M* / F*	M / F
CELL DIVISION	M* ; M*	M ; F	M* ; F*	F ; F	M* ; F*	M ; F
UNION OF HALF CELLS	[M*/M] [M*/F]		[M*/F] [F*/F]		[M*/M] [F*/F] [M*/F] [M/F*]	
SEX OF CHILD	♂	♀	♂	♀	STERILE ♂	♀

*INDICATES THAT THE CELLS BELONG TO FATHER

to a sequence of white and black beads in independent draws from a bag. Assuming that a child develops from a cell which is the union of half cells contributed by father and mother, the existence of two sexes shows that the cell of at least one parent is composed of two dissimilar half cells (like black and white beads). The three possible types of parental cells are shown in Table 13.7. Our inference on the mechanism of sex determination implies that the four possible combinations of half cells one from each parent are equally frequent. The three possible types of parental cells are all consistent with the inferred chance mechanism. Therefore, there is a need for collecting further evidence to choose one among them.

Data on pedigrees whose members suffer from a rare malady like haemophilia throw some light on this problem. These data show that a woman may carry this disease without showing any symptoms and when married to a normal male produces male children half of whom on the average inherit the disease while the other half are completely free, and female children half of whom on the average are carriers like herself while the other half are completely free. Or in other words a woman carrying but not exhibiting the disease produces sons of two different types and also daughters of two different types in equal numbers on the average. We shall examine which of the three possibilities in Table 13.7 support the observations.

Let us suppose that a woman is a carrier when the M half of her cell is defective under the models 1 and 3 of Table 7. Labelling this half as M_d we find that all sons receive M_d while no daughter receives M_d under model 1 and vice versa under model 3. This contradicts observed facts that two types of sons and two types of daughters are born. Similar contradiction arises if the F half is assumed to be defective. The hypothesis that both M and F halves are defective is clearly untenable. There is only one possibility left, viz. that of model 2 in Table 13.7. It is easily verified by assuming one F to be defective in the female, that four types of children are possible, namely

M*	M*	F*	F*
F	F_d	F	F_d

with equal frequency on the average. The first two types have the male sex and last two the female sex. Then half the number of daughters are like the mother while the other half are defect free. With the further hypothesis that a male is affected when the F half is defective we have two types of sons, one type exhibiting the disease and another completely free. Thus model 2 is consistent with observed data. We have demonstrated how by a completely statistical approach it is possible to probe into the constitution of male and female cells and establish an essential difference.

13.4. SCRUTINY AND EDITING OF PRIMARY RECORD-CROSS EXAMINATION OF DATA

In investigations where observations are recorded in the field and investigators have no chance of repeating the measurements, the problem of "scrutinising and editing" the primary records assumes paramount importance. The magnitude and the proportion of recording errors are sometimes extremely large in field investigations and the analysis based on such data may result in wrong conclusions. The importance of scrutiny or what Fisher calls, cross examination of data, must be emphasized right at the start of the statistical training.

The Indian Statistical Institute undertakes the processing of huge volume of socio-economic data collected from all over India by the National Sample Survey. In addition, the scientists at the Institute produce large masses of data from laboratory investigations, which are subject to statistical analysis. Thus, there is enough live material for the students to worry their heads.

Scrutiny is indeed a difficult job. No definite rules can be laid down in deciding whether a recorded figure is correct or not without having the opportunity to check it from the original source. The students have to

Table 13.8. Frequency distribution of artificial and imaginary data.

No. of black beads	Frequency			
	Artificial data of Table 2	Imaginary data (1)	Expected value	Imaginary data (2)
0	5	2	6.25	5
1	27	20	31.25	32
2	64	78	62.50	63
3	68	80	62.50	61
4	32	17	31.25	33
5	4	3	6.25	6

learn mostly from experience. Reading of some published papers on the subject will help the student in understanding the problem and in providing broad guide lines.

There is an excellent paper by Mahalanobis (1933), who used very ingenious methods in rectifying the errors in Risley's published record of anthropometric measurements, which was considered to be full of inconsistencies and discrepancies by anthropologists. Other publications by Mahalanobis, Majumdar and Rao (1949), Mukherji, Rao and Trevor (1955) and Majumdar and Rao (1958) contain extensive accounts on scrutiny of data.

Attempts have been made, in a recent investigation at the Indian Statistical Institute, to use the computer in scrutiny of data. Programs for detecting outliers (possibly recording errors), investigator bias, incomplete information etc., written by the students were used for the purpose. Students find such projects extremely interesting and stimulating. Often there is competition among students in detecting errors in primary records.

A statistician should also acquire skill in examining whether data quoted by others are genuine or faked. To bring out the difference between these two types of data, each student in a class of 20 was asked to write down a series of B's and W's imagining the occurrence of events in 50 independent drawings from a bag containing black and white beads in equal numbers. There were 1000 observations providing an imaginary series (which we shall label as 1) from which a frequency distribution of the number of white beads in sets of 5 was obtained. The frequency distributions for the imaginary data (1) and artificial data of Table 13.2 are compared in Table 13.8. The imaginary data (1) contained more sets with 2 or 3 black beads than expected under a chance mechanism so that students were biased towards sets in which the difference between black and white beads is small. At this stage one of the students was shown the expected values and asked to write a series of 1000 observations to conform to a binomial distribution.

267

The frequency distribution obtained from imaginary data (2) is also given in Table 13.8. The tendency, when the expected values were known, was to produce a frequency distribution which agreed more closely with the expected values than was normally possible under a chance mechanism. Generally faked data are detected by systematic bias towards certain kinds of events and/or by too close an agreement with an assumed hypothesis. An article by Fisher (1936) illustrates such a case from published data.

13.5. ERRORS OF MEASUREMENTS—CONCEPT OF TRUE VALUE

The study of the natural sciences offers excellent scope for students to get acquainted with errors of measurements, errors due to limitations of measuring instruments and due to investigator bias. Some possible exercises in physics and chemistry are given below.

Rods differing slightly in length would be supplied and students would be required to measure the lengths of these rods. The object of the experiment is to compare the results obtained by the same student on different days, or by different students, or by different methods and also to find what is the smallest difference in the lengths of two rods which can be distinguished by such measurements. The experiment has to be carefully designed. Such exercises would supply a basis for the "operational" aspect of the concept of length.

The data provided by such an experiment would be ideal for illustrating simple statistical techniques—comparison of means and variabilities between students, testing for differences between rods and comparing the efficiencies of different methods of measurement. Hagen's hypothesis about the symmetry of error distribution can be examined through the computation of the third moment, or Pearson's β_1 coefficient. The data will be useful for more sophisticated treatment by analysis of variance later in the course.

Experiments with simple or Krater's pendulum, calorimeter, spectrometer etc., will provide data of similar but slightly more complicated nature for statistical analysis.

Calibration of burettes and pipettes, use of balance, preparation of standard solutions and testing of Avogadro's law are some exercises which might involve the students in understanding principles of design of experiments and testing of hypotheses.

13.6. AN INVESTIGATION IN BIOLOGY—EMPHASIS ON QUANTITATIVE APPROACH

It is not generally known that a coconut tree can be classified as left handed or right handed depending on the direction of its foliar spiral. Some years

Table 13.9.

| Pollen parent | Seed parent | Progeny | | Prop. of left to total |
		Left	Right	
Right	Right	28	35	0.44
Right	Left	32	36	0.47
Left	Right	20	24	0.45
Left	Left	14	16	0.47

ago an investigation into the study of this aspect of coconut trees was undertaken by T. A. Davis, Professor of biology at the Indian Statistical Institute. The results are briefly summarised, as the investigation is a good example of the statistical approach to a biological problem, worthy of discussion in a statistical course. The questions raised and the evidence provided by observations are as follows. The material is ideal for application of χ^2- and t-tests.

Is left and right foliar spirality genetically inherited? The question can be answered by considering parent plants of different combinations of foliar spirality and scoring the progeny for the same characteristic. The data collected for this purpose are given in Table 13.9.

It is seen from the table that the proportion of plants with left foliar spiral does not depend on the type of parents and consequently there is no genetic basis for the determination of left or right spirality.

However, the deviation of the overall proportion of left to total, is somewhat less than half. This could not be explained until data from various parts of the world could be collected. Table 13.10 gives the numbers of plants with left and right spirality from 22 countries in the Northern hemisphere and 11 countries in the Southern hemisphere.

It is seen that the proportion of left-plants is more than half in the Northern hemisphere and less than half in the Southern hemisphere, which may be the influence of one way rotation of the earth, as in the explanation of the phenomenon of the bath tub vortex which under well controlled conditions is shown to be counter-clockwise in the northern hemisphere and clockwise in the southern hemisphere (Shapiro, 1962).

Table 13.10.

Hemisphere	Left	Right	Prop. of left to total
North	18,968	17,843	0.515
South	4,090	4,540	0.473

Table 13.11.

Category	No. of trees		Mean yield 12 years (1949–60)	6 years (1955–60)
Healthy	L	58	57.69	65.60
	R	70	49.82	54.28
Early diseased	L	60	32.95	36.54
	R	66	30.55	33.10
Late diseased	L	56	22.05	23.63
	R	64	20.04	20.33

A more exciting part of the investigation is the difference in yield rates of the left and right trees. The figures of annual yields of nuts are given in Table 13.11.

It appears that a left palm tree gives about 10 per cent more yield than the right palm tree, a conclusion of great economic importance though unexplainable at the present stage of investigation.

13.7. SOME PRACTICAL EXERCISES—MULTI DISCIPLINARY APPROACH

As I have mentioned earlier, the late Professor J. B. S. Haldane took an active interest in discussions on the nature and content of the B. Stat. course. He had suggested a set of practical exercises of an interdisciplinary nature for students in statistics, which are given below.

1. After previous training in surveying and determinations of elasticity, a tree will be strained by a rope stretched to a neighbouring building, and its deformation observed with a thedolite. The observations will be repeated in a high wind. This may be regarded as an exercise in (*a*) surveying, or applied trigonometry, (*b*) statistics, (*c*) quantitative biology, (*d*) meteorology.

2. Before a chemical balance is systematically used, its theory will be studied. Its periods of oscillation at different loads will then be measured, and the theory verified.

3. Before the compound microscope is used, its theory will similarly be studied, and the performance of the instrument used will be calculated from optical principles. The theory will then be verified.

4. Volumetric gas analysis will be taught. The results will be used (*a*) to verify Avogadro's law, (*b*) to measure human respiration at rest and at work, (*c*) to analyse coal mine air, determining methane, carbon dioxide,

and oxygen. This introduces the notion of chemical controls for the prevention of industrial accidents.

5. The use of a flame spectrometer will be taught. It should be possible to use the same instrument for (a) physical measurements, (b) soil analysis (in conjunction with experiments on the growth of plants in different soils), (c) ore analysis, (d) human blood plasma analysis.

While many of the biological exercises will not lend themselves to co-operation with the physicists and chemists, they will yield data suited for statistical analysis. This is most obvious in the case of the genetical course. But a few other examples are given.

1. The class will carry out simple anthropometric measurements on one another. These will be used for the calculation of means, variances and correlations.

2. They will study life cycles in a frog and a silk-worm moth. Daily counts of survivors will enable them to construct life tables.

3. Observations on a simple and rapid piece of animal behaviour, e.g., the successive ascents of a koi fish for air, will be made in such a way as to furnish data for the estimation of time trends and serial correlations. Five hours' continuous observation will give a series of about 80 intervals, which can be treated by the methods used for rainfall records over 80 years.

Throughout the biological and chemical courses at least, a psychologist will attend whenever quantitative data is obtained to make it possible to compare the performances of different students, e.g., the accuracy with which they make up standard solutions. This will allow them to assess their own and each others' aptitudes, and may obviate the need for practical examinations.

REFERENCES

1. Davis, T. A. (1962): The non-inheritance of asymmetry in Cocus nucifera. J. Genetics, 58, 42–50.
2. Davis, T. A. (1963): The dependence of yield on asymmetry in coconut palms. J. Genetics, 58, 186–215.
3. Davis, T. A. (1968): Biology in the tropics. Haldane and Modern Biology, pp. 327–333, Johns Hopkins Press, Baltimore.
4. Fisher, R. A. (1936): Has Mendel's work been rediscovered? Annals of Science, 1, 115–137.
5. Mahalanobis, P. C. (1933): A revision of Risley's anthropometric data relating to the tribes and castes of Bengel. Sankhyā, 1 (1), 76–105.
6. Mahalanobis, P. C., Majumdar, D. N. and Rao, C. R. (1949): An anthropometric survey of the United Provinces, 1941—A statistical study—Sankhyā, 9, 90–324.

7. Mahalanobis, P. C. (1965): Statistics as a key technology. American Statistician.
8. Majumdar, D. N. and Rao, C. R. (1958): Bengal anthropometric survey, 1945. —A statistical study—Sankhyā, 19, 201–408.
9. Mukherji, R. K., Rao, C. R. and Trevor, J. (1955): The ancient inhabitants of Jebal Moya, Cambridge University Press.
10. Shapiro, A. H. (1962): Bath tub vortex. Nature, 196, 1080–1081.

272

14. Remarks on the teaching of probability

Alfréd Rényi

Mathematical Institute of the Hungarian Academy of Sciences
Budapest, Hungary

14.1. INTRODUCTION

The following remarks deal with the teaching of probability in general, without specifying the level and type of school, the age of the students, etc. In other words, I shall deal with such questions, which are relevant for the teaching of probability at any level. My remarks will be grouped around three basic questions: (1) why should probability be taught; (2) what should be taught; and (3) how should it be taught. Thus, I shall deal with the aims, content and methods of teaching probability.

My remarks are, of course, based on and influenced by my personal experiences. I have the most experience in teaching at the university level; however, I have also given courses of probability at the so-called Free University of Budapest, to an audience consisting mainly of high school students, who participated voluntarily; I have also given some series of lectures on probability in the Hungarian television, where one does not really know exactly who is listening, but the audience is certainly very mixed, consisting partly of young people, partly of grown-up people with very different backgrounds.

14.2. WHY SHOULD PROBABILITY BE TAUGHT?

It seems at the first sight, that a definite answer to this question can be given only when the level and type of school is specified. Nevertheless, I think that something can be said without this specification too. I shall list what I think are the main aims of the teaching of probability in general; what I mean is that these three aims should all be kept in mind in working out the curriculum of any course on probability, giving, of course, different weights to these aims corresponding to the type of course in question. These three aims are as follows:

A. Probability should be taught because it is important for the mental development of the students.

273

B. Probability should be taught for its practical uses in everyday life and in different fields of knowledge.

C. Probability should be taught because its teaching is an important and even indispensable part of mathematical education.

I shall now give some comments on each of these aims.

Comments on A.—There was at the University of Budapest a professor of law, who used to ask his students at oral examinations the following question: "If you look down on the city from St. Gellert's hill (a hill in the middle of Budapest) what do you see?" The students were supposed to answer: "Objects and subjects of law." I do not know what the reaction of this professor would have been if a student would have answered to his question that he would see stochastic processes. Probably the professor would not have understood the answer at all, in spite of it being much more meaningfull than the answer he expected. The understanding of the notion of probability is really indispensable for an understanding of the world around us. It is a keystone of a scientific outlook to the world. The teaching of any branch of mathematics helps the mental development of the students, teaches them to think logically in clearly defined terms, etc. What I have in mind saying that the study of probability theory is important for the mental development of the students is however something more, including what was said about the teaching of any branch of mathematics, but going beyond this. The study of probability teaches the student that clear logical thinking is of use also in situations when one is confronted with uncertainty (what is in fact the case in almost every practical situation). The study of probability has an advantageous effect on the character of the students too. For instance, it strengthens their courage if they understand that some failure may be due simply to chance and is no reason to give up some effort. Primitive people are inclined to be oversuspicious. If they have some trouble, they usually try to explain it by attributing it to the malice of somebody, even if this is not the case. The reason of this irrational behavior is often that they do not understand the notion of chance. The study of probability may help to eradicate these remnants of the magic way of thinking of the stone-age. The study of probability makes, also, people more understanding for the point of view of others and thus helps them to adjust themselves to social life.

Comments on B.—In life, everybody is constantly facing certain risks; probability theory teaches us a reasonable behavior concerning risks and hazards of everyday life. Making a reasonable use of available insurance is a good example of how anybody can apply probability in his own life. In planning

274

the family budget, or a trip abroad, etc., everybody has to make estimates of expenses which to some extent depend on chance. These examples show that everybody needs some knowledge of the laws of chance.

In view of the growing importance of the application of probability theory in sciences, in technology, economics, etc., more and more people need a certain amount of knowledge of probability theory for their professional work. It depends on the type of school how far this has to be taken into account. I want to emphasize, however, that nowadays every educated citizen, independently of his or her profession has to understand to some extent such things as atomic energy, radioactivity, genetics, etc., and for even a superficial understanding of these things some knowledge about probability is necessary. Nowadays when weather forecasts speak about the probability of having rain tomorrow, everybody should know what this really means.

Comments on C.—Acquaintance with the elements of probability theory helps to understand the relation of mathematics to the real world, to grasp the notion of a mathematical model of reality. If probability theory is completely missing from the mathematical education of a group of students, they do not get an adequate picture about what mathematics really is and what it can do for them. It is common misunderstanding among people not familiar with probability theory that mathematical methods can be applied only in situations where simple and strict laws are valid between a small number of exactly measurable quantities. One often hears even nowadays statements that mathematical methods can not be applied to the study of certain phenomena because they are "too complex". This prejudice is characteristic of those who have studied some mathematics but not probability, has hindered for some time the development of the application of mathematical methods in economy, sociology, biology, psychology, etc., at least in certain countries.

I would like to add that the inclusion of the teaching of probability into the teaching of mathematics at the pre-college level is in conformity with other modern trends in mathematical education, and can very easily be coordinated with these to the benefit of both. For instance, the teaching of probability is made easier if the students have before this got acquainted with the elements of set theory and of Boolean algebra; on the other hand studying probability is an excellent occasion for using the mentioned notions, and thus helps their thorough understanding.

14.3. WHAT SHOULD BE TAUGHT?

As I want to deal only with questions which are relevant for the teaching of probability at every level, and the content of a course of probability has clearly to depend heavily on the type of school in question, on the age of the students, their general mathematical background, etc., I shall restrict myself to some general remarks only.

I think that every course of probability theory should contain a certain amount of material concerning each of the four topics listed below:

A. The empirical background of probability theory, that is the exhibition of statistical regularities in everyday life, in nature, in games of chance, etc.;

B. The mathematical theory of probability;

C. Applications of probability theory to the description and prediction of random mass phenomena in different fields;

D. The history of probability theory, including the discussion of the philosophical questions connected with the notion of probability.

The arrangement of these four points corresponds to the logical order in which—according to my opinion—these questions should be treated. To avoid misunderstandings, I want to emphasize that when I am saying that the course should be started by making the students familiar with the notion of statistical regularity, I do not mean that the course should start with statistics. On the contrary, I have found all attempts to teach statistics before and without some preliminary knowledge of probability theory, highly unsatisfactory from a logical as well as from a didactical point of view. What I mean by saying that it is desirable that the course should start with making the students familiar with the notion of statistical regularity, is that this notion should be explained through well-chosen examples and experiments, which make it clear to the student what are the basic facts that the mathematical theory of probability should help to understand and explain. After this one should pass to the exposition of as much of probability theory as can be taught in view of the age and mathematical background of the students, taking, of course, the duration and particular aims of the course also into account. As regards mathematical statistics as an independent course, I think that this should be taught only at the college level, for those students who are interested in it.

As regards the applications of probability theory, I have sometimes encountered the view that the practical importance of probability theory can be made clear only through the teaching of statistics. I think that this is not the case. A large part of the most important applications of probability theory can be fully understood on the basis of an introductory course of probability theory. Of course, even a short course of probability should make it clear that in reality the basic parameters have to be determined in most cases empirically; however, if large samples are available, this does not require sophisticated statistical methods. Nevertheless it should be made clear to the students of an introductory course on probability that the study of the inverse problems of probability theory (when one starts from the observations and wants to make from these inferences about the parameters of the underlying probability distribution) is the subject of a separate discipline, namely mathematical statistics, which is based on probability theory; but nevertheless, is an independent discipline, not a part of probability theory. Of course, Bayesian statistics can be considered a part of probability theory, and a limited amount of Bayesian statistics can be included in an introductory course of probability if time permits this.

As regards D), I think that while the inclusion of some historical material is useful and desirable in the teaching of any subject, this is particularly helpful in teaching probability. I think that it is also very important to discuss to some extent, even in a short introductory course, the philosophy of probability, because this helps the students to learn the probabilistic way of thinking. The discussion of the philosophical questions concerning probability can be most easily done in course of giving a short account of the history of probability, this being at the same time the history of the philosophy of probability.

Finally, I would like to emphasize that I consider *entropy* and *information* as basic concepts of probability, and I strongly recommend that the teacher should spend some time in the discussion of these notions too.

14.4. HOW SHOULD PROBABILITY BE TAUGHT?

Concerning this group of questions, the difficulty is quite the opposite as with respect to the previous group. Here so much could be said—even without specifying the level—that some selection has to be made. Leaving many important questions aside, I shall give some remarks on the following three questions only:

A. The question of rigour;
B. The performance in class of experiments on random events;
C. The introduction of the notion of a probability space.

A. I am in general in favour of a reasonable amount of rigour in teaching mathematics, because I feel that mathematics without rigour is not mathematics at all. This, of course, does not mean that every statement made should be rigorously proved. Some theorems can be stated without any proof, some with a heuristic reasoning supporting it, and only some with full proofs. However, a sharp distinction has to be made between these different ways of conveying information. The student should always know what has been proved and what not. Especially a heuristic argument should never be called a proof. Similarly sharp distinction should be made between definitions and theorems. All this applies to the teaching of any branch of mathematics, but as in teaching probability these basic rules are often violated, I thought it is worth while to emphasize them. I want to add, that if the teacher wants that his students should appreciate why rigour is necessary, he has to convince them about this, by well-chosen examples in which a perfunctory treatment leads to definitely false results. In general, well chosen examples should form the backbone of the teaching of mathematics, and nowhere is there such a great choice of exciting and nevertheless elementary examples as in probability theory.

B. Statistical regularity can be exemplified on figures taken from books or newspapers, etc., but it makes a greater impression on the students if the data analyzed are obtained from experiments performed before their eyes, and if possible, by themselves. Some teachers object to this, because they are afraid that the experiments lead to results which are not quite as expected, and which, by the very nature of such experiments, cannot be exactly foreseen. I think that this fear is not justified, and if the teacher understands probability well, he cannot come into an embarrassing situation. Of course, the teacher has to react quickly, and the evaluation of the data which the teacher himself cannot foresee is a more difficult task than the discussion of examples where the teacher can work out the results in advance. But the advantages of experimenting in class are so great, that in spite of these difficulties I am strongly in favour of such experiments. Of course, these experiments have to be prepared with care. For instance, in course of my popular lecture series in TV I wanted to perform Buffon's famous experiment with needles. I was surprised to find that while a large percentage of textbooks of probability mentions Buffon's experiment, none of these books gives any practical advice how to carry out this experiment in such a way that the basic assumptions should be fairly well realized. Finally, I had to devise myself a simple mechanism for this purpose. I had similar experience with another classical experiment, Galton's desk. I have found that if one realizes the experiment without caution, the results obtained will strongly deviate from what one expects, because the deviations of the balls at different levels will be strongly correlated. In this case, I had to construct a special apparatus to obtain the results which one expects. As regards dice, the best which I have seen are the dice of icosahedral form, prepared in Japan for the production of random digits for purposes of quality control. As far as I know, these are manufactured in Japan in large quantities. I do not think that it would be too difficult to manufacture reliable ordinary dice for the use in teaching probability. In connection with dice, I want to mention that in my TV lectures, I have performed experiments not only with ordinary dice, but with bones such as have been used by the Greeks and Romans of ancient times. Of course, there are many other simple experiments suitable for performing them in class: Throwing coins, drawing cards from a well-shuffled pack, playing roulette, etc. I have realized what a valuable help can be obtained from examples concerning games of chance, when my colleague, Dr. P. Révesz told me his experiences in teaching probability in Ethiopia. He told me that he had great difficulties because games of chance are totally unknown in Ethiopia, and as they are strictly forbidden, he was advised not to mention such games in his lectures. Many ingenious devices are used in quality control, which can be used in class. For instance, in my TV lectures, I have performed experiments with a bag of small plastic balls and a plastic shovel in which there are 100 small holes arranged in a 10×10 square; if the shovel is merged among the balls, the holes are filled with balls which are attracted by electrostatic forces to the shovel. I have filled the bag with two sorts of balls, white and red, so that the percentage of red balls was quite small (1 %). In this way, I obtained data, which could be well fitted by the Poisson distribution. I would like to mention that the data obtained from experiments can be analyzed in various ways, and this analysis can lead to much more than the understanding of the notion of statistical regularity, namely to the understanding of the notion of independence and the less obvious properties of randomness. As an example, I would like to mention that I have often shown to the students two sequences of zeros and ones; I have told them that I obtained one of them by throwing a coin (0 meaning heads and 1 tails) and that the other one is artificial, a rather poor imitation of a real random sequence. The sequences had length about 150: The students has to guess which of the two is the real random sequence and which is the imitation. (The point was that the artificial sequence was too regular, it did not contain long runs of either zeros or ones, and of course, the real sequence did.)

C. Finally, I would like to give an account about how I recently introduced the notion of a probability space. At the first sight, the innovation seems to be of terminological character only, but I shall try to show that there is more behind it.

What is usually called a probability space, i.e., a triple $(\Omega, \mathcal{A}, P)$ where Ω is a non-empty set, $\mathcal{A}$ a σ-algebra of subsets of Ω, and P a measure on α such that $P(\Omega) = 1$, is called in my terminology an *experiment*. The elements

ω of Ω are called the possible *outcomes* of the experiment. Every subset A of Ω is called an *event*, consisting in that the outcome of the experiment belongs to the set A; those subsets which belong to the family $\mathcal{A}$ are interpreted as *observable events*, while those subset of Ω which do not belong to $\mathcal{A}$ as not observable events. $P(A)$ is, of course, interpreted as usual as the probability of the observable event A: It is emphasized that the probability of not observable events is not defined at all.

A standard example is the experiment consisting in throwing two indistinguishable dice: In this case Ω consists of the 36 pairs of numbers (a, b) where $1 \leqslant a \leqslant 6$ and $1 \leqslant b \leqslant 6$, while $\mathcal{A}$ consists of those subsets of Ω which have the property that if $(a, b) \in A$, then $(b, a) \in A$; among the 2^{36} subsets of Ω only 2^{21} have this property: These are the observable events.

This example shows, that even if Ω is finite, it may be reasonable to take for $\mathcal{A}$ not the family of all subsets of Ω, but a more restricted algebra of subsets of Ω. Of course, in the example mentioned above, one may take for Ω instead of the set of ordered pairs (a, b) with $1 \leqslant a \leqslant 6$, $1 \leqslant b \leqslant 6$, the set of all such unordered pairs, and in this case, $\mathcal{A}$ may be taken as the family of all subsets of Ω. However, in most cases, it is more advantageous to deal with a wider set of outcomes, but restrict the family of sets on which the probability is defined.

This approach leads in a logical way to the supposition that $\mathcal{A}$ has to be an algebra of sets. As a matter of fact, it is obvious that if an event is observable, so is its contrary. Further that if we consider two observable events, the event consisting in that at least one of the mentioned two events occurs is also observable. (This is not true in quantum mechanics, but certainly true concerning "classical" observations.)

I have tried out this method of introducing the concept of a probability space at different levels (including the pre-college level) and I have found that the emphasis laid on the notion of observability makes it easier for the students to understand the notion of a probability space. Of course, some of the advantages of this method become obvious only at a later stage. It facilitates the understanding of the general notion of conditional probability and of conditional expectation if the student gets used from the beginning to the fact that the family of sets on which a measure is defined does not necessarily coincide with the largest family to which it could be extended. Many textbooks motivate the fact that a probability measure is usually defined only on a certain σ-algebra of subsets of the basic space and not on all its subsets, by saying that it is often impossible by purely mathematical reasons, to extend the measure in question to all subsets. While this is literally true, I think that this motivation is nevertheless misleading, because usually it would be quite pointless to extend the probability measure to all subsets of the basic space, because this extension would lose its meaning (e.g., as a conditional probability). I do not want to go into the details of this question as this concerns only the teaching of advanced probability theory. Coming back to elementary courses on probability I want to emphasize that I have found that it facilitates the understanding of the notion of probability—more exactly of the mathematical setup of probability theory—if the notion of observability of events for which probability is defined, is made part of the setup right from the start.

15. Relations, Functions and Expectations

L. Råde

Chalmers Institute of Technology, Göteborg, Sweden
and
CEMREL-CSMP, CARBONDALE, Illinois, U.S.A.

15.1. INTRODUCTION

In this paper I will discuss the treatment of some fundamental notions of probability theory in the Elements of Mathematics Program (EM) of the Comprehensive School Mathematics Program (CSMP). I will center the discussion on how the careful treatment of relations and functions in this program can be utilized in the teaching of probability.

The EM program is one component of CSMP. It is a program for capable students aimed at developing a sequence of carefully planned textbooks to be used in independent study. A detailed description of this program can be found in (1).

It is planned that Book 9 in the EM series will be a book on probability (2). The students who will use this book have the following characteristics (among others):

1. They are highly verbal and motivated students (upper 15–20 %).
2. They are 14–16 years old.
3. Their previous study includes an explicit treatment of basic mathematical logic (statement calculus, first order predicate calculus and proof theory), set theory, relations and functions.

In this discussion I will try to show what such a background can mean for the teaching of basic probability theory. In the year 1968–69 this treatment has been tried out with two groups of students. First a group of students was taught the material by classroom lecturing supplemented with written problem work. Based on the lecture notes and making use of the experience from this class, a textbook is being written. This textbook is being studied individually by the second group of students.

In this discussion I will be especially concerned with how the careful treatment of relations and functions in the EM program can be utilized in the teaching of probability. Further disconnected comments on other aspects of teaching probability at this level are at the end of this paper.

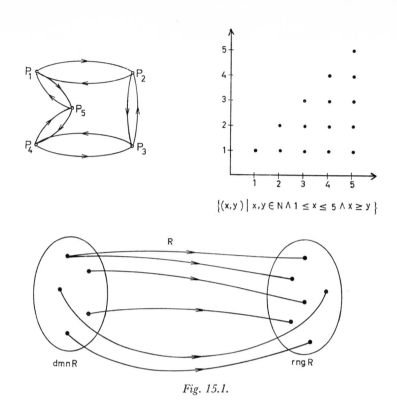

$$\{(x,y) \mid x,y \in N \wedge 1 \leq x \leq 5 \wedge x \geq y\}$$

Fig. 15.1.

15.2. RELATIONS AND FUNCTIONS IN THE EM PROGRAM

Relations and functions are treated in Books 6 and 7 of the EM program. The treatment is based on the notion of an *ordered pair*, which is defined as a set according to Kuratowski and Wiener. Relations are defined as sets of ordered pairs and functions as relations with the special property that no two ordered pairs of the relation have the same first component. The treatment includes a lot of graphical work. Relations and functions are portrayed by different kinds of arrow diagrams and graphs in coordinate systems. Matrix representation is also discussed. Figure 15.1 shows some illustrations from the book on relations.

Two notions connected with relations and functions have been of special importance for the treatment of probability in this program, namely *composition of relations* and the *function induced by a relation*. The composition $R \circ S$ of two relations R and S needs no discussion here. The function induced by a relation is defined as follows:

Let f be a relation. Then $\mathring{f}$ (*the f-induced function*) is a function such that

$$\mathring{f} : \mathcal{P}(\text{domain} f) \rightarrow \mathcal{P}(\text{range} f)$$

284

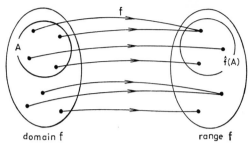

domain f   range f

Fig. 15.2.

and for all $A \in \mathcal{D}(\text{domain } f)$

$$\hat{f}(A) = \{y \mid (\exists x)\, (x \in A \wedge (x, y) \in f)\}.$$

Thus $\hat{f}$ is the function with $\mathcal{D}(\text{domain } f)$ (the set of all subsets of the domain of f) as domain and which assigns to each subset A of the domain of f the image of A under f. The image of A under f is the set of those elements in the range that are second components of ordered pairs of f with the first component in A. Figure 15.2 illustrates this for a function f.

The following properties of $\hat{f}$ are essential:

(1) $\hat{f}(\phi) = \phi$ and $\hat{f}\,(\text{domain } f) = \text{range } f$
(2) For all subsets A and B of domain f

$$\hat{f}(A \cup B) = \hat{f}(A) \cup \hat{f}(B).$$

Of special interest in probability theory is the function $\hat{f}^{-1}$, where f is a function and f^{-1} its converse (or the inverse if it exists). This function has the properties:

(1) For all subsets A of the range of f

$$\hat{f}^{-1}(A) = \{x \mid x \in \text{domain } f \wedge f(x) \in A\}.$$

(2) For all subsets A and B of range f, if $A \cap B = \phi$, then

$$\hat{f}^{-1}(A) \cap \hat{f}^{-1}(B) = \phi.$$

Usually $\hat{f}^{-1}(A)$ is called the *inverse image* of A (under f).

The notion of the induced function will also be used in connection with the composition of relations. The following property is especially useful:

If f and g are relations such that range $f \subset$ domain g, then,

$$\widehat{g \circ f} = \hat{g} \circ \hat{f}.$$

This is illustrated in Figure 15.4 for functions f and g.

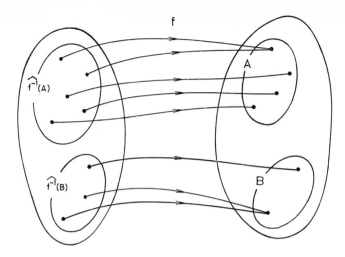

Fig. 15.3.

15.3. FINITE PROBABILITY SPACES,
CONDITIONAL PROBABILITY AND INDEPENDENCE

In this section I give a short summary of how the notions in the title above are treated. In later sections I will discuss in more detail how relations and functions are used after the basic notions have been treated. Throughout the paper I will center my discussion on the mathematical structure of the subject. However, in the actual presentation to the students *all new concepts are motivated and introduced by appeal to practical situations*. All concepts in probability theory have their root in features of practical experiments. Probability theory, more than most areas of mathematics, offers many op-

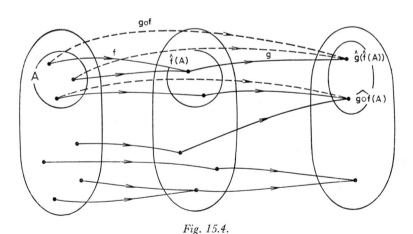

Fig. 15.4.

portunities to demonstrate the interplay between the real world and mathematics.

We begin with the following definition of a finite probability space.

Definition: For all Ω, P the ordered pair (Ω, P) is a *finite probability space* (*fps*) if and only if

1. Ω is a finite set
2. $P : \mathcal{P}(\Omega) \to R$
3. $(\forall A)\ (A \in \mathcal{P}(\Omega) \Rightarrow 0 \leqslant P(A) \leqslant 1)$
4. $P(\Omega) = 1$
5. $(\forall A, B)\ [(A, B \in \mathcal{P}(\Omega) \land A \cap B = \phi) \Rightarrow P(A \cup B) = P(A) + P(B)]$.

The set Ω is called the *outcome set* and P the *probability measure* of the fps (Ω, P). An fps is also called an *experiment*. The definition above is often presented as a sequence of axioms. In this course, however, this cannot be done as there are no new undefined terms introduced. The treatment of probability theory is here made within set theory.

The basic properties of an fps are now easily derived. The point probability function (ppf) p of an fps (Ω, P) is defined as follows:

$$p : \Omega \to R$$

and

$$p(w) = P(\{w\}) \text{ for all } w \in \Omega.$$

Furthermore it is shown that for a function t such that

$$t : \Omega \to R \text{ (where } \Omega \text{ is a finite set)}$$

$$\sum_{w \in \Omega} t(w) = 1$$

$$t(w) \geqslant 0 \text{ for all } w \in \Omega$$

there exists one and only one P such that t is the ppf of (Ω, P).

An fps (Ω, P) is said to have a *uniform probability measure* if the ppf is a constant function. It is shown in this case that for all $A \in \mathcal{P}(\Omega)$,

$$P(A) = \frac{\#(A)}{\#(\Omega)}.$$

If (Ω, P) is an fps and A an event such that $P(A) > 0$ it is easy to verify that

$$p_A = \{(w, p(w)/P(A)) \mid w \in A\} \cup \{(w, 0) \mid w \in \Omega - A\}$$

is a ppf (on Ω). The fps (Ω, P_A) is called the *conditional fps given A* and the measure P_A is called the conditional probability measure given A. It is shown that for all events A and B with $P(A) > 0$

$$P_A(B) = \frac{P(A \cap B)}{P(A)}.$$

Now independence can be introduced as a relation as follows. If (Ω, P) is an fps, the relation

$$\{(A, B) \mid A, B \in \mathcal{P}(\Omega) \wedge P(A \cap B) = P(A)\, P(B)\}$$

is called the *independence relation for* (Ω, P) and is denoted by "$I_{(\Omega, P)}$". It is shown that if $(A, B) \in I_{(\Omega, P)}$ ("A and B are independent") then

$$(B, A) \in I_{(\Omega, P)}$$
$$(\bar{A}, B) \in I_{(\Omega, P)}$$
$$(\bar{A}, \bar{B}) \in I_{(\Omega, P)}$$

where $\bar{A}$ is the complement of A, relative to Ω.

Independence is extended to three events by introduction of the following ternary relation "I_3" ($I_{(\Omega, P)}$ is now denoted by "I_2") where

$$I_3 = \{(A, B, C) \mid A, B, C \in \mathcal{P}(\Omega) \wedge (A, B) \in I_2 \wedge (A, C) \in I_2$$
$$\wedge\, (B, C) \in I_2 \wedge P(A \cap B \cap C) = P(A)\, P(B)\, P(C)\}.$$

15.4. MAPPING OF AN FPS

Let (Ω, P) be an fps and f a function with domain Ω. Then it is shown that $(\hat{f}(\Omega), P \circ \hat{f}^{-1})$ is an fps. This new fps determined by the basic fps (Ω, P) and the function f is called the f-*image of* (Ω, P) and it is also denoted by "(Ω_f, P_f)". Thus we have

$$(\Omega_f, P_f) = (\hat{f}(\Omega), P \circ \hat{f}^{-1}).$$

This definition is natural as the practical situation illustrated in Figure 15.5 shows.

In the figure the outcome set

$$\Omega = \{1 \text{ dot, } 2 \text{ dots, } 3 \text{ dots, } 4 \text{ dots, } 5 \text{ dots, } 6 \text{ dots}\}$$

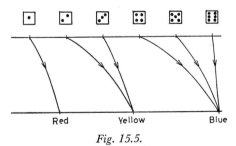

Red   Yellow   Blue

Fig. 15.5.

288

of the fps or experiment of tossing a symmetric die is portrayed. The die is colored according to a "coloring function" c such that

$$c(1 \text{ dot}) = \text{Red}$$
$$c(2 \text{ dots}) = c(3 \text{ dots}) = \text{Yellow}$$
$$c(4 \text{ dots}) = c(5 \text{ dots}) = c(6 \text{ dots}) = \text{Blue}.$$

(Coloring a set of objects such that each object is colored in one color can be described by a function!) If the die is tossed after it has been colored (and the paint is dry!) a suitable outcome set is the set

$$\{\text{Red, Yellow, Blue}\} = \hat{c}(\Omega).$$

What is the probability of the singleton event {Blue}, (that is, $P_c(\{\text{Blue}\})$? This event occurs if and only if the event {4 dots, 5 dots, 6 dots} occurs using the original die. Thus

$$P_c(\{\text{Blue}\}) = P(\{4 \text{ dots, 5 dots, 6 dots}\}) = \tfrac{1}{2}$$

or

$$P_c(\{\text{Blue}\}) = P(\hat{c}^{-1}(\{\text{Blue}\}))$$

because {4 dots, 5 dots, 6 dots} is the inverse image under c of {Blue}. It is thus natural to assign the probability (in the original fps of tossing a symmetric die) of the inverse image under c of {Blue} in the new fps. Also observe that

$$P_c(\{\text{Blue}\}) = (P \circ \hat{c}^{-1})(\{\text{Blue}\}).$$

Within probability theory as well as within numerous applications it is interesting to study composed mappings of an fps. The following theorem is fundamental.

Fundamental theorem on compositions of mappings of an fps (FTCMFPS)

Let (Ω, P) be an fps and f a function with domain Ω. Furthermore let g be a function such that range $f =$ domain g. Then the g-image of (Ω_f, P_f) is also the $(g \circ f)$-image of (Ω, P). Or, shorter:

$$((\Omega_f)_g, (P_f)_g) = (\Omega_{g \circ f}, P_{g \circ f})$$

The proof of this theorem is indicated below.

$$\Omega_{g \circ f} = \hat{g} \circ \hat{f}(\Omega) = (\hat{g} \circ \hat{f})(\Omega) = \hat{g}(\hat{f}(\Omega))$$
$$(\Omega_f)_g = \hat{g}(\Omega_f) = \hat{g}(\hat{f}(\Omega))$$

$$P_{g \circ f} = P \circ \widehat{(g \circ f)}^{-1} = P \circ (\hat{f}^{-1} \circ \hat{g}^{-1}) = P \circ (\hat{f}^{-1} \circ \hat{g}^{-1})$$
$$(P_f)_g = P_f \circ \hat{g}^{-1} = (P \circ \hat{f}^{-1}) \circ \hat{g}^{-1}$$

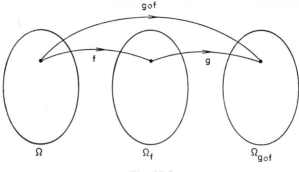

Fig. 15.6.

This proof is easily mastered by the students because they know how to find the converse of a composition and that composition of functions is associative.

15.5. RELATIONS AS OUTCOME SETS

Now we turn our interest to fps's with a relation (set of ordered pairs) as outcome set. Figure 15.7 shows two examples of such fps's.

In the following we use the first and second projection functions $pr_{(1, A)}$ and $pr_{(2, A)}$ with domain A, where A is a relation. For these functions the following holds:

$$pr_{(1, A)} : A \xrightarrow{\text{onto}} \text{domain } A$$

$$pr_{(1, A)} ((x, y)) = x \text{ for all } (x, y) \in A$$

$$pr_{(2, A)} : A \xrightarrow{\text{onto}} \text{range } A$$

$$pr_{(2, A)} ((x, y)) = y \text{ for all } (x, y) \in A.$$

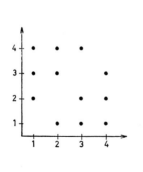

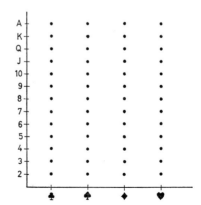

Fig. 15.7.

290

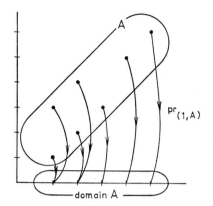
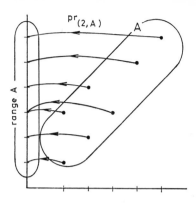

Fig. 15.8.

Now let (Ω, P) be an fps and Ω a relation. Then the $pr_{(1,\Omega)}$- and $pr_{(2,\Omega)}$-images of (Ω, P) are called the first and second marginal fps's of (Ω, P). Denote them by "(Ω_1, P_1)" and "(Ω_2, P_2)". Then

$$\Omega_1 = \text{domain } \Omega, \quad P_1 = P \circ \widehat{pr_{(1,\Omega)}^{-1}}$$

$$\Omega_2 = \text{range } \Omega, \quad P_2 = P \circ \widehat{pr_{(2,\Omega)}^{-1}}.$$

It is easy to see the practical significance of these fps's for the cases in Figure 15.7 (assuming for instance a uniform probability measure).

It is not difficult to find examples of fps's (Ω, P) with Ω a relation and such that

$$\Omega = \Omega_1 \times \Omega_2$$

and

$$P(A \times B) = P_1(A) \cdot P_2(B) \text{ for all } A \in \mathcal{P}(\Omega_1) \text{ and } B \in \mathcal{P}(\Omega_2).$$

In this case (Ω, P) is said to have *independent marginal fps's*. Furthermore, it is shown that for given fps's (Γ_1, T_1) and (Γ_2, T_2) there exists one and only one fps (Ω, P) such that (Γ_1, T_1) and (Γ_2, T_2) are the independent marginal fps's of (Ω, P). This fps has the outcome set $\Gamma_1 \times \Gamma_2$ and the probability measure P is determined by the point probability function p such that

$$p((u, w)) = t_1(u) \cdot t_2(w) \text{ for all } (u, w) \in \Gamma_1 \times \Gamma_2.$$

Here t_1 and t_2 are the ppf's determined by Γ_1 and Γ_2. This fps is also called the (independent) product of (Γ_1, T_1) and (Γ_2, T_2). If $\Gamma_1 = \Gamma_2$ and $T_1 = T_2$ we have two independent trials of the same fps (or experiment).

Figure 15.9 portrays an important special case: two independent trials of a Bernoulli fps (or experiment); that is, an fps with a doubleton set $\{w_1, w_2\}$ as outcome set and with $p(w_1) = \varrho$, $p(w_2) = 1 - \varrho$.

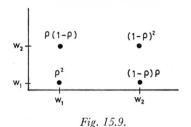

Fig. 15.9.

The notions discussed in this section are extended to "higher" (ternary and so on) relations without going into much detail. The definition of n independent trials of a Bernoulli experiment is especially important.

15.6. EXPECTATION OF REAL FPS'S AND REALVALUED FUNCTIONS

A real fps (rfps) is an fps (Ω, P) with Ω a subset of the set of real numbers. For rfps's one can find sums of outcomes and products of outcomes and probabilities and so on. This gives possibilities to introduce new concepts, especially the expectation $\mu_{(\Omega, P)}$ of an rfps:

$$\mu_{(\Omega, P)} = \sum_{x \in \Omega} xp(x)$$

This definition is motivated by some practical experiments with real numbers as outcomes. Using the stability of relative frequency concept it is easy to motivate the definition of the expectation as a prediction of the mean of the observed outcomes in a large number of trials.

Now consider the expectation of an rfps which is the image under a realvalued function ξ of an fps (Ω, P).

In our previously introduced notation this rfps is named

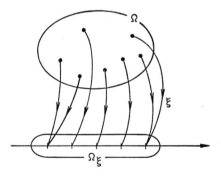

Fig. 15.10.

292

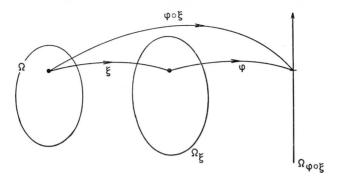

Fig. 15.11.

$$(\Omega_\xi, P_\xi)$$

and its expectation is

$$\mu_{(\Omega_\xi, P_\xi)} = \sum_{x \in \Omega_\xi} x p_\xi(x).$$

As another name for this expectation we introduce

$$E_{(\Omega, P)}(\xi)$$

or simply "$E(\xi)$" when it is clear what the basic fps (Ω, P) is. Much of the following treatment of expectation rests on the following theorem.

Fundamental theorem on realvalued mappings and expectations (FTMEXP)

Let (Ω, P) be an fps and $\xi : \Omega \to R$. Then

$$E_{(\Omega, P)}(\xi) = \sum_{w \in \Omega} \xi(w) p(w).$$

This theorem is proved by a rearrangement of the terms in the sum

$$\sum_{x \in \Omega} x p_\xi(x).$$

Now consider the following situation. (Ω, P) is an fps and $\xi : \Omega \xrightarrow{\text{onto}} \Omega_\xi$ (range $\xi = \Omega_\xi$) and $\varphi : \Omega_\xi \to R$. Then $(\Omega_{\varphi \circ \xi}, P_{\varphi \circ \xi})$ is an rfps and according to FTCMFPS it is the φ-image of (Ω_ξ, P_ξ). Thus

$$E_{(\Omega, P)}(\varphi \circ \xi) = E_{(\Omega_\xi, P_\xi)}(\varphi)$$

and according to FTMEXP

$$E_{(\Omega, P)}(\varphi \circ \xi) = \sum_{x \in \Omega_\xi} \varphi(x) p_\xi(x).$$

Observe that we have three ways to find $E_{(\Omega, P)}(\varphi \circ \xi)$:

293

$$E_{(\Omega, P)} (\varphi \circ \xi) = \sum_{x \in \Omega_{\varphi \circ \xi}} x p_{\varphi \circ \xi}(x)$$

$$= \sum_{w \in \Omega} \varphi(\xi(w)) \, p(w)$$

$$= \sum_{x \in \Omega_\xi} \varphi(x) \, p_\xi(x).$$

15.7. EXPECTATIONS AND THE RING OF REALVALUED FUNCTIONS DEFINED ON Ω

Let (Ω, P) be an fps and S_Ω the set of all realvalued functions with domain Ω. If $\xi, \eta \in S_\Omega$ then $\xi + \eta$ and $\xi \cdot \eta$ are elements of S_Ω such that

$$(\xi + \eta) \, (w) = \xi(w) + \eta(w) \quad \text{for all } w \in \Omega$$
$$(\xi \cdot \eta) \, (w) \ \ = \xi(w) \, \eta(w) \quad \text{ for all } w \in \Omega.$$

If, furthermore, $c \in R$, then $c\xi$ and c_Ω are elements of S_Ω such that

$$(c\xi) \, (w) = c\xi(w) \quad \text{ for all } w \in \Omega$$
$$c_\Omega(w) = c \quad \quad \text{ for all } w \in \Omega.$$

The function c_Ω is called a *constant function on* Ω.

Now with the aid of FTMEXP the following is easily proved:

$$E_{(\Omega, P)} (\xi + \eta) = E_{(\Omega, P)} (\xi) + E_{(\Omega, P)} (\eta)$$
$$E_{(\Omega, P)} (c\xi) \ \ \ = E_{(\Omega, P)} (c_\Omega \cdot \xi) = c E_{(\Omega, P)} (\xi)$$
$$E_{(\Omega, P)} (c_\Omega) \ \ \ = c$$

For instance the first of these formulas is proved as follows:

$$E_{(\Omega, P)} (\xi + \eta) = \sum_{w \in \Omega} (\xi + \eta) \, (w) \, p(w)$$

$$= \sum_{w \in \Omega} (\xi(w) + \eta(w)) \, p(w)$$

$$= \sum_{w \in \Omega} \xi(w) \, p(w) + \sum_{w \in \Omega} \eta(w) \, p(w)$$

$$= E_{(\Omega, P)} (\xi) + E_{(\Omega, P)} (\eta)$$

15.8. THE FUNCTION $\langle \xi, \eta \rangle$

Let (Ω, P) be an fps and $\xi, \eta \in S_\Omega$. Then we define a function $\langle \xi, \eta \rangle$ such that

$$\langle \xi, \eta \rangle : \Omega \to R \times R$$

and

$$\langle \xi, \eta \rangle \, (w) = (\xi(w), \eta(w)) \text{ for all } w \in \Omega.$$

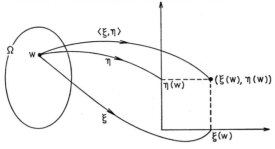

Fig. 15.12.

Thus for given functions ξ and η with domain Ω the function $\langle \xi, \eta \rangle$ assigns to each outcome in Ω the ordered pair $(\xi(w), \eta(w))$. This definition is illustrated in Figure 15.12.

The function $\langle \xi, \eta \rangle$ is of great interest and is used very much in statistics (usually called a "two-dimensional random variable").

The $\langle \xi, \eta \rangle$-image of (Ω, P) is $(\Omega_{\langle \xi, \eta \rangle}, P_{\langle \xi, \eta \rangle})$. Now it is easily proved that (see Figure 15.13)

$$pr_{(1, \Omega_{\langle \xi, \eta \rangle})} \circ \langle \xi, \eta \rangle = \xi$$

$$pr_{(2, \Omega_{\langle \xi, \eta \rangle})} \circ \langle \xi, \eta \rangle = \eta.$$

Here,

$$pr_{(1, \Omega_{\langle \xi, \eta \rangle})} \quad \text{and} \quad pr_{(2, \Omega_{\langle \xi, \eta \rangle})}$$

are first and second projection functions on $\Omega_{\langle \xi, \eta \rangle}$.

It now follows from FTCMFPS that (Ω_ξ, P_ξ) is not only the ξ-image of (Ω, P) but also the first projection image of $(\Omega_{\langle \xi, \eta \rangle}, P_{\langle \xi, \eta \rangle})$. Thus we immediately get the following formulas for the ppf's p_ξ, p_η and $p_{\langle \xi, \eta \rangle}$:

$$p_\xi(x) = \sum_x p_{\langle \xi, \eta \rangle}((x, y)) \quad \text{for all} \quad x \in \Omega_\xi$$

$$p_\eta(y) = \sum_y p_{\langle \xi, \eta \rangle}((x, y)) \quad \text{for all} \quad y \in \Omega_\eta$$

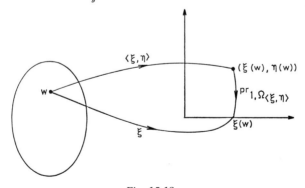

Fig. 15.13.

295

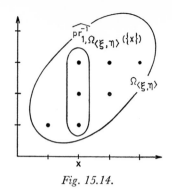

Fig. 15.14.

In the first formula the summation is done for all y in $\widehat{pr^{-1}_{(1,\Omega_{\langle\xi,\eta\rangle}}}(\{x\})$ that is the inverse image of $\{x\}$ under the first projection function on $\Omega_{\langle\xi,\eta\rangle}$. Similarly in the second formula the summation is for x in $\widehat{pr^{-1}_{(2,\Omega_{\langle\xi,\eta\rangle}}}(\{y\})$. Furthermore from FTMEXP we get the following new formulas for

$$E_{(\Omega,P)}(\xi) \quad \text{and} \quad E_{(\Omega,P)}(\eta):$$

$$E_{(\Omega,P)}(\xi) = \sum_{(x,y)\in\Omega_{\langle\xi,\eta\rangle}} x p_{\langle\xi,\eta\rangle}((x,y))$$

$$E_{(\Omega,P)}(\eta) = \sum_{(x,y)\in\Omega_{\langle\xi,\eta\rangle}} y p_{\langle\xi,\eta\rangle}((x,y))$$

The following indicates how the first formula is proved:

$$E_{(\Omega,P)}(\xi) = E_{(\Omega,P)}(pr_{(1,\Omega_{\langle\xi,\eta\rangle}}\circ\langle\xi,\eta\rangle)$$

$$= E_{(\Omega_{\langle\xi,\eta\rangle},P_{\langle\xi,\eta\rangle}})(pr_{(1,\Omega_{\langle\xi,\eta\rangle}})$$

$$= \sum_{(x,y)\in\Omega_{\langle\xi,\eta\rangle}} pr_{(1,\Omega_{\langle\xi,\eta\rangle}}((x,y)) p_{\langle\xi,\eta\rangle}((x,y))$$

$$= \sum_{(x,y)\in\Omega_{\langle\xi,\eta\rangle}} x p_{\langle\xi,\eta\rangle}((x,y))$$

We can now also derive new formulas for $E_{(\Omega,P)}(\xi+\eta)$ and $E_{(\Omega,P)}(\xi\cdot\eta)$.

First we define two functions. Let $A\subset R\times R$ (A is a set of ordered pairs of real numbers). Then the "plus function" $+_A$ and the "dot function" $\cdot_A$ on A are functions such that

$$+_A : A \to R$$

and

$$+_A((x,y)) = x+y \quad \text{for all } (x,y)\in A$$

and

$$\cdot_A : A \to R$$

and

$$\cdot_A((x,y)) = xy \quad \text{for all } (x,y)\in A.$$

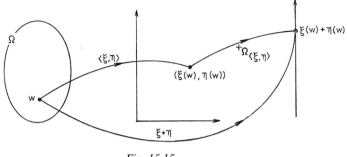

Fig. 15.15.

Now it is easy to prove that (see Figure 15.15)

$$\xi + \eta = +_{\Omega_{\langle \xi, \eta \rangle}} \circ \langle \xi, \eta \rangle$$

$$\xi \cdot \eta = \cdot_{\Omega_{\langle \xi, \eta \rangle}} \circ \langle \xi, \eta \rangle$$

Thus we get, with the aid of FTCMFPS and FTMEXP

$$E_{(\Omega, P)}(\xi + \eta) = E_{(\Omega, P)}(+_{\Omega_{\langle \xi, \eta \rangle}} \circ \langle \xi, \eta \rangle)$$

$$= E_{(\Omega_{\langle \xi, \eta \rangle}, P_{\langle \xi, \eta \rangle})}(+_{\Omega_{\langle \xi, \eta \rangle}})$$

$$= \sum_{(x, y) \in \Omega_{\langle \xi, \eta \rangle}} +_{\Omega_{\langle \xi, \eta \rangle}}((x, y)) \, p_{\langle \xi, \eta \rangle}(x, y)$$

$$= \sum_{(x, y) \in \Omega_{\langle \xi, \eta \rangle}} (x + y) \, p_{\langle \xi, \eta \rangle}(x, y).$$

Similarly one proves that

$$E_{(\Omega, P)}(\xi \cdot \eta) = \sum_{(x, y) \in \Omega_{\langle \xi, \eta \rangle}} xy p_{\langle \xi, \eta \rangle}((x, y)).$$

15.9. INDEPENDENT FUNCTIONS

Figure 15.16 portrays the following situation. To the 50 individuals in a population Ω are assigned real numbers by functions ξ and η. Now let (Ω, P) be the fps with this set Ω as outcome set and a uniform probability measure. This is a mathematical model of the practical experiment of choosing one of the 50 individuals at random. The figure also shows $\Omega_{\langle \xi, \eta \rangle}, p_{\langle \xi, \eta \rangle}, \Omega_\xi, p_\xi, \Omega_\eta,$ and p_η. In the figure the upper numbers in the boxes are those assigned by ξ and the lower numbers those assigned by η. Observe that in this case (Ω_ξ, P_ξ) and (Ω_η, P_η) are independent marginal fps's of $(\Omega_{\langle \xi, \eta \rangle}, P_{\langle \xi, \eta \rangle})$. This means that

297

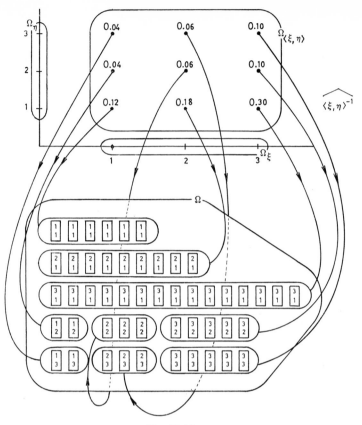

Fig. 15.16.

$$\Omega_{\langle \xi, \eta \rangle} = \Omega_\xi \times \Omega_\eta$$

and

$$p_{\langle \xi, \eta \rangle}((x,y)) = p_\xi(x)\, p_\eta(y) \quad \text{for all} \quad (x,y) \in \Omega_{\langle \xi, \eta \rangle}.$$

When this is the case ξ and η are said to be *independent*. In this case

$$E_{(\Omega, P)}(\xi \cdot \eta) = E_{(\Omega, P)}(\xi)\, E_{(\Omega, P)}(\eta)$$

because

$$E_{(\Omega, P)}(\xi \cdot \eta) = \sum_{(x,y) \in \Omega_{\langle \xi, \eta \rangle}} xy p_{\langle \xi, \eta \rangle}((x,y))$$

$$= \sum_{(x,y) \in \Omega_\xi \times \Omega_\eta} x p_\xi(x)\, y p_\eta(y)$$

$$= \Big(\sum_{x \in \Omega_\xi} x p_\xi(x) \Big) \Big(\sum_{y \in \Omega_\eta} y p_\eta(y) \Big)$$

$$= E_{(\Omega, P)}(\xi)\, E_{(\Omega, P)}(\eta).$$

298

15.10. SOME CONCLUDING REMARKS

I hope that the presentation above has shown how easily the basic results concerning mappings and expectations of fps's can be derived if the students master the notions of functions and relations. In the following I will add some more comments on the EM probability course.

1. *Notation*

My first comment is about the notation used in the teaching of probability theory. The importance of a precise and consistent notation cannot be overemphasized. This is especially so in the treatment of probability for the EM students who are young and are studying probability theory in a sequence of mathematical topics. Unfortunately much notation commonly used in probability theory is not in agreement with that used in other mathematical areas. Also the notation used is sometimes vague or ambiguous.

For instance, in some textbooks on probability the letter "P" is used for all probability measures introduced. Very often no notational distinction is made to distinguish a probability measure P and the related measure P_f determined by a function f. This can be confusing for students. It is also not unusual to find formulas like the following

$$P(A \times B) = P(A) \, P(B),$$

$$p((u, v)) = p(u) \, p(v)$$

where obviously three different probability measures are involved in each formula but all are denoted by the same letter "P" or "p".

It is common to call real-valued functions defined on the outcome set of an fps random (or stochastic) variables. This is a well-established tradition in the teaching of probability. (The history of this tradition is unknown to me.) This terminology perhaps does no harm at the college level, but young students find it confusing. (I would also like to know why the word "sample space" has such wide usage when "outcome set" or "outcome space" seems to be more natural and more descriptive.)

In the EM course a clear distinction is made between the two functions f and $\hat{f}$ since these are different functions. Usually this distinction is not made in textbooks on probability (and in other parts of mathematics)· Though it may be a little easier to write "$f^{-1}(A)$" instead of "$\hat{f}^{-1}(A)$", the first notation is very confusing for the beginner for two reasons: first A is not an element of the domain of f^{-1} and second, f^{-1} may not be a function.

The function, which in this course has been denoted by "$\langle \xi, \eta \rangle$" is usually called a two-dimensional random variable and is denoted "(ξ, η)". However, "(ξ, η)" is the standard notation for an ordered pair with ξ and

η as first and second components and (ξ, η) is not a function. (Observe that $\{(\xi, \eta)\}$ is a function but not the function usually intended by the notation "(ξ, η)".) Also, the word "expectation" is used in the EM-course instead of "mean" or "mean value". The latter should be reserved for the mean $(1/n) \sum_{i=1}^{n} \xi_i$ of n real-valued functions with the same domain.

The notation "$E_{(\Omega, P)}(\xi)$" used here indicates that the expectation not only is determined by the function ξ but also by the fps (Ω, P). Observe that $E_{(\Omega, P)}$ can be considered a function that assigns a real number to every real-valued function with domain Ω. It is in fact a linear transformation on the vector space S_Ω. Also observe the important formula

$$E_{(\Omega, P)}(\varphi \circ \xi) = E_{(\Omega_\xi, P_\xi)}(\varphi).$$

It is also a (bad) practice not to distinguish in notation between a "constant c" and a constant function c_Ω, which takes the value c on the set Ω. Thus one finds formulas like the following

$$E(b) = b$$
$$E(a\xi + b) = E(a\xi) + E(b) = aE(\xi) + b.$$

Here, "b" is used in "$E(b)$" as a name for a function and in "b" as name for a real number. Even if this saves in the amount of actual writing, it is very confusing for the beginner. Hence the time saved in writing often has to be used in clearing up the resulting confusion. (In hope of not offending my colleagues by these remarks on bad notation in probability textbooks, I have taken the examples cited above from different versions of my own textbooks.)

2. Textbooks in probability all refer to "nonmathematical creatures" like tacks, dice, roulettes, arrivals of customers, coin tossings, gambling, occurrences, indistinguishable objects (!), and so on. Many students of probability are attracted (I have always been!) by these creatures and this terminology (How to gamble if you must!) but for others they cause confusion. Sometimes these creatures are found not only in examples and problems but also in theorems and proofs. Of course this is not at all incorrect (and contributes to the charm of probability theory) as these creatures can easily be made part of the mathematical object language, for instance, by naming special fps's (or more general probability spaces) with these names.

For the beginner, however, it may be helpful if the mathematical theory of probability and the real world are clearly distinguishable. For instance, when a phrase like "a symmetric die is tossed" it should be made clear whether the intention is to describe a real world activity or a specific finite probability space.

300

3. As was pointed out in the introduction, students in the EM program have received an introductory course in mathematical logic in grade 6 or 7. This course happens to be very controversial among mathematicians. My experiences working with these students, however, are very positive. In the actual textbook on probability in the EM program, the language of logic is not overly visible since the students are reading and writing very abbreviated proofs at this stage and these proofs look very much like "usual" proofs. Only a few references to the deduction theorem and inference schemes like PGU (principle of generalizing to a universal statement) and IU (inference from a universal statement) make the language somewhat different from what normally appears in books on probability theory. The logic seems to give EM students an unusual security in their work. I have found in these students an interest in proof and an ability to follow and make long proofs (especially proofs of existence) which is unusual with such young students. Also the experience these students have had proving theorems about sets, fields, ordered fields, relations, functions, etc., makes it easier for them to create proofs of their own. Obviously the logic is also of great help in this activity. Even if early experience in mathematical logic is not a possible way to mathematics for all students, there does seem to exist a reasonable number of students for whom this background is appropriate and very valuable.

REFERENCES

1. Comprehensive School Mathematics Program. Basic Program Plan, Spring 1969, Central Midwestern Regional Educational Laboratory, Inc., (CEMREL), St. Ann, Missouri.
2. R. Exner, C. E. Heidema, J. S. Karmos, B. A. Kaufman, L. Råde, H. G. Steiner, Elements of Mathematics, Book 9, Finite Probability Spaces.

16. On the teaching of probability and statistics at the pre-college level in Australia

J. B. Douglas

University of New South Wales
Kensington, Australia

16.1. GENERAL INTRODUCTION

Each of the six States which constitute the Commonwealth of Australia (population 12 million) has its own Department of Education which controls the public schools, primary and secondary, in that State. About three quarters of all school children attend these schools, the rest being denominational (about 80 % Roman Catholic) or "independent". Schooling is compulsory up to 15 or 16 years of age; primary schools run from ages 5 to 12 years approximately (kindergarten, and grades 1 to 6), and secondary schools from 12 to 17 or 18 years approximately (forms 1 to 5 or 6).

The syllabuses for the various stages are covered by recommendations by various Committees within each State, with no formal associations across States. At every stage a good deal of uniformity within a State, and especially within the public school system, is achieved by these Committees' published syllabuses, but especially at the higher stages of secondary programmes this uniformity is very substantial. At these stages, the Committees contain a high proportion of University nominees whose eyes are often fixed on University entrance requirements, and the Committees control either directly or indirectly public examinations which may not only lead to the award of a "Leaving Certificate" but may also be used for purposes of matriculation. (In three States the Leaving examination precedes the Matriculation examination by a year.) Matriculation requirements differ from State to State, and even from University to University within a State.

In what follows, the syllabus extracts quoted are those prescribed by the various Committees, and hence have to be given State by State. In almost every case, there are long explanatory notes together with reference and text books both for teachers and pupils—these are omitted to save space, although two examples are given under the State of Victoria for illustrative purposes. Because the topics of probability (except as an example of permutations and combinations) and statistics are relatively new, these explanatory notes are often very long compared with those relating to other parts of the syllabus—they have been intended to constitute one form of inservice training of teachers, necessary because many practising teachers have not themselves had any formal instruction in these topics. At least for some teachers, and especially for those near or in the capital cities, formal courses have been provided by Departments of Education during special conferences, after school hours, and in vacations—in many of these activities University staff have participated, sometimes indeed a University acting as the organizing body. In the public image, it is probably true that "sets" are thought of as the "New Mathematics" but probability and statistics would run second.

Developments in syllabuses overseas have affected Australian practice to varying degrees, sometimes varying within a State as well as between States. In a smaller and less populous State (e.g. Tasmania, with an area of 26,000 square miles and a population of 380,000) a single individual may have been responsible for changes quite impossible for one person to have produced in a larger State (e.g., New South Wales, with area 310,000 square miles and population 4,350,000). As well, the roles played by the newer Universities, against the only relatively recently breached belief that no State needs more than one University (there are now 14), were seen differently in the different States: in some cases representatives of the older Universities became identified with the status quo, with a consequent unwillingness to see change as other than criticism of their previous, often carefully thought out but now outdated, practices. Thus Tasmania produced at an early stage very comprehensive and far reaching syllabuses in probability at the matriculation level; while New South Wales managed to produce a "modern" syllabus for the first four forms of secondary school work but a highly "traditional" top for the last two forms leading to matriculation.

16.2. SYLLABUSES IN PROBABILITY AND STATISTICS

Brief summarising comments are made on the overall picture within Australia—for the reasons already given, these are in the nature of "averages" and the "variances" about these "averages" are very large. The modifications and qualifications necessary appear in the detailed syllabuses, which are arranged with Matriculation level courses coming first; these comments start at the opposite end, at the Primary level, since there is the greatest agreement across States there. Although applications of statistics appear in a number of places—e.g. social sciences, agricultural science— almost all statistics proper appears in mathematics courses, and it is these which are described in detail.

Curriculum Officers of the Departments of Education of each State agreed, in 1964 at a Conference arranged through the independent Australian Council for Educational Research, on the general direction of revision of Primary school syllabuses in Mathematics. The intention was to take account of changes generally recognized as desirable in mathematics teaching at all levels, and in pursuance of this a jointly written and produced book appeared in 1966, with title, *Background in Mathematics/A Guidebook to Elementary Mathematics for Teachers in Primary Schools*. Individual States remain responsible for their detailed syllabuses with differing emphases, but an indication of the type of work prescribed is given by noting that in New South Wales, for example, sets are first met at the Kindergarten level, and returned to in each following year. Little or no formal use of these notions is made with respect to probability at these levels: the notion of randomness, developed experimentally, and long run stability of relative frequencies, are the most which is included. Amongst descriptive statistics, however, is included graphical work dealing with bar graphs, pie diagrams and the like, together with simple measures of central tendency and perhaps the range. The Australian Broadcasting Commission (roughly parallel to the B.B.C. in its functions) participates very substantially in school broadcasts and telecasts at every level, and has produced (at least) two primary mathematics telecasts on graphs.

In the junior forms of the secondary schools the "formal" apparatus of Statistics is carried a good deal further. The mean, median and mode are dealt with, for example, both with respect to small samples and in frequency distributions; and a good deal of attention is paid to the correct use and interpretation of graphical material, partly in preparation for future work. Mostly, standard deviation (*not* for grouped distributions) is not included, though the range may be. Little formal work on probability is introduced, the most common tendency being to think of probabilities as being long run relative frequencies (following the graphical work). The only alternative work on probability deals exclusively with the "equally likely" case and direct enumeration.

At the senior Secondary level, near Matriculation, the picture is greatly complicated by the existence of alternative syllabuses: by some students no mathematics at all may be taken (rather exceptionally), while for those who do, syllabuses range from those intended for a general education to those intended for mathematical specialists—which latter tend to contain less statistics but perhaps more rather formal and old fashioned probability.

The use of set representations in sample spaces is rather general, though this is often not taken beyond the most elementary level of equally likely points. (However, the empirical stability of relative frequencies, sometimes before and sometimes after the elementary measure "theory" mentioned, is generally discussed to enable a treatment of non-equally likely cases.) At this level, conditional probability is introduced, and formal relations for probabilities of unions and intersections often developed. The more formal counting techniques (permutations and combinations) do not appear universally, and when they do they are sometimes in a separate section. The binomial distribution, with an informal treatment of random variables, is discussed, and sometimes both the Poisson and normal distributions as well, together with an introduction to questions of estimation. Mathematical expectations are often included; rather more unusual are regression, and product moment correlation, following a brief treatment of bivariate distributions.

As courses of study stand at present, there is a rather uneasy compromise n the treatment of probability, between the strict limitation to finite sample spaces with equally weighted points (rarely, in this case, using this kind of language), and the introduction of theory more in line with modern views of probability models. This flows partly from the conservatism of many (school and university) teachers of mathematics, and one of the consequences of the restricted approach is that courses containing it tend also to restrict their treatment of statistics to descriptive aspects. The notion of random variable is little more than implicitly included, and statistical inference of any kind hence almost entirely omitted. Such courses as these are in the minority, and do not reflect the general tendency of course revision. In the more common case, however, it is possible to see rather frequently a good deal of confusion in the treatment of conditional probability (independence), and the existence of numerous textbooks sometimes rather hurriedly written after the revision of syllabuses suggests that the confusion will be present for some years.

The information which follows, and a good deal of what precedes, this acknowledgement has been obtained through the very willing assistance of all Education Departments of the various States, Public Examination bodies, the Australian Council for Educational Research, and a number of University staff members particularly concerned with secondary courses. Without their continued help in answering my queries and supplying information, this survey would not have been possible.

16.3. DETAILED SYLLABUSES

NEW SOUTH WALES (population 4,350,000)

(The Australian Capital Territory (population 110,000), which includes the national capital, follows N.S.W. Syllabus details.)

First Level

6. Theory of Probability

(*a*) Statistical regularity. Random experiments. Relative frequency as an empirical measure of probability.

(*b*) Random experiments with a finite number of possible outcomes. Simple events, composite events. Probability of an event. Mutually exclusive events; the opposite (complementary) event. The algebra of events. Theorem of total probability.

(*c*) Two stage random experiments. Independent events. The product rule.

(*d*) Systematic enumeration in a finite sample space leading to the definition of $^{n}P_{r}$ and $^{n}C_{r}$.

(*e*) Binomial probabilities and the binomial distribution.

(*f*) The notion of a random variable, illustrated mainly in connection with the binomial distribution. The expected value of a random variable. The expected value of the binomial variable.

Second Level

19. Theory of Probability
    As for first level.

Third Level

11. Probability and Random Variables.

(i) The probability of an event for a finite sample space with equally weighted points. Application to problems, and the simplest "theorems" of probability. Interpretation of probabilities as relative frequencies; the inverse use of this to set up reasonable probability models.

(ii) The "addition" theorem, and the simplest conditional probabilities (the "product" theorem).

(iii) Random variables: binomial random variables in numerically specified cases.

JUNIOR SECONDARY

Advanced Level

7. Statistics

Collection and tabulation of data. Visual representation and interpretation: pictorial, column, bar, sector and line graphs. Cumulative frequency graphs. Mean, median and mode. Weighted mean. Measures of dispersion: range, interquartile range, standard deviation. Elementary notion of probability.

Ordinary Level	Extensions
9. Statistics.	
Collection and tabulation of data, with precise definition of the scope of the survey.	
Sampling.	Midpoint of interval
Range, class interval.	Relative frequency, cumulative relative frequency.
Counting techniques: tally marks, frequency, cumulative frequency.	
Visual representation and interpretation.	Cumulative frequency graph.
Influence of scale on interpretation.	Deviation from mean.
Histograms, frequency polygons.	Sum of deviations from the arithmetic mean is zero.
Arithmetic mean. Calculation of arithmetic mean of a frequency distribution, median and mode.	Weighted mean.
Value of mean, median, mode as measures of central tendency.	

Modified

4. Statistics.

Interpretation of pictorial, column and line, bar and sector graphs. Collection and tabulation of data, with precise definition of the scope of survey. Sampling. Range. Tally marks as a counting technique, frequency. Visual representation and interpretation. Value of mean, median, mode as measures of central tendency.

PRIMARY

Pictographs, bar graphs, interpretation of line graphs.

QUEENSLAND (population 1,720,000)

MATRICULATION (Senior Public Examination)

General Mathematics

Statistics

1. Frequency distributions: mean, median, standard deviation; mean deviation, semi-interquartile-range; variance, coefficient of variation.

2. Sampling: standard error of the mean; approximate 95 % confidence limits for the true (population) mean.

3. Bivariate observations: the general concept of regression; product–moment correlation and its computation.

4. Miscellaneous practical topics: moving averages; weighted averages.

Mathematics I

Statistics

1. Descriptive statistics: mean, standard deviation.
2. Probability; the binomial theorem.
3. The normal distribution.

PRIMARY

Picture graphs—construction and interpretation. Charts and bar graphs.

SOUTH AUSTRALIA (population 1,120,000)

(The Northern Territory (population 60,000) also follows these syllabuses.)

MATRICULATION

Statistics:

As for Intermediate Arithmetic, and in addition: Elementary discussion of the scope of statistics; displaying of numerical data by picturegrams, histograms, pie diagrams and continuous graphs. The concept of a statistical distribution and the collection and tabulation of data, relative frequencies of class and combinations of classes; expected class frequencies in samples from extensive data. Calculation of the mean (including data tabulated by class intervals) and mode. The cumulative frequency graph; median, quartiles, interquartile range, percentiles. The standard deviation as a measure of dispersion; its calculation (including data tabulated by class intervals).

LEAVING MATHEMATICS

Probability and Statistics

Simple extensions of the sum and product laws of probability. Binomial probability distribution. Frequency graphs; mean; median, quartiles, percentiles. Measures of dispersion: range, interquartile range.

INTERMEDIATE MATHEMATICS

Statistics and Probability

Statistics:

Meaning, collection, tabulation, representation, and interpretation of data. Frequency tables, pictograms, line charts, bar charts (or histograms), pie charts (or circular graphs). Measures of central tendency; mean and median. Sampling: opinion polls.

Probability:

A practical, experimental approach to a definition of an event A (e.g. as a subset of the set of N equally likely possible outcomes of an experiment); the probability $P(A)$ of an event A (e.g. $P(A) = n(A)/N$; $0 \leqslant P(A) \leqslant 1$; the graphical representations of the rules for the combination of probabilities of (a) independent events

$$P(A \text{ and } B) = P(A \cap B) = P(A) \cdot P(B),$$

(b) mutually exclusive events

$$P(A \text{ or } B) = P(A \cup B) = P(A) + P(B).$$

LEAVING ARITHMETIC

As for Matriculation Mathematics.

INTERMEDIATE ARITHMETIC

Collection and representation of data; use of pictograms (objects of equal size); histograms (representing equal intervals only); pie diagrams (two or three divisions of the circle only); graphical representation of data on squared paper; column or bar graphs; construction of line graphs; readings (including interpolation) from the graph.

TASMANIA (population 380,000)

MATRICULATION

Probability

1. Intuitive approach to probability.

   (i) Single repeated experiments with coins, dice and cards; the notion of sample space and event; mutually exclusive and complementary events.

   (ii) The notion of probability of an event; independent events; conditional probability.

   (iii) Random numbers and their use in simple experiments.

2. Formal approach to probability.

   (i) More formal treatment of sample space; events, compound events; probability; probability of compound events from probability of simpler events; conditional probability, independence.

   (ii) Mathematical expectation.

3. The law of chance for repeated trials—the binomial distribution.

   (i) Case of 2 and 3 trials; extension to n trials.

   (ii) Binomial probability tables and their use.

Statistics

Collection and tabulation of data with precise definition of the scope of the survey. Sampling, range, class interval. Counting techniques: tally marks, frequency, cumulative frequency. Visual representation and interpretation. Influence of scale on interpretation. Histograms, frequency polygons. The mean, mode and median of a frequency distribution. Value of mean, mode and median as measures of central tendency. Weighted mean.

PRIMARY SCHOOL SYLLABUS

Graphs: pictographs, bar graphs, line graphs, circle graphs. Empirical investigation of random events. Simple measures of central tendency (including activities leading to empirical normal distributions).

VICTORIA (population 3,300,000)

MATRICULATION

General Mathematics

5. *Probability and Statistics.*—Elementary ideas on probabilities, including the sum and product theorems. Frequency and probability distributions and their graphical representation. The mean as an expected value, and as a measure of location; other measures of location and dispersion, including the standard deviation and coefficient of variation. Elementary ideas on estimation; statistics and parameters. The binomial and Poisson distributions; probabilities for sampling without replacement (i.e. hypergeometric). Informal treatment of the normal distribution. Elementary ideas on significance and confidence limits. Informal treatment of regression.

Notes: (Given as an example.)

(1) Probability should be discussed both as a ratio of numbers of equally likely events and as long-run relative frequency. Conditional probability is included. Stress should be placed on the statistician's special interest in a small probability as indicating that an event is unlikely to happen.

(2) Although occasionally of interest in themselves, frequency distributions are mainly important in giving an idea of underlying probability distributions. Graphical representation will be taken to include correct and appropriate use of the histogram and probability or frequency polygon, the probability density curve, and the corresponding cumulative graphs. The generation of a variate by means of a spinner (i.e., a disc with numbers or numbered divisions marked round the edge constructed with the aid of the cumulative graph) helps students to appreciate the concepts associated with a probability distribution, and may be used to provide sample data and to operate simulation models.

(3) The use of a working zero and unit will not be obligatory in working out means and standard deviations, nor will infinite integrals be required. Use of the

divisor n in the calculation of the standard deviation will be permitted, since the reasons for the use of $n-1$ cannot be discussed properly at this stage. It will be taken as a rough working rule that a variate "very probably" lies within two standard deviation from the mean and "almost certainly" within three standard deviations from it.

The median and other quantities may be obtained from the cumulative graph; the mode may be estimated visually, the possibility of accidentally high frequencies being borne in mind.

(4) Statistics which are estimates of parameters are often used as approximations to their values, but the two concepts should be kept quite distinct. The convention of using Roman letters m, s, p, etc., for statistics and Greek letters μ, σ, π, etc., for the corresponding parameters is strongly recommended.

(5) The use of the binomial and Poisson as exact distributions should be distinguished from their use as approximations (e.g., to the distributions of counts of defectives in samples taken without replacement).

Knowledge and application of the formulae for the mean and standard deviation of these two distributions will be required, but not formal derivation except in particular cases of the binomial. It is suggested that the formulae should be assumed and verified numerically in particular cases.

(6) The normal distribution should be handled by means of tables and graphs, being regarded as a first approximation to the typical roughly symmetrical humped distribution. Mathematical manipulation of the normal integral will not be required.

(7) The ideas of statistical significance and confidence limits should be handled by direct and inverse use of the three-sigma limits (i.e., $\mu \pm 3\sigma$) applied to a single observed variate value deviating from a possibly unknown mean (e.g. a binomial or Poisson count from an underlying count-rate).

(8) The least-squares method of fitting a straight regression line will not be required: a reasonably accurate simple method is to divide the data into two halves, corresponding to higher and lower values of the independent variable, and to join the mean-points for the two halves. Stress should be placed on the interpretation of a regression line as a locus of means.

Books:

The whole syllabus is covered in Fitzpatrick, J. B., General Mathematics. (Jacaranda.)

Additional references for Statistics are:

E. L. Unthank, Statistics for Matriculation General Mathematics. (Hall.)
M. J. Moroney, Facts from Figures. (Pelican.)
B. C. Brookes and W. F. L. Dick, Introduction to Statistical Method. (Heinemann.)
R. Loveday, Statistics: A First Course. (C. U. P.)
R. Loveday, Statistics: A Second Course. (C. U. P.)

General Mathematics—Alternative Syllabus

5. *Probability and Statistics.*—Elementary ideas on probabilities, including the sum, product and conditional probability formulas.

The binomial, Poisson and hypergeometric distributions. Informal treatment of the normal distribution. Graphs of the probabilities and cumula-

312

tive probabilities, and their use in finding percentage points (quantiles). The mean μ, as a location parameter and as an expected value. The variance σ^2, and standard deviation, σ, as dispersion parameters. A knowledge of the formulas for these in the binomial and Poisson cases, and the role of these parameters in the normal case. Variance, σ^2/n, and standard deviation, $\sigma/\sqrt{n}$, for an average of n independent variates each having variance σ^2.

Applied Mathematics—Alternative Syllabus

1. *Probability and Statistics.*—Review work of Leaving Mathematics II, with a few harder "permutation-combination" type problems. Dependent events and conditional probabilities: the formula

$$Pr[A\,|\,B] = Pr[A \cap B]/Pr[B] \quad \text{(if } Pr[B] \neq 0),$$

and its simplification in the independent case. Binomial, Poisson, hypergeometric and normal distributions, together with the verification that the binomial and Poisson probabilities sum to one over the sample space; statement of same (without derivation) for hypergeometric and normal distributions.

Definitions of mean (μ) as a measure of location, variance (σ^2) and standard deviation (σ) as measure of dispersion.

Derivations of μ, σ^2 and σ for binomial and Poisson distributions; statement of same (without derivation) for hypergeometric and normal distributions. Variance and standard deviations of sums and difference of independent variates, and in particular of averages of n independent variates.

LEAVING CERTIFICATE

Mathematics II—Alternative Syllabus

4. *Statistics.*—(*a*) Probability Theory: the concepts of sample point, sample space, events, union and intersection thereof, complements (making use of set notation). The ideas of probability of a sample point, sample space, event generally. (Simple examples only: cards, dice, etc.) The formulae:

$$Pr[A] = 1 - Pr[A'],$$
$$Pr[A \cup B] = Pr[A] + Pr[B] - Pr[A \cap B],$$
$$Pr[A \cap B] = Pr[A] \cdot Pr[B], \text{ if } A, B \text{ are independent.}$$

(*b*) Binomial Probabilities.

Notes: (Given as an example.)

In this unit the aim is to present an introduction to that part of probability theory that can be handled rigorously at this stage, viz., the study of experiments that can have more than one, but a finite number of possible outcomes. Limiting concepts are to be avoided.

313

Terminology:

A sample point is a possible result of an experiment. A sample space (E) is the collection of all sample points.

4. *Statistics*

An event denoted by A, B, ..., is a collection of sample points (including E, ϕ as extreme cases). The corresponding set theory terminology is element, universal set, and null set respectively; these terms should be mentioned as alternatives.

The probability of a sample point is an undefined concept, but is the theoretical abstraction corresponding to the proportion of times the sample point would occur in many repetitions of the experiment.

The probability of an event A is denoted by $Pr(A)$, and is the sum of the probabilities of the sample points in A.

We have the properties

$Pr(A) \geqslant 0.$

$Pr(\phi) = 0.$

$Pr(A \cup B) = Pr(A) + Pr(B)$, if $A \cap B = \phi$.

These are just the defining properties of a "measure". However, in addition, the probability measure satisfies also

$Pr(E) = 1,$

$0 \leqslant Pr(A) \leqslant 1,$

$Pr[A'] = 1 - Pr[A].$

Independent Events:

Definitions: Two events A and B are independent if

$Pr[A \cap B] = Pr[A] \cdot Pr[B].$

Three events, A, B, and C, are independent if

$Pr[A \cap B] = Pr[A] \cdot Pr[B],$

$Pr A[\cap C] = Pr]A[\cdot Pr[C],$

$Pr[B \cap C] = Pr[B] \cdot Pr[C],$

and $Pr[A \cap B \cap C] = Pr[A] \cdot Pr[B] \cdot Pr[C].$

Similarly, an arbitrary number of events are independent if all intersections of them (two at a time, three at a time, etc.) satisfy the above multiplication property for probabilities.

"An experiment is repeated independently" means that events relating to different repetitions are independent. This leads into binomial probabilities: If an experiment is repeated n times independently and if π is the probability that an event, A, occurs in any particular repetition, then the probability that A occurs exactly x times in the n repetitions is

$$\binom{n}{x} \pi^x (1 - \pi)^{n-x}, \quad x = 0, 1, 2, \ldots, n.$$

Numerical work should be used to illustrate the above concepts. Examples can be drawn from coin tossing, dice, cards, industrial applications when defective and non-defective items are manufactured, from random sampling (i.e., with equal probabilities) for public-opinion polls, etc.

Mathematics A

D. *Mathematics in the Social Sciences.*—Further practice on the work in statistics prescribed for Mathematics A (fourth year), including the calculation of means from frequency tables. Graphical representation and comparison of time series, with concept of trend and seasonal cycle. Elementary ideas on probability, including addition, multiplication and expected values.

Application of these methods in the social sciences, including index numbers (notably the cost-of-living index with mention of basic wage calculations), sample surveys, crude and standardized death rates, and the life table.

JUNIOR SECONDARY

Mathematics A

Arithmetic.—Statistics: Averages (mean, weighted mean, median, mode). Construction of scatter diagrams.

Mathematics A—Alternative Syllabus.—3. Statistics

(*a*) Presentation of data via histograms, relative frequency polygons, cumulative frequency polygons, "scatter diagrams" for regression type relations.

(*b*) Measures of location: mean, weighted mean, median, mode.

Mathematics B—Alternative Syllabus.—As for Mathematics A—Alternative Syllabus.

PRIMARY

Pictorial representation, bar graphs and line graphs—interpretation and construction. Interpretation of circle graphs. Investigation of random events. Simple measures of central tendency: median, mode, arithmetic mean

WESTERN AUSTRALIA (population 890,000)

MATRICULATION

Mathematics I—General Mathematics

4. *Statistics*

1. Representations of data. Frequency tables, frequency graphs, cumulative frequency graphs. (Dot frequency diagrams, histograms, bar graphs, pie charts, ideographs.)

2. Summation notation.

3. Summarising data. Median (determined by counting or from cumulative frequency graph). Mode (visually from frequency graph or table). Mean $\bar{x}$ (calculated). Percentiles (determined from cumulative frequency graph). Range. Standard deviation

$$s = \sqrt{\frac{1}{n} \sum (x_i - \bar{x})^2};$$

corresponding formulae for grouped data. Use of standard deviation in the rough rule that (a) an observation "very probably" lies in the interval $(\bar{x} - 2s, \bar{x} + 2s)$ (b) an observation "almost certainly" lies in the interval $(\bar{x} - 3s, \bar{x} + 3s)$.

5. *Probability*

1. Counting Techniques. Permutations and combinations (i.e. arrangements and selections) of n distinct objects taken r at a time.

2. Intuitive approach to probability (using language of sets). Concept of random variable, sample space, event, occurrence of an event. (Examples confined to finite sample spaces where outcomes are equally likely.) Probability of event defined as ratio of number of favourable outcomes to total number of possible outcomes. Counting of outcomes by

(i) counting points in sample space diagram or listing elements.

(ii) application of procedure in 1. Probability as long-run relative frequency.

3. Probability of compound events

(a) Complementary events.

(b) Calculation of probability of a compound event

(i) by enumeration of cases in simple examples.

(ii) by use of addition law for mutually exclusive events

(iii) by use of multiplication law for both independent events, for example, selection without replacement or transference from one "urn" to another. Probability of A and B = (Prob. of A) × (Prob. of B on assumption A has occurred).

4. Normal probability distribution. Concept of population and sample, parameter and statistic. Continuous probability distribution as limit of empirical frequency distribution. Notation for mean and standard deviation, μ, σ. Standard normal variate $z = (x - \mu)/\sigma$. Notation of probability as area under probability curve. Normal distribution tables to find probability that variable lies in a certain interval.

316

6. Collection and tabulation of data. Graphical representation of data. Pictographs, bar graphs, pie graphs, column graphs, line graphs. Graphical representation of frequency distributions. Measures of central tendency: mode, median and mean. Cumulative frequency. Range. Relative frequency. Introduction to probability as long-run relative frequency. (No formulae for grouped data needed.)

PRIMARY

Line, bar and pie graphs. Measures of central tendency.

17. Teaching of probability and statistics in the French lycée

P. L. Hennequin

Université de Clermont
Clermont-Ferrand, France

17.1. INTRODUCTION

In France, secondary school is terminated by "Baccalauréat". Until 1966 this exam was given in two parts: the first at the end of the class "Première", the second at the end of the class "Terminale". Nowadays, only the last part is used. Pupils in this "Terminale" are generally between 17 and 20 years old.

Until 1967, probability and statistics were taught in the section called "Technology and Economy" (this contained only 1% of the candidates for Baccalauréat), and taught also (but in infinitesimal quantity) in the section called "Experimental Science" (this contained about 30% of the candidates). In Appendix I, the corresponding programs for these sections are listed.

Since 1968, there are five sections for the Baccalauréat:

A. Philosophy, Human and Social Sciences   45% of the candidates
B. Economical Sciences   4% of the candidates
C. Sciences (Mathematics and Physics)   15% of the candidates
D. Sciences (Physics, Chemistry, Natural History)   30% of the candidates
E. Technology   6% of the candidates

Probability and statistics are now taught in Section A (a short introduction) and in Section B and D. In Appendix I the actual programs are given, and also the planned programs as outlined by a minesterial commission (Chairman: André Lichnerowicz). These programs will be taught next year (1969) in the second class, in 1970 in the first class, and in 1971 in the "Terminale".

The introduction of these subjects presents a heavy task for the teachers of mathematics because most of them have never studied these notions at the university. For that reason, the French "Association des Professeurs de Mathématiques" has published many articles in its bulletin (see Appendix

II, 1) and has asked my colleague Guerber and me to write two books (see Appendix II, C) on probability and statistics. Also, conferences and presentations on these subjects have been organized in each academy for the teachers who will teach these subjects.

17.2. SOME REFLECTIONS ABOUT THE PROGRAMS

We shall discuss the content of Section B (it contains that of Section D). The authors of the actual program had chosen the following plan.

(*a*) Descriptive statistics (one or many variables)

(*b*) Notions of probability (finite cases, countable cases, continuous cases)

(*c*) The principles of statistical inference (applications of the normal distribution in connection with the estimation of an expectation, test of significance in connection with the difference between two means).

The members of the "Commission Lichnerowicz" proposed a different order:

(*a*) Descriptive statistics of one variable

(*b*) Notions of probability (finite cases)

(*c*) Descriptive statistics of many variables

(*d*) Probability (continuous cases)

(*e*) Introduction to estimation

The suggestions of the commission have the advantage of permitting a probabilistic discussion of the method of linear approximation by least squares. The physicists hope that in the future error calculus will be taught in such a way that "random errors" can be used, and that instead of formulas using addition of absolute values, formulas using addition of variances will be introduced. (See Appendix II, A, [14].)

Our opinion is that one critical point in these programs is the introduction of the continuous case. It is not possible to define the mathematical expectation in this case without introducing the improper integrals $\int_{-\infty}^{+\infty} f(x)\, dx$. But analysis courses in the programs present only the definition of $\int_a^b f(x)\, dx$ for finite a and b.

Similarly, for the introduction of expectation in the countable case, it is necessary to handle with infinite series $\Sigma p_i x_i$ and this notion is not in the suggested program of analysis. It is always dangerous in mathematics to *use* concepts before they have been studied.

We think that, at the level of secondary school, a program could be built according to the following scheme (see Appendix II, 3):

(a) *Statistical data, observations and results, graphical methods*
(b) *Characteristics of statistical data*
   Location characteristics (mode, median, mean)
   Dispersion characteristics (range, interquartile range, mean deviation,
      standard deviation)
   Comparison of these characteristics
(c) *Probability and random variables on a finite set*
   Events related to an experiment (see Section 3 below)
   Probability
   Random variables
   Expectations, moments, medians
(d) *Simultaneous study of two real variables*
   Linear approximation (least squares method) (see Section 4 below)
   Regression lines, linear correlation
   Application to time series
(e) *Dependence and independence. Product spaces and finite sequences of random
   variables*
   Conditional expectation and conditional probability
   Independence
   Product spaces and sequences of independent variables
   Binomial distribution
   The Poisson approximation
   The normal approximation (with the use of tables)
   The weak law of large numbers (see Section 5 below)
(f) *Estimation from a subset or from a sample of a finite set*
   Sampling with or without replacement
   Estimation from a sample
   Inadmissible hypotheses
   Confidence sets

This program has the advantage of using only very simple mathematical concepts. Essentially it makes use of the $\sum_{i=1}^{n}$ symbol, finite mean operators, minimization of trinomials of second degree, graphical methods and numerical tables. It permits establishing unity in mathematics, showing, for example: the isomorphism between the Boolean (finite) ring of events related to an experiment and the subsets of a finite set; the analogy between mathematical expectation and variance on one hand, and center of gravity and moment of inertia on the other; the analogy between regression lines and conjugate diameters of a conic; the analogy between the construction of the probability product measures and the theory of area and volume.

In the following I shall develop, as examples, three ideas:

(*a*) The choice of axioms for the set of events related to an experiment, based on the *implication* relation;

(*b*) The comparison of different norms in the problem of linear approximation;

(*c*) The weak law of large numbers in the case of finite probability spaces.

17.3. CHOICE OF AXIOMS FOR A SET OF EVENTS

We start from the usual, rather imprecise, notion of "description of an event related to an experiment E". We call $\mathcal{E}$ the (very large) set of these descriptions; we note its elements by $M, N, \ldots$ We shall make precise the language to be used for this description. When an experiment E is performed we can say if an event occurs or not.

On $\mathcal{E}$ we now define an *implication relation*, designated by $\subset$, as follows:

$$M \subset N \text{ iff "}M \text{ occurs" implies "}N \text{ occurs".}$$

Axiom 1: $\forall M \in \mathcal{E}, M \subset M$ (reflexivity)

Axiom 2: $\forall M, N \in \mathcal{E}, M \subset N, N \subset P$ implies $M \subset P$ (transitivity)

Thus $\mathcal{E}$ is pre-ordered. Let $\mathcal{A}$ be the quotient set of $\mathcal{E}$ determined by the relation

$$M \sim N \text{ iff } M \subset N \text{ and } N \subset M.$$

Then $\mathcal{A}$ is the set of events related to E; we note its elements by $A, B, \ldots$ The relation $\subset$ induces on $\mathcal{A}$ a relation, also designated by $\subset$, which is an *order* relation on $\mathcal{A}$.

Axiom 3: $\forall A, B \in \mathcal{A}$, for this order $\subset$, there exists a g.l.b., $A \cap B$, and a l.u.b., $A \cup B$, such that

$$A \cap B \subset A \subset A \cup B, A \cap B \subset B \subset A \cup B$$

and

$$X \subset A, X \subset B \;\Rightarrow\; X \subset A \cap B$$

$$A \subset X, B \subset X \;\Rightarrow\; A \cup B \subset X.$$

Thus $\mathcal{A}$ is a lattice. Associativity and commutativity of $\cap$ and $\cup$ are *consequences* of the axioms, and also *idempotence* and the *inclusion*

$$(A \cap B) \cup C \subset (A \cup C) \cap (B \cup C)$$

Axiom 4: $(A \cup C) \cap (B \cup C) \subset (A \cap B) \cup C$

Thus $\mathcal{A}$ is a *distributive* lattice.

Axiom 5: $\mathcal{A}$ possesses for the order $\subset$ a greatest element Ω and a least element ϕ.

Axiom 6: $\forall A \in \mathcal{A}, \exists \complement A$ such that $A \cup \complement A = \Omega$ and $A \cap \complement A = \phi$.

We then prove the uniqueness of $\complement A$ and the classical properties of $\complement$, $\cup$, $\cap$, ϕ, and Ω. Furthermore, we can prove that $\mathcal{A}$ is a unitary ring for Δ and $\cap$ (where $A\Delta B = (A \cap \complement B) \cup (B \cap \complement A)$).

If we define an elementary event A by

$$\begin{cases} A \neq \phi \\ B \subset A, B \neq A \Rightarrow B = \phi \end{cases}$$

we can easily establish, when $\mathcal{A}$ is *finite*, the isomorphism between this ring $\mathcal{A}$ and the ring $\mathcal{P}(\Omega^*)$ of the set of all subsets of the set Ω^* of elementary events.

Conversely, on every unitary Boolean ($\forall A, A \cap A = A$) finite ring, we can define an order $\subset$ by

$$A \subset B \quad \text{iff} \quad A \cap B = A.$$

Then, we can define, as usual, a probability measure P on $\mathcal{A}$. In this process we axiomatize the properties of the frequency of an event A among n trials $\omega_1, \omega_2, \ldots, \omega_n$,

$$f_n(A) = \frac{1}{n} \sum_{i=1}^{n} 1_A(\omega_i)$$

and also the mathematical expectation $E(X)$ of a random variable X.

We can also, as suggested in Appendix II. A, [10], after Pascal define E as a linear positive form on the space of all the mappings of Ω in R_1, such that $E(1_\Omega) = 1$, and find the probability of A by $P(A) = E(1_A)$.

17.4. LINEAR APPROXIMATION AND COMPARISON OF NORMS

One of the fundamental problems of experimental sciences is the following: n realizations (x_i, y_i) of a phenomenon, with an unknown law $y = \varphi(x)$ have been observed. We choose φ in a class Φ of functions which, in general, depend on m parameters with $m < n$. It is usually not possible to find $\varphi \in \Phi$ such that $\varphi(x_i) = y_i$, $1 \leqslant i \leqslant n$; but we can suppose that the experimental measurements have been made with all possible care so that the set $\{|y_i - \varphi(x_i)|, 1 \leqslant i \leqslant n\}$ contains only "small numbers". It is possible to associate with this set the vector $y - \varphi$ in R^n whose components are $y_i - \varphi(x_i)$, $1 \leqslant i \leqslant n$, and a norm $\|y - \varphi\|$ of this vector.

From a topological point of view, the choice of the norm is not important, because R^n is finite dimensional and hence all norms are equivalent. But it is not this point of view that interests us, we wish to determine $\varphi \in \Phi$ so that $\|y - \varphi\|$ is minimum.

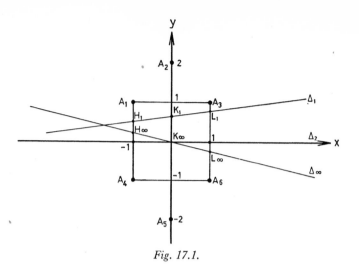

Fig. 17.1.

It is interesting and worth while to discuss this problem at a very elementary level because this discussion points out that:

(a) Even if *existence* of a minimum with some (non strictly convex) norms can be proved, this is not always the case for *uniqueness*.

(b) The solution depends essentially on the choice of the norm.

Let me give an elementary example about these two points. Consider on R^n the three norms:

$$\|X\|_1 = \sum_{i=1}^{n} |x_i|,$$

$$\|X\|_2 = \left(\sum_{i=1}^{n} x_i^2\right)^{\frac{1}{2}},$$

$$\|X\|_\infty = \underset{1 \leqslant i \leqslant n}{\text{Max}} |x_i|$$

where X denotes the vector whose components are x_i. (We could amplify the problem by assigning to each component x_i a mass λ_i, taking into account the quality of each measurement.)

(a) *First example*

Let us consider the six points

$$A_1(-1, 1),\ A_2(0, 2),\ A_3(1, 1),\ A_4(-1, -1),\ A_5(0, -2),\ A_6(1, -1).$$

By using symmetry, we see that

$$\|Y - aX - b\|_2^2 = \sum_{i=1}^{6} (y_i - ax_i - b)^2$$

324

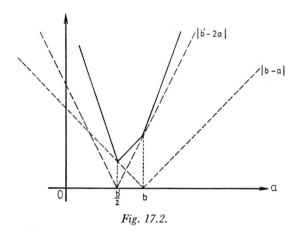

Fig. 17.2.

is minimum for $a = b = 0$, and this minimum is a strict one, therefore it is unique. The corresponding straight line of approximation Δ_2 is the x-axis.

Let H, K, L be the points on the straight line Δ with abscissa $-1, 0, 1$. Then we have

$$\| Y - aX - b \|_\infty = \text{Max } \{HA_1, HA_4, KA_2, KA_5, LA_3, LA_6\}.$$

Now

$$\text{Max } (KA_2, KA_5) \geqslant \frac{KA_2 + KA_5}{2} \geqslant 2$$

and HA_1, HA_4, LA_3, LA_6 are smaller than 2 if H is between A_1 and A_4 and L is between A_3 and A_6. In this case the minimum is obtained for $KA_2 = KA_5 = 2$ and for each H between A_1 and A_4; that is, for $b = 0$ and $|a| \leqslant 1$ (indetermination of order one).

Finally, we have

$$\| Y - aX - b \|_1 = HA_1 + HA_4 + KA_2 + KA_5 + LA_3 + LA_6$$

$$\geqslant A_1A_4 + A_2A_5 + A_3A_6 = 8$$

with equality iff H is between A_1 and A_4 and L is between A_3 and A_6 (this implies that K is between A_2 and A_5). There is now a double indetermination and the conditions for minimum are $|a + b| \leqslant 1$ and $|b - a| \leqslant 1$.

(b) *Second example*

Let us consider the three points

$$M_1(-1, 0), \ M_2(0, 1), \ M_3(2, 1)$$

and a straight line $y = ax + b$ such that $\| Y - aX - b \|_k$ is a minimum.

325

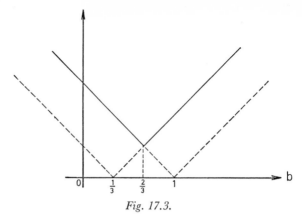

Fig. 17.3.

(1) $k = \infty$

$$\| Y - aX - b \|_\infty = \mathrm{Max}\ \{|b-a|,\ |1-b|,\ |1-2a-b|\}$$

Let us first consider the function $a \to \mathrm{Max}\ \{|b-a|,\ |b'-2a|\}$.

If we assume $b' < 2b$ (the other case is analogous), we find (see Figure 17.2) that this function has a unique minimum for

$$b - a = 2a - b' \quad \text{or} \quad a = \frac{b+b'}{3}.$$

If $b' = 1 - b$, the function $\mathrm{Max}\ \{|b-a|,\ |1-2a-b|\}$ has a minimum for $b = \frac{2}{3}$ (see Figure 17.3).

Thus the norm $\| Y - aX - b \|_\infty$ has a minimum equal to $\frac{1}{3}$ for $a = \frac{1}{3}$, $b = \frac{2}{3}$.

(2) $k = 1$

$$\| Y - aX - b \|_1 = |b-a| + |1-b| + |1-2a-b|$$

With fixed b and b', the function $a \to |b-a| + |b'-2a|$ has a minimum for $a = b'/2$ (see Figure 17.4).

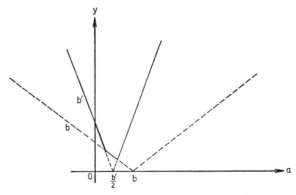

Fig. 17.4.

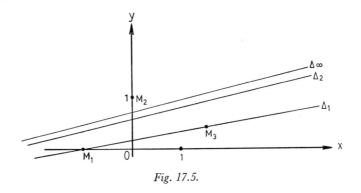

Fig. 17.5.

If $b' = 1 - b$, the function $|b - a| + |1 - b - 2a|$ has a minimum equal to $\frac{2}{3}$, for $b = \frac{1}{3}$ and $a = \frac{1}{3}$.

(3) $k = 2$

$\|Y - aX - b\|_2^2 = 2b^2 + (2a - 4)b + 5a^2 - 4a + 2$ has, for fixed a a mini-

mum for $b = \dfrac{2 - a}{3}$ and this minimum in equal to $\dfrac{14a^2}{3} - \dfrac{8a}{3} + \dfrac{2}{3}$. This func-

tion has a minimum for $a = \frac{2}{7}$ and thus $b = \dfrac{2 - a}{3} = \dfrac{4}{7}$.

In Figure 17.5 we have pictured the three points M_1, M_2, M_3 and the three straight lines Δ_∞, Δ_1, Δ_2 corresponding to the three norms. The lines Δ_∞ and Δ_1 are parallel, Δ_1 going through M_1 and M_3 (this can easily be proved), and Δ_∞ goes through the midpoint of M_1M_2. The line Δ_2 goes through the center of gravity of the triangle $M_1M_2M_3$, but is not parallel to Δ_1 and Δ_∞.

Among the three norms we can now see that $\|\ \|_2$ possesses two advantages:

(a) Uniqueness of the minimum

(b) The minimum can be determined by finding a derivative, that is easier than working with absolute values as is required in the other cases.

Although this elementary discussion is not properly of probabilistic nature, it seems interesting as a good introduction to applied mathematics.

17.5. LAW OF LARGE NUMBERS ON FINITE SPACES

Now we return to probability. In this section we discuss how the law of large numbers can be treated in an elementary course of probability.

Is it possible to prove a non-trivial law of large numbers in the case of a finite space?

It is trivial that a set $\{X_1, \ldots, X_n\}$ of independent variables, each taking at least two values with a strictly positive probability, takes 2^n distinct values with strictly positive probability and, therefore, is necessarily defined on a set Ω with cardinality $\geqslant 2^n$. It is not possible, therefore, to define an infinite sequence of independent non-constant variables on a finite set Ω.

To avoid such difficulty, we shall define $\{X_1, \ldots, X_n\}$ on a space Ω_n with cardinality increasing with n, using the following proposition.

Proposition 1:

Consider n distribution functions F_j (increasing step functions with a finite number of jumps). We may construct a finite probability space $(\Omega^n, \mathcal{A}^n, P^n)$ and n random variables on this space, such that:

(*a*) The distribution function of X_j is F_j, $1 \leqslant j \leqslant n$.
(*b*) The X_j are independent.

Principle of the construction

Let a_j^i, $1 \leqslant i \leqslant n_j$ be the abscissa of the jumps of F_j; p_j^i the amplitude of the jump at the point a_j^i:

$$p_j^i \geqslant 0 \quad \text{and} \quad \sum_{i=1}^{n_j} p_j^i = 1$$

Let Ω_j be an arbitrary set $\{\omega_j^1, \ldots, \omega_j^{n_j}\}$ whose cardinality is n_j, and let P_j be the probability measure on $\mathcal{P}(\Omega_j)$ such that $P_j(\{\omega_j^i\}) = p_j^i$.

Let $\varUpsilon_j$ be a mapping of Ω_j into R defined by

$$\varUpsilon_j(\omega_j^i) = a_j^i, \quad 1 \leqslant i \leqslant n_j.$$

Now,
$$\Omega^n = \prod_{j=1}^n \Omega_j, \quad \mathcal{A}^n = \mathcal{P}(\Omega^n), \quad P^n = \bigotimes_{j=1}^n P_j.$$

Let $\omega \in \Omega^n$; $\omega = \{\omega_1, \omega_2, \ldots, \omega_n\}$, $\omega_j \in \Omega_j$, and define

$$X_j(\omega) = \varUpsilon_j(\omega_j).$$

Then $P^n(\{X_j(\omega) \in B\}) = P_j(\{\varUpsilon_j(\omega_j) \in B\})$ and F_j is the distribution function of X_j. Furthermore,

$$P^n \left(\bigcap_{j=1}^n \{X_j(\omega) \in B_j\} \right) = \prod_{j=1}^n P_j(\{\varUpsilon_j(\omega_j) \in B_j\})$$

$$= \prod_{j=1}^n P_j(\{X_j(\omega) \in B_j\}).$$

Hence the X_j are independent.

Thus we can formulate the following weak law of large numbers.

328

Proposition 2:

Let $\{F_j\}$ be an infinite sequence of distribution functions and let m_j and σ_j^2 be the corresponding expectations and variances. Let for each $n \in \mathcal{N}$, $(\Omega^n, \mathcal{A}^n, P^n)$ be the probability space and X_j $(1 \leqslant j \leqslant n)$ the n independent random variables, associated with F_j as described in Proposition 1. Then, if

$$\lim_{n \to \infty} \frac{1}{n^2} \sum_{j=1}^{n} \sigma_j^2 = 0,$$

it is the case that

$$\forall \, \varepsilon > 0, \ \lim_{n \to \infty} P^n \left(\left\{ \left| \frac{1}{n} \left| \sum_{j=1}^{n} (X_j - m_j) \right| \geqslant \varepsilon \right\} \right) = 0.$$

This proposition immediately follows from the conjunction of the Bienaymé and Chebychev inequalities.

We note that it does not give exactly the convergence in probability, because P^n must be defined on each Ω^n on which $\{X_1, \ldots, X_n\}$ are defined.

Appendix I

PROGRAMMES

A. *Programmes en vigueur de 1947 à 1966*

SÉRIE SCIENCES EXPÉRIMENTALES

Combinaisons — Probabilités simples.

SÉRIE TECHNIQUE ET ECONOMIQUE

1re *partie — Notions de Mathématiques Statistiques*

I. Les séries statistiques : définition. Représentation graphique. Graphique à échelle arithmétique, à échelle logarithmique. Construction et interprétation de ces graphiques. Polygone et courbe de fréquence, courbe cumulative. Critique des apparences graphiques.

II. Eléments caractéristiques d'une série statistique, paramètres de position : Valeurs typiques. Médiane. Moyennes (arithmétiques pondérées, géométriques). Dominante.

Evaluation de la dispersion : Intervalles de variations; quartiles, déciles, centiles, écart moyen arithmétique écart type fluctuation, écart équiprobable.

III. Ajustement linéaire : Ajustement par moyennes discontinues. Méthode des moindres carrés. Ajustement pouvant se ramener au premier degré par un changement de variable.

IV. Séries chronologiques. Mouvement de longue durée : Droite de longue durée. Données régularisées.

Variations saisonnières : Mise en évidence par graphiques et tableaux.

Elimination : procédés de la moyenne mensuelle, de la moyenne mobile, des chaînes de rapport.

V. Notions de corrélation : Définition. Coefficient de corrélation linéaire. Droite de régression.

2ᵉ partie — Notions de Mathématiques Statistiques

I. Notions de calcul de probabilités : Probabilités simples. Probabilités totales. Probabilités composées. Espérance mathématique.

Loi des grands nombres : lemme de Bienaymé et son utilisation par Tchebicheff; théorèmes de Bernoulli et de Borel, épreuves répétées dans le cas de deux éventualités dont les probabilités sont constantes; utilisation du binôme de Newton, pour un exposant positif entier et rappel des notions d'écart moyen, fluctuation, écart quadratique moyen, écart équiprobable, écart réduit; moments de divers ordres.

II. Lois statistiques : Distribution binomiale, ses caractéristiques. Distribution des moyennes. Distribution normale : courbe de Laplace-Gauss.

III. Principes de la méthodologie statistique : Applications des propriétés de la distribution normale au problème du jugement par échantillon : valeur significative d'une moyenne.

Estimation de la moyenne vraie à l'aide d'un échantillon; valeur significative de la différence entre deux moyennes d'échantillons.

IV. Application à la vie économique. Etude descriptive et critique des documents statistiques.

V. Indications sur les questions suivantes : les nombres indices : leur confection, leur utilisation. Indices de prix de production. Emploi de la statistique dans la conduite et le contrôle des entreprises. Contrôle des matières premières, de la production; analyse des stocks. Statistique de direction : prévisions.

B. *Programmes actuels depuis 1966*

CLASSE DE PREMIÈRE A

Statistique. Présentation de documents statistiques; représentations graphiques. Eléments caractéristiques d'une série statistique. Médiane, moyennes, quantiles.

CLASSE DE TERMINALE A

Statistiques et Probabilités. Problèmes de dénombrements et applications simples. Principe du calcul des probabilités. Variable aléatoire. Notion de loi de probabilité : loi de Gauss ou normale.

CLASSE DE PREMIÈRE B

Initiation à la statistique

1) Séries statistiques. Présentation des documents statistiques : observation, enregistrement et groupement des données. Tableaux numériques. Diverses représentations graphiques. Polygone et courbe de fréquence, courbe cumulative. Eléments caractéristiques d'une série statistique. Médiane, moyennes, dominante. Evaluation de la dispersion : quartiles, écart moyen arithmétique, fluctuation, écart-type.

2) Les indices de la vie économique. Indices simples, synthétiques. Confection, utilisation. Indices usuels.

3) Ajustement lineaire. Méthode graphique, méthode des moyennes discontinues, méthode des moindres carrés.

4) Séries chronologiques. Les composantes fondamentales du mouvement d'ensemble : mouvement de longue durée, mouvement cyclique, variations saisonnières (divers procédés d'élimination), variations accidentelles.

5) Notions sur la corrélation. Définition. Droite de régression, covariance, co-efficient de corrélation linéaire.

Statistique et probabilités

Notions sur le calcul des probabilités et la méthode statistique.

1) Principes du calcul des probabilités. Probabilités. Probabilités simples; probabilités totales et probabilités composées.

2) Variable aléatoire. Notion de loi de probabilité. Valeurs typiques d'une loi de probabilité : espérance mathématique (moment d'ordre 1), moment d'ordre 2; variance, écart quadratique moyen ou écart-type.

Inégalite de Bienaymé–Tchébitcheff.

3) Lois importantes de probabilité : loi binômiale, loi de Laplace-Gauss ou loi normale, loi de Poisson.

4) Loi des grands nombres. Enoncés commentés des théorèmes de Bernoulli et de Borel.

5) Principe de la méthode statistique. Applications des propriétés de la distribution normale au jugement sur échantillon. Estimation d'une moyenne. Valeur significative d'une moyenne; intervalle de confiance.

Valeur significative de la différence entre les moyennes de deux échantillons.

Initiation à la Statistique

1) Séries statistiques

a) Présentation de documents statistiques :
observation, enregistrement et groupement des données. Tableaux numériques. Diverses représentations graphiques. Polygone et courbe de fréquence, courbe cumulative.

b) Eléments caractéristiques d'une série statistique. Médiane, moyennes, dominante. Evaluation de la dispersion, quartiles, écart moyen arithmétique, fluctuation, écart-type.

2) Ajustement lineaire. Méthode graphique, méthode des moyennes disconti-nues, méthode des moindres carrés.

3) Séries chronologiques. Les composants fondamentaux du mouvement d'ensemble, mouvement de longue durée, mouvement cyclique, variations saisonnières (divers procédés d'élimination), variations accidentelles.

4) Notions sur la corrélation. Définition, Droite de régression, covariance, co-efficient de corrélation linéaire.

Statistique et Probabilités

1) Préliminaires d'analyse combinatoire. Permutations, arrangements, com-binaisons sans répétition. Formule du binôme. Problèmes de dénombrement et ap-plications simples.

2) Principe de calcul des probabilités. Variable aléatoire. Notion de loi de pro-babilité : loi binômiale, loi de Gauss ou normale, loi des grands nombres, loi de Poisson.

3) Statistique appliquée. Estimation d'une moyenne (dans le seul cas où la loi de distribution est normale). Valeur significative d'une moyenne, intervalle de confiance.

C. *Projets de la commission* « *Lichnerowicz* »

(doivent en principe rentrer en vigueur en 1970 et 1971)

Statistique et Probabilites

1) Description de phénomènes concernant des populations homogènes importantes; example des indices de la vie économique. Présentation de documents statistiques : observation, enregistrement, groupement des données. Représentations
graphiques et tableaux numériques. Fréquence, polygone de fréquence.

2) *Le modèle mathématique correspondant : espaces probabilisés finis.*
L'ensemble Ω des évènements élémentaires; correspondance entre la terminologie
ensembliste et la terminologie probabiliste (élément = évènement élémentaire;
partie = évènement; complémentaire = évènement contraire; partie vide = évènement impossible; partie pleine = évènement certain; réunion = évènement A ou B,
le « ou » étant inclusif; intersection = évènement A et B; parties disjointes = évènements incompatibles).

Notion de loi de probabilité sur Ω (associe à tout évènement A un nombre
$P(A) \geqslant 0$ de telle sorte que $P(\Omega) = 1$, et que $P(A \cup B) = P(A) + P(B)$ lorsque $A \cap B =$
$= \varnothing$). Croissance; formule $P(A) + P(B) = P(A \cup B) + P(A \cap B)$. Exemples d'espaces
probabilisés où les évènements élémentaires sont équiprobables par raison de symétrie (dès, cartes, urnes, etc. ...).

Variable aléatoire X sur un espace probabilisé fini; évènements liés à cette
variable aléatoire (par exemple $X = a$ donné, $X \leqslant a$ donné).

3) Moments d'ordre 1 et 2 en statistique : moyenne empirique, variance empirique; inegalité de Bienaymé–Čebičev.

On pourra faire connaître aux élèves les sens des mots : médiane, quartiles,
etc. ...

4) Espérance (ou moment d'ordre 1) d'une variable aléatoire X, d'une somme,
du produit par une constante. Notation $E(X)$.

Moment d'ordre 2 d'une variable aléatoire X; variance, notation $M_2(X)$. Ecart
quadratique moyen (ou écart type); notation σ_X. Formule $M_2(X) = E(X)^2 + \sigma_X^2$.
Inégalité $P(|X - E(X)| \geqslant t\sigma_X) \leqslant 1/t^2$. Inégalité de Bienaymé–Čebičev. Variable aléa-
toire réduite.

Statistique et Probabilités

1) Séries statistiques à deux caractères. Fréquences marginales. Moment mixte
d'ordre 2; covariance empirique. Droite de régression d'une variable sur une autre;
coefficient de corrélation.

2) Loi de probabilité à densité continue et monotone par intervalles. Fonction de
répartition.

Examples : loi uniforme sur un intervalle fini; loi de Gauss (à partir d'une représentation graphique et d'une table).

3) Usage (sans justification) des méthodes d'estimation d'une moyenne en Statistique; valeur significative; intervalle de confiance pour une approximation donnée.

Valeur significative de la différence entre les moyennes de deux échantillons.

Statistique et Probabilités

1) Description statistique des populations et de leurs échantillons. Documents statistiques. Représentations graphiques. Effectifs et fréquence. Fréquence relative.

2) *Le modèle mathématique correspondant : espaces probabilisés finis.*
L'ensemble Ω des évènements élémentaires; correspondance entre la terminologie ensembliste et la terminologie probabiliste (élément = événement élémentaire; partie = événement; complémentaire = événement contraire; partie vide = événement impossible; partie pleine = événement certain; réunion = événement A ou B, le « ou » étant inclusif; intersection = événement A et B; parties disjointes = événements incompatibles).

Notion de loi de probabilité sur Ω (associe à tout événement A un nombre $P(A) \geqslant 0$ de telle sorte que $P(\Omega) = 1$, et que $P(A \cup B) = P(A) + P(B)$ si $A \cap B = \varnothing$). Croissance; formule $P(A) + P(B) = P(A \cup B) + P(A \cap B)$. Exemples d'espaces probabilisés finis où les événements élémentaires sont équiprobables par raison de symétrie (dès, cartes, urnes, etc.).

Variable aléatoire sur un espace probabilisé fini; événement liés à celle-ci.

3) Application de l'analyse combinatoire (c′·a′·d′·le 2) des « Notions générales » à des calculs de probabilités. Loi binômiale pour le jeu de pile-ou-face.

4) Moments d'ordre 1 et 2 en statistique : moyenne empirique, variance empirique; inégalité de Bienaymé–Tchebicheff.

5) Espérance (ou moment d'ordre 1) d'une variable aléatoire X, d'une somme, du produit par une constante. Notation $E(X)$. Moment d'ordre 2 d'une variable aléatoire X; variance; notation $M_2(X)$. Ecart quadratique moyen (ou écart type); notation σ_X. Formule $M_2(X) = E(X)^2 + \sigma_X^2$. Inégalité $P(|X - E(X)| \geqslant t\sigma_X) \leqslant 1/t^2$. Inégalité de Bienaymé–Tchébicheff. Variable aléatoire réduite.

Statistique et Probabilités

1) Séries statistiques à deux caractères. Fréquences marginales. Moment mixte d'ordre 2; covariance empirique. Droite de régression d'une variable sur une autre; coéfficient de corrélation.

2) Loi de probabilité à densité continue et monotone par intervalles. Fonction de répartition.
Exemples : loi uniforme sur un intervalle fini; loi de Gauss (à partir d'une représentation graphique et d'une table).

3) Loi binômiale; loi de Poisson.

4) Usage (sans justification) des méthodes d'estimation d'une moyenne en statistique; valeur significative; intervalle de confiance pour une approximation donnée.
Valeur significative de la différence entre les moyennes de deux échantillons.

Appendix II

BIBLIOGRAPHIE

A. *Articles consacrés à l'enseignement des Probabilités et de la Statistique au niveau élémentaire*

1. G. Darmois, L'enseignement du calcul des probabilités et des méthodes statistiques. Bulletin de la Société Française de Pédagogie n° 107, 1954 et cahiers pédagogiques pour l'enseignement du second degré 2ᵉ année, n° 3, 15.11.55.
2. L. Leboutet, Etude sur les difficultés des étudiants en statistique. Bulletin A. P. M. 37 n° 191, Mars 1958, 240–243.
3. R. Fortet, Le calcul des probabilités. Les grandes lignes de son développement et ses principaux champs d'application. Bulletin A. P. M. 38 n° 198, Mars 1959, 182–193.
4. M. Barbut, Mathématiques et sciences Humaines. Bulletin A. P. M. 40 n° 213, Décembre 1960, 179–183.
5. A. Huisman, Le bon sens réduit au calcul. Bulletin A. P. M. 40 n° 215, Mai 1961, 331–355.
6. G. Guitel, Un exemple de présentation géométrique en analyse combinatoire. Bulletin A. P. M. 42 n° 231, Mai 1963, 367–378.
7. P. Rosensthiel, Algèbre et Probabilités. Bulletin A. P. M. 44 n° 241, Octobre 1964, 27–46.
8. P. Rosensthiel et A. Warusfel, Algèbre de Boole et publicité. Bulletin A. P. M. 45 n° 251, Juillet 1966, 21–34.
9. P. Kree, Exposé introductif aux probabilités et aux statistiques. Bulletin A. P. M. 45 n° 253, Juillet 1966, 386–388.
10. M. Barbut, De Pascal à Savage, un chapitre de l'algèbre linéaire : le calcul des probabilités. Bulletin A. P. M. 45 n° 254, Septembre 1966, 527–539.
11. A. Badrikian, L. Guerber, P. L. Hennequin, L'enseignement du calcul des Probabilités en Terminales. Bulletin A. P. M. 46 n° 259, Décembre 1967, 335–340.
12. J. R. P. Ibarra, Démocratie et statistique. Bulletin A. P. M. 47 n° 262, Mai 1968, 217–223.
13. Piednoir, Probabilités et Aléas. Bulletin A. P. M. 47 n° 262, Mai 1968, 267–272.
   Bulletin A. P. M. n° 263, Juillet 1968, 369–371.
14. R. Lachaud, J. Lequeux, Rasse, S. Rouault, J. Marsan, G. Voreux, Statistiques et Probabilités, erreurs et incertitudes.
   Bulletin Union des Physicians 62 n° 505, Mai 1968, 929–1018.

B. *Principaux ouvrages en usage dans les établissements Français du second degré*

1. Boissonnade et Halbique, Statistique et Probabilités, Ligel 1968
   — Exercices, Ligel 1969
2. Chambadal, Eléments de calcul des Probabilités, Dunod 1968
3. Cluzel et Vissio, Mathématiques, Terminale D, Delagrave 1968
4. Combes et Saada, Exercices de Probabilités et Statistiques, Vuibert 1968
5. Cossart et Theron, Mathématiques, 1ʳᵉ B, Bordas 1968
   — Mathematiques, 1ʳᵉ D, Bordas 1967

6. Cuenat, Cours de statistique élémentaire, Magnard 1968
7. Hagege, Notions de statistique et de Probabilités (A), O.C.D.L. 1967
   — Initiation à la statistique (1re)
   — Eléments de calcul des probabilités (terminales)
8. Lamat, Statistique et Probabilités, Technique et Vulgarisation 1962
9. Lebosse-Hemery, Mathématiques 1re B, Nathan 1967
   — Mathématiques 1re D
   — Mathématiques Terminale B
   — Mathématiques Terminale D
10. Lespinard et Pernet, Mathématiques 1re B, Desvigne 1967
    — Mathématiques 1re D
    — Mathématiques Terminale B
    — Mathématiques Terminale D
11. Louquet, Les mathématiques en 1re D, Les mathématiques en Terminale D, Armand Colin 1967
12. Monge, Mathématiques 1re, Terminales, Belin 1968
13. Monjallon, Introduction à la méthode statistique, Vuibert 1954
    — Elements de statistique mathématique, Vuibert 1963
14. Pace, Statistique 1re A, B, D, Technique, Licet 1968
    — Statistique et Probabilités, Terminale Bac
    — 100 corrigés détaillés de statistiques
    — Statistique descriptive
15. Pochard, Statistique (1re D), Gauthier Villars 1967
    — Mathématiques (Terminale D)
16. Reeb-Fuchs, Statistiques commentées, Gauthier Villars 1967

C. *Livres écrits à l'intention des professeurs de l'enseignement secondaire*

1. Guerber et Hennequin, Initiation à la Statistique, A. P. M., 1967
2. Guerber et Hennequin, Initiation aux Probabilités, A. P. M., 1968

18. The introduction of probability and statistics on the pre-college level in western Australia

Beryl Hume

University of Western Australia
Nedlands, Western Australia

18.1. INTRODUCTION

Although the introduction of probability and statistics at the pre-college level is of prime importance in this report, it is necessary first to describe one of our first year university courses which has had considerable influence on the first of our high school courses to include these topics.

18.2. FIRST YEAR COLLEGE LEVEL (UNIVERSITY OF WESTERN AUSTRALIA). FIRST YEAR MATHEMATICS COURSE FOR BIOLOGICAL AND SOCIAL SCIENCE STUDENTS

This service course of some 75 lectures, approximately half on calculus and the remainder on probability and statistics, was implemented in 1959 at the request of the Faculty of Agriculture. I was involved in designing the course, in conjunction with Dr. J. Gani,[1] and frequently have been responsible for teaching it. My previous experience of school teaching was particularly useful in that the students of this course enter with widely differing backgrounds and levels of mathematical ability.

The usefulness of the course is perhaps best indicated by enrolments which in this course have risen from some 80 students in 1959 to 400 in 1968, while total university enrolments have risen from 3200 to 6500 over the same period. Students in the course now come from Science, Arts, Agriculture, Medicine, Education, Economics and Commerce.

The course serves as a basic introduction to probability and statistics (with the supporting course of elementary calculus) suited to all fields of application and covers descriptive statistics, probability (addition law, conditional probability etc.), standard distributions (binomial, Poisson, nor-

---

[1] At that time Senior Lecturer in the Department of Mathematics, University of Western Australia.

mal), hypothesis testing and types of errors, χ^2-test of goodness of fit, use of random number tables, sampling distribution of the mean and of difference of means, confidence limits, t-test, variance ratio test, linear correlation and regression. (An introduction to the theory of single server infinite queues has been included when time has permitted.)

More specific statistical methods are left to the individual departments in succeeding years. The aim of our course is not to turn out skilled statisticians, which is impossible in one year and especially with students who are often far from strong mathematically, but to teach an appreciation of the basic concepts. It is hoped that students will be able to read research papers intelligently, see the need of consulting a statistician for design of experiments and analysis of results, and be able to communicate with the statistician.

Mathematical treatment of the statistics is given where appropriate to the students' level of mathematics—otherwise a heuristic approach is used. (This contrasts with the "cook book" courses given in some other departments which rely on only a knowledge of elementary algebra and a sequence of mechanical steps to follow in applying a statistical test.)

18.3. INTRODUCTION OF PROBABILITY AND STATISTICS AT THE PRE-COLLEGE LEVEL

Revision of school mathematics courses in Western Australia has been gathering momentum since 1961. In some cases revision has taken place at different age levels almost simultaneously, whereas in others, revision at a higher level has preceded that at a lower level. Consequently further revisions will be necessary as students come through better prepared from lower courses. We are now in this position with regard to the introduction of probability and statistics in our strong school courses. (See (*b*) below.)

Second Mathematics Stream (*Last Two Years of High School*)

In 1964 the Leaving Mathematics Syllabus Committee in Western Australia (of which I am one of the university representatives) decided that there was a need for a single mathematics subject at the Leaving/Matriculation level which would be suitable as (i) a terminal course and (ii) a preparation for the first year university course for biological and social sciences referred to above. Inclusion of some probability and statistics in this course was therefore an obvious choice, from the point of both (i) and (ii), and necessarily at a pre-calculus level. Since this course was to cater for those students not wishing to pursue a strong mathematics course at tertiary level, it was not expected that students attempting this course would be from the top mathematical stream. (Examination results and teachers' comments have shown that these students are often far from "bright" mathematically!)

Because of my interest in and experience of the first year university course for which this was to be a preparation, I was directly involved in the preparation of the syllabus. (See J. B. Douglas's paper in this book, pp. 303–317 for the probability and statistics sections—the remainder is largely algebra.) Our next tasks were to prepare the teachers through in-service courses, and to find suitable texts. Unfortunately there was no text in probability and statistics at the required level—material was treated too sketchily or too deeply, or too little or too much was included—and the only thing to do was produce our own. This I agreed to do, because at first we thought that it would be sufficient to slightly modify the experimental text "Introductory Probability and Statistical Inference" prepared for the Commission on Mathematics, College Entrance Examination Board. However, closer examination showed that this text was not at quite the right level for our students to read for themselves, and hence my task evolved into something far greater than at first envisaged. I have been the Chief Examiner for this subject since it was first examined in 1965 (the students in that year working with my text in cyclostyled form). The emphasis in the problem sections of the paper is on the "practical" side. My subjective feeling is that teachers, and hence students, have steadily improved in dealing with descriptive statistics and the application of the normal distribution, but the students' performance on the less routine type probability questions leaves much to be desired. However, many teachers have commented on the students' interest in these sections of the course, and especially on the benefit of practical experiments. My personal opinion is that the course would be of greater value if it could go as far as some simple statistical inference, but at present this does not seem practicable.

Strong Mathematics Stream (Last Two Years of High School)

In the past few years the syllabus committee has been working on new syllabuses to replace the present calculus and pre-calculus courses at Leaving/Matriculation. The committee appreciated the value of including probability and statistics in the new syllabus but felt that there was not room for this with so much basic algebra remaining to be done. However, by 1972, all students will have come through on the new courses in the first three years of high school, and there will be the need to prune the Leaving/Matriculation syllabuses of overlapping material. Hence it is that in 1969–70 we must consider further changes, and, in view of the committee's earlier thinking, it seems that preference will be given to the inclusion of probability and statistics. Apart from the question of the amount of material which can

339

be included there is also the question of method of treatment, and in particular, should the probability and statistics precede, parallel or follow the calculus section.

Junior Secondary and Primary

As indicated by the syllabus on Page 317 of J. B. Douglas' paper in this book, the work at these levels is confined to descriptive statistics and very simple probability.

18.4. SCHOOL MATHEMATICS ENRICHMENT COURSES

The summer residential courses run in Western Australia over the past five years for mathematically bright school students prior to their last school year have included lecture programs on material outside the school syllabuses. A popular lecture course has been that on probability. Most of these students have not yet encountered calculus in their school course, and the probability work is confined mostly to finite sample spaces. However, with students of this calibre, there is the opportunity for lectures to proceed at a reasonably fast rate and for a discussion on an axiomatic approach. In the 1969 course, where I had 10 lectures in this course, we went as far as the binomial distribution (mention made of mean, but not of variance), simple hypothesis testing and the use of the χ^2-test for goodness of fit. (The latter was preceded by a brief discussion on continuous probability distributions.) This use of statistical inference proved very interesting to the students, in that they were able to apply tests to practical experiments with dice and coins. This experience of teaching these students, who are admittedly a biased sample of our student population, has confirmed my opinion that some simple work on statistical inference in our schools would be of great value.

19. On the teaching of probability and statistics at the pre-college level in Sweden

Lennart Råde

Chalmers Institute of Technology, Gothenburg, Sweden
and
CEMREL-CSMP, Carbondale, Illinois, U.S.A.

19.1. INTRODUCTION

A new gymnasium (grades 10–12 of high shool) was established in Sweden in 1966. This gymnasium is organized in four lines: humanities and social science, economics, science, technology. In many cases the courses are the same for the different lines. For instance in grade 10, where all students have to study mathematics, there are only two different mathematics courses.

Probability and statistics are included in the mathematics curricula for all lines. This starts with a course in descriptive statistics in grade 10. Some of the students in the humanities line will not study mathematics after this grade. For them a short introductory course to probability including stability of relative frequencies and an orientation about probability theory limited to finite outcome sets is also included in grade 10.

The main part of the course in probability and statistics occurs in grade 12. Here the course in probability includes a discussion of the application of probability to statistics in connection with estimation and decision making.

Probability and statistics were introduced in the new gymnasium as the result of a survey dealing with the outcomes of mathematics teaching in the old gymnasium and the demands from universities and other institutes receiving students from the gymnasium. (See (3).) This survey showed an overwhelming desire that students leaving the gymnasium have a knowledge of probability and statistics. The results also showed that gymnasium students at that time were poorly prepared in these fields. This was especially pointed out by professors of social science, physics, chemistry and biology.

The work of the Scandinavian Committee for Modernizing School Mathematics was also of great importance in the introduction of probability and statistics in the new gymnasium. This committee started its work in 1960 and published its final report in 1967. (See (6).) An abridged version of this report appears in English (7). The committee published an experimental text in probability and statistics (1), which was tried out (mostly in grade 12) in the Scandinavian countries. The following extract concerning experiences obtained from the use of this experimental text comes from the final report:

The students have in general been very much interested in the subject. To a large extent this interest appears to come from contact with realistic problems and situations and the possibilities offered to use knowledge from other parts of mathematics.

According to many teachers descriptive statistics should be studied earlier in school. It has been pointed out that the interest in this field may be greater at an earlier stage. It was considered of great value that the students learned to handle large sets of numerical data. It was reported that in some cases desk calculators had been used.

The probability part of the course interested the students more than the course in descriptive statistics. It was hard to predict the level of difficulty for different concepts in probability theory. The structure itself has often been easy for the students to master but many problems have been difficult. A very important feature of the experimental text is that it treats the relationship between relative frequencies and probabilities. This gives the students a good understanding of the empirical background of probability concepts, which is needed for the later abstract treatment based on outcome sets and random variables. Without having this relationship treated, there is a danger that probability theory would turn out to be a field of mathematics where tricky and abstract problems are solved.

Some teachers considered that the treatment of random variables is too theoretic for this level. Other teachers, however, pointed out how extremely easy the concept was mastered by students; the reason was thought to be their good background in set theory and the basic function concept.

19.2. DESCRIPTIVE STATISTICS IN GRADE 10

The following extract from the curriculum (5) gives the recommendations for the treatment of descriptive statistics in grade 10.:

The students are to master the usual graphical methods to present statistical data materials and to calculate numbers describing essential properties of such materials. However, if possible, one should already at this stage discuss other areas of statistics, like statistical handling of data collection and data interpretation. At this stage it is also possible to indicate why probability theory is important in statistics.

Presentation of statistical data material in a frequency table is to be treated. Different choices of class intervals should be discussed, as well as what to do with observations falling at the limits between class intervals. The study is mainly limited to the following graphical pictures: bar diagram, histogram and cumulative frequency polygon. Also sector diagrams and other types of diagrams can be discussed. In connection with this, one can give some popular examples showing how statistical data materials are presented by picturing the quantities under discussion in different sizes.

The following measures of location are treated: mean, median and quartiles.

Also the mode is mentioned. The median is defined as the "middle" observation when the number of observations is odd and as the mean of the two "middle" observations when the number of observations is even. For statistical data given in a frequency table, the median and the quartiles are defined with aid of the cumulative frequency polygon. No general formulas for this case are given as the method is only an application of linear interpolation. The following measures of spread are treated: variance and standard deviation. Also range is mentioned. In the definition of the variance for statistical data with n observations, $n-1$ is used as numerator.

In connection with calculations of means and variances, it is suitable to introduce the summation symbol and to develop some laws for its use. Numerical calculation of means, variances and standard deviations is also treated for statistical data given by frequency tables. One should avoid extensive machinery of formulas. One can, for instance, give verifications of given formulas for only three or four observations. By calculation of means and variances for large data materials the students are trained to use desk calculators.

The actual statistical data used in demonstrations and by the students should relate to different applications of statistics in such fields as physics, biology, technology, economics and sociology. It is appropriate to let the students themselves collect data from statistical publications or other sources. One can also let the students collect data by doing some simple practical experiments, such as guessing the length of a line segment, observing traffic or performing some random experiment like tossing dice.

For students in the social science and economics lines, index numbers are also treated. This is done so that the students' knowledge of percentages is used and enlarged. As an introduction one can treat such index calculations where in a given set of data all numbers are multiplied by a constant so that one of the numbers or the mean of the numbers is changed to 100. One example is the comparison of productions or sales during different periods of time. Different types of index numbers are treated. The use of chain index is mentioned. One should also mention some official index numbers.

19.3. PROBABILITY AND STATISTICS IN GRADE 12

The following extract from the curriculum (5) shows the recommendations for the treatment of probability and statistics in grade 12. This course is preceeded by a course in combinatorics treating the multiplication principle and the combinatorial meaning of factorials and binomial coefficients.

One of the aims of the course in probability is to give the students an understanding of the concept of a probability. They should also be able to manipulate probabilities. Different applications of probability theory in such fields as operations research, statistics, insurance, economy, etc. should be presented. It is especially important that the application of probability in statistics is treated in order to give the students an introduction to statistical inference.

The probability concept is introduced from the start in connection with relative frequencies and stability of relative frequencies. At the beginning, frequencies and relative frequencies for an event in a number of trials of an experiment are defined and examples of the stability of relative frequencies are demonstrated. It is appropriate

343

to let the students themselves perform trials of some simple experiments, such as tossing of coins, tacks or dice. Doing such experiments the students get a concrete insight in the empirical phenomenon which is the basis of probability theory. Also demographic and other kinds of data can be used to illustrate this phenomenon. It is important that the students get contact both with experiments having "symmetry" and experiments where this is not the case.

After this introduction, probability distributions for experiments having a finite number of outcomes are treated. The set of outcomes is called the outcome set and events are introduced as subsets of the outcome set. The probability distribution is introduced by assigning each outcome an (elementary) probability. The case in which the elementary probabilities are equal (uniform probability distribution) is considered carefully. The relation between the probability of an event and its complementary event and the law

$$P(A \cup B) = P(A) + P(B)$$

for disjoint events A and B are considered. Also independent events are defined.

The problem work is to be limited to simple applications of the laws of probability and combinatorics.

The use of the binomial distribution is illustrated with simple examples concerning drawing with replacement, tossing of coins, applications from quality control, genetics, and so on. The students are taught to use a table dealing with the binomial distribution. Due to time limitations, it is not possible to treat in detail the extension of probability theory to the case with infinite outcome sets. As an example with a denumerable outcome set the Poisson distribution is treated briefly and examples of its application are given. It is also shown how to find probabilities from integration of a probability density. The main example covered is the normal distribution. The connection between the form of the normal probability density curve and the two parameters in its equation is dicussed. The students learn how to use a table dealing with the normal probability distributions. Applications involving the use of such a table are given.

The course is finished with a general introduction to statistical inference, including a discussion of the different steps in a statistical investigation: to collect and present data, to interpret data and to make decisions. Some concrete examples of a decision situation leading to the application of the binomial distribution are discussed. By considering the power function one can discuss the probability of making wrong decisions under various alternatives. A penetrating discussion of general decision problems is not possible. Various aspects of such problems (like the effect of sample size and the choice of decision criterion) are discussed only in connection with the concrete problem.

The following explains how the calculation of a confidence interval is treated. First it is shown how, with a single observation involving a normal distribution with known standard deviation, a confidence interval for the expectation is derived. It is not necessary to introduce the names "expectation" and "standard deviation." Then a sample mean can be considered as one observation from a normal distribution, and thus it is shown how to find the confidence interval for the expectation in this case. For economics majors one also treats the fitting of a straight line by the least squares method.

For the students majoring in economics a short introduction to *time series* is also included. The recommendations for this course are as follows:

344

A short qualitative discussion of the concepts of trend, seasonal variations, cyclical variations and random variations is given. After this it is shown (using practical examples) how a trend is estimated by a free hand curve or by the calculation of moving averages. Furthermore, mention is made of the description of a seasonal variation by a comparison with moving averages.

Students in the social science and economics lines are also given an introduction to *sampling methods*. The recommendations for this course are as follows:

The treatment of different sampling methods is to be started with a general discussion of advantages of sampling methods as compared to total population investigations like smaller costs, rapid results and results with greater scope and greater precision. One should also describe briefly the different steps in a sample survey: statement of the aim of the survey, definition of population, choice of sampling method, organization of field work and treatment and analysis of the collected data. Some sampling methods are then described using concrete examples; for instance, simple random sampling, stratified sampling and sequential sampling. Also cluster methods can be mentioned.

In the list of references at the end of this article several textbooks are mentioned, treating the courses described above. The courses are usually integrated in textbooks covering the whole mathematics curriculum. A book containing only the courses described above (somewhat enlarged) is (2).

19.4. TEACHER TRAINING

A problem that had to be solved in connection with the introduction of the courses above involved the training of teachers. Only a few teachers in the gymnasium had studied probability and statistics at the university. The problem was solved by intensive summer courses and by offering all teachers a correspondence course. (See (4).) This course covered the necessary background for the teaching of the courses described above. At present probability and statistics are included in the university courses taken by those who are going to teach mathematics in the gymnasium.

REFERENCES

1. Ajne, B. & Råde, L., Statistik och sannolikhetslära för gymnasiet. Nordiska kommittén för modernisering av matematikundervisningen. Stockholm 1960.
2. Bergendal, G., Håstad, M. & Råde, L., Statistik och sannolikhetslära. Biblioteksförlaget. Stockholm 1968.
3. Dahlöf, U., Kraven på gymnasiet, undersökningar vid universitet och högskolor i förvaltning och näringsliv. Statens Offentliga Utredningar 1963:22. Stockholm 1963.

4. Råde, L., Sannolikhetslära och statistik. Fortbildningskurs. Hermods-NKI. Malmö 1965.
5. Läroplan för gymnasiet. Skolöverstyrelsens skriftserie 80. SÖ-förlaget, Stockholm 1965.
6. Nordisk skolmatematik. Nordisk utredningsserie 1967:9. Stockholm 1967.
7. New School Mathematics in the Nordic Countries. Nordisk utredningsserie 1967:11. Stockholm 1967.

Textbooks

The following different series of textbooks consist each of several volumes, usually one book for each school year and its course.
8. Bergendal, G., Håstad, M. & Råde, L., Matematik för gymnasiet. Biblioteksförlaget, Stockholm.
9. Brolin, H., Sjöstedt, C. E., Thörnquist, S. & Vejde, O., Matematik för gymnasiet. Natur och Kultur, Stockholm.
10. Ekbom, L. & Hilding, S., Matematik för gymnasiet. Svenska Bokförlaget, Stockholm.
11. Greger, K. & Häggmark, P., Gymnasiets matematik. Akademiförlaget Gumperts, Göteborg.
12. Nyman, B., Matematik för gymnasiet. Svenska Bokförlaget, Stockholm.

20. A Collection of Problems in Probability and Statistics

S. Holm

Chalmers Institute of Technology
Gothenburg, Sweden

PROBABILITY, FINITE OUTCOME SPACE

1. *A game*

Two persons play a game as follows: One of the persons (call him A) hides an object in one of his hands. The other person (call him B) has to guess in which hand A has the object. If B guesses correctly, he gets 4 cents, and if he guesses left hand when it is in the right hand, he has to pay 2 cents, and if he guesses right hand when it is in the left hand, he has to pay 7 cents. B randomises his decisions by choosing the left hand with probability p. Determine the expectation of what he earns as a function of p for the two cases:

1. A has the object in his left hand.
2. A has the object in his right hand.

Is there some value of p which is especially good for B to use?
Discuss!

2. *Stopping experiments*

Independent trials of an experiment (e.g., tossing a die), in which an event A occurs with probability p, are performed. You don't receive information about the results of the trials, but you are asked to stop the experiments when you think the event has occurred an odd number of times.

If you stop after n trials, what is the probability that the event has occurred an odd number of times? What values of n for $p < 1/2$, $p > 1/2$ and $p = 1/2$ maximize this probability?

3. *Tossing dice*

If you throw an ordinary six-sided die, what is the probability that the total number of points on the face up and on the face down is an odd number?

If you throw two ordinary dice, what is the probability that the total number of points on the faces up on the two dice is an odd number?

Perform many trials of these experiments to obtain frequency tables for odd and even sums. Compare with the probabilities!

4. Getting a new ace

A deck of cards is shuffled and then divided into two parts with an equal number of cards in each part. You draw one card from one of the parts and it happens to be an ace. You place the ace in the other part, shuffle it, and draw a card. What is the probability that you get an ace again?

5. Simplified "rencontre" problem

A deck of n cards marked $1, 2, \ldots, n$ is shuffled. While counting $1, 2, \ldots, n$, you take one card at a time without replacement. If you get the card with the same number you are counting, a rencontre occurs. If q_n is the probability that at least one rencontre occurs, then a classical problem is to determine $\lim_{n \to \infty} q_n$, which is equal to $1 - 1/e$. The problem is considerably simplified if the cards are taken with replacement. Show that the same limiting result holds.

6. A lottery

Ten thousands tickets (numbered from 1 to 10,000) are sold at 1 dollar each in a lottery in which the prizes are as follows: 1 prize of 2000 dollars, 2 prizes of 1000 dollars, 10 prizes of 100 dollars and 25 prizes of 50 dollars. Assume that a fair method is used for choosing the winning tickets (at random and without replacement), and that Mr. X buys 4 tickets.

    (a) What is the probability that he wins 300 dollars?
    (b) What is his expected gain (or loss)?

If, in addition to the above prizes, consolation prizes of 100 dollars are awarded to each ticket whose number differs by 1 from the 2000 dollar prize ticket, comment on the changes this makes in the calculation in (a) and (b). In this case, would Mr. X increase or decrease his expected gain by buying his tickets from different ticket sellers? (Assume ticket sellers have books of consecutively numbered tickets.)

7. "Negative information"

An event A is said to carry negative information about an event B if $P(B|A) < P(B)$, and this is denoted by $A \searrow B$. Examine the following three statements, and prove them, or disprove them, by supplying counterexamples:

    (a) $A \searrow B \Rightarrow B \searrow A$
    (b) $(A \searrow B \quad \text{and} \quad B \searrow C) \Rightarrow A \searrow C$
    (c) $(A \searrow B \quad \text{and} \quad C \searrow B) \Rightarrow A \cap C \searrow B$

8. Who baked the cake?

Three cooks A, B and C bake a special kind of cake with probabilities 0.06, 0.05 and 0.02 respectively that the cake fails to rise. In the establishment where all three work, A bakes 25 % of these cakes, B bakes 60 % and C 15 %. One day a waiter, who knows that only A and B are cooking that day, sees a "failure" being thrown out. What is the probability that the failure was A's?

9. Through the network

Consider a big squared network such that the lengths of the sides of the square are b units. A ball of radius $r(r<b/2)$ is randomly thrown perpendicular to the network. What is the probability that it goes through the network without touching it?

10. Different information?

In a box there are three balls. Previously each ball was painted either red or green, with probability 1/2 for a color being selected, and the coloring of each ball was independent. Now suppose you have such a box, but you don't know the color of the balls.

(a) Find the conditional probability that there are at least two red balls, if you get the information that there is at least one red ball.

(b) Now suppose instead that you handle the box carelessly and one ball falls out. It is red. At first sight you would seem to have gotten the same information as in case (a), but have you really? Find the conditional probability that there are at least two red balls (including the one you dropped) in the box in this case.

11. Playing "craps" unfairly

The game "craps" is played in the following way: You first toss two dice. If you get the sum 7 you win, but if you get the sum 2, 11, or 12 you lose, and if you get some other sum you have to toss the two dice time after time until you get the same sum again or the sum 7. If you get the same sum again you win, and if you get the sum 7 you lose.

(a) What is the probability of winning the game if you use two ordinary (symmetric) dice?

(b) What is the probability of winning the game if you use two dice which are heavily loaded in one corner so that die 1 can give only 3, 4, and 6, with probability 1/3 each, and die 2 can give only 1, 3, and 4, with probability 1/3 each.

(c) Show that the probability of winning by any loading of this kind (giving probability 1/3 to *any* three numbers on each die) cannot exceed 8/9. How should you load the dice to get this probability?

PROBABILITY, ANALYSIS USED

1. *Soccer*

When two teams play a soccer game, the number of goals for the two teams can be considered as two independent Poisson processes with intensities 1/45 goals/minute and 1/90 goals/minute. Determine the probability that the two teams get the same number of goals in a 90-minute game.

2. *Two inequalities (discrete)*

(a) Let X be a random variable of the discrete type, which can take the values ka, $k=0, 1, 2, \ldots$, with non-increasing probabilities $P(X=ka)$. Show that for $k \neq 0$ and $a > 0$

$$P(X=ka) \leqslant 2E(X)/k^2a.$$

(b) Let Y be a random variable of the discrete type, which can take the values ka, $k=0, 1, 2, \ldots$, and has expectation μ. Show that, if $P(X=ka)$ is a non-increasing function of k for $ka > \mu$, then

$$P(Y=y) \leqslant \frac{3 \operatorname{Var}(Y) a}{(y-\mu)^3} \quad \text{for} \quad y > \mu, (a > 0).$$

3. *Two inequalities (continuous)*

(a) Let X be a non-negative random variable of the continuous type with non-increasing density f. Show that

$$f(x) \leqslant \frac{2E(X)}{x^2} \quad \text{for all} \quad x > 0.$$

(b) Let Y be a random variable of the continuous type, with expectation μ. Show that, if the density f is non-increasing for $x > \mu$, then

$$f(x) \leqslant \frac{3 \operatorname{Var}(Y)}{(x-\mu)^3} \quad \text{for all} \quad x > \mu.$$

4. *A simplified queuing problem*

In a certain serving system, serving always takes the same time T, and serving is continued cyclically in such a manner that serving is started only at times $0, T, 2T, 3T, \ldots$. During each serving interval there arrive $0, 1,$ or 2 customers with probabilities $1/2, 1/4,$ and $1/4$, and the number of customers arriving during different serving intervals are independent. During each

350

serving interval one customer is served if there is at least one customer queuing at the beginning of the interval; otherwise, none is served. Determine a stationary probability distribution for the queue length just before serving is started, i.e., a probability distribution such that if the queue length has this distribution at one serving start, it has the same distribution at the next serving start. Determine also the expectation of the queue length when it has this stationary distribution.

5. *Misprints*

Suppose that when a text is in proof-sheet form, there are a number of misprints which are Poisson distributed with parameter λ. Suppose further that if there are n misprints in the proof sheet, the number of discovered and corrected misprints has a binomial distribution with parameters n and p. What is the probability that there are no misprints after the proofreading?

6. *Insurance*

A car insurance company receives daily claims in a Poisson process with average $\lambda = .5$ claims/day. These claims are either for 10 dollars or for 100 dollars, with probabilities .8 and .2 respectively. Find the average daily rate of receipt of premiums needed to cover the claims.

7. *Playing at marbles*

A poem by a Swedish author begins: "We played at marbles in the square one day, a first year schoolboy and I; I had fifty he had five; we played; he lost the few he had, ..." Suppose that they play in such a way that in each game one or the other of them wins one marble from the other, and that they play until one of them has no marbles left. Show that, if they play equally well, i.e., they each have both probability $1/2$ of winning in each game, then the first year schoolboy has a probability of only $1/11$ to win "totally". (Hint: Let q_n = probability of winning "totally" when starting with n marbles against $55 - n$. Show that $q_n = (1/2)q_{n+1} + (1/2)q_{n-1}$.

8. *"Hong-Kong"*

In order to illustrate the mathematics of epidemics, we consider the following very simplified situation: In a group consisting of six persons, one person has contracted an infectious influenza. Suppose that at one special moment before he gets ill he can instantaneously transfer the infection to some other person, and that he is at that moment in contact with one of the other persons in the group (randomly chosen). At the moment when the second person can transfer the infection to someone else, the first person who had the influenza is well again. The second person is at that moment in contact with some randomly chosen person in the group. If this is the person who has already had the influenza, the epidemic stops. If it is someone else, the epidemic will continue, and at the moment when this person can transfer the infection he is in contact with someone (randomly chosen) from the group, etc.

(a) Determine the probability that the total number of persons in the group who get the influenza is 2, 3, 4, 5, and 6.

(b) Determine the expectation of the number of persons in the group who get the influenza.

STATISTICS, FINITE OUTCOME SPACE

1. Ecology

When ecologists want to estimate the number of insects of some kind, e.g., in a field or a wood, they first catch a number, say M, of insects, mark them and then let them free in the same area. After some time they again catch a number, say n, of insects in the area. This gives the estimate $(Mn)/X$ of the total number of insects, say N in the area, where X is the number of marked insects in this second capture.

(a) What is the probability distribution of X for given N, M, and n?

(b) For the expectation of X it is the case that $E(X) = (nM)/N$, but the expectation of $(Mn)/X$ is not equal to N. Explain!

(c) Now study the expectation of the estimate of N, but in order to avoid difficulties with the (rare) possibility $X=0$, use instead the estimate $Y = (M+1)(n+1)/(X+1)$.

Show that $E(Y) = (N+1)\left(1 - \dfrac{\binom{M+1}{n+1}}{\binom{N+1}{n+1}}\right).$

2. A traffic count

A statistician sitting in a café observes the number of cars passing in 1 minute time intervals. The observed numbers, doing this for 10 consecutive 1 minute intervals, are 3, 4, 2, 1, 2, 4, 3, 2, 1, 2. He knows from experience that the maximum number of cars which could pass bumper to bumper is 8. Assuming that the number of cars passing form a binomial process and estimating the binomial probability p from his data, the statistician wishes to calculate the probability that no car arrives during the one minute he needs to cross the street. What is this probability? If he can actually cross successfully provided there are fewer than 3 cars, what is the probability that he can cross successfully?

3. *Small probabilities*

Assume an *a priori* distribution for the probability p of an event A, which is uniform on $(0, 1)$, and that n independent trials of the experiment are performed.

(*a*) Find the $100\, q\%$ Baye's confidence interval $(0 < q < 1)$ for p of the form $(0, p_u)$, if the event has not occurred in any of the experiments.

(*b*) How many trials must be performed in which A has not occurred, in order to get $p_u < 0.01$ as a 95 % confidence interval?

8. *Wrong judgements*

For an investigation a medical scientist has to compare two photographic pictures of something, one taken before a medical treatment and one after the medical treatment, and he has for each pair to judge "better after treatment" or "worse after treatment". In order to estimate the probability of making wrong judgements, he makes two independent judgements for each of n pairs. Suppose that the n experiments are independent and that the probability that it really becomes better after the medical treatment is p. Suppose further that the probability of making a wrong judgement is q (independent of if it has really become better or worse). As an estimate of q he uses $X = 2n_d/n$, where n_d is the number of pairs of judgement, in which he makes opposite judgements for the two times. Show that this is reasonable for small q by determining $E(X)$ and by showing

$$\lim_{q \to 0} \frac{E(X)}{q} = 1.$$

5. *Random walk statistics*

A particle starts at time $t=0$ at a point $x=0$ on a line. At time $t=1$ it jumps to $x=1$ with probability p and to $x=-1$ with probability $1-p$. At times $t=2, 3, \ldots, n$ it jumps one unit to the right (x increases by 1) with probability p and one unit to the left (x decreases by 1) with probability $(1-p)$. The steps at times $t=1, 2, 3, \ldots, n$ are independent. Let the position of the particle after n steps be X_n.

(*a*) Determine the expectation of X_n.
(*b*) Suggest a good estimate of p.
(*c*) What is the variance of that estimate?

6. *A roulette wheel has no memory*

If one listens to the people playing roulette, one can often hear them say something like this: "Now Red has occurred ten times in a row, so the next spin should have a large probability of giving Black. I will bet on Black."

If they thought a little more, I think they would rather say: "Since Red has occurred ten times in a row, there is a possibility that something is wrong with the roulette wheel, and I will take advantage and bet on Red."

In order to illustrate this we simplify the situation as follows: Consider a box with four balls. Two of them ought to be black and two ought to be red, but there is some small probability, say 1/1000, that by mistake there are three red balls and one black.

(*a*) A ball is drawn (with replacement between the drawings) 10 times, and each time it is red. What is the probability that there are three red balls and one black ball in the box?

(*b*) Assume that if you bet $2.00 on one color in the next drawing, you get $3.00 if that color is drawn and nothing if the other color is drawn. What is the expectation of the amount of dollars you win or lose if you bet on red and black respectively?

7. *Quality control*

The quality of lots of 2000 items of some kind is controlled by taking a sample of n items (randomly without replacements) from each lot. If there is at least one defective item in the sample, the lot is rejected.

(*a*) Determine the probability that a lot having 200 defective items is rejected if $n=20$.

(*b*) What is the smallest sample size such that a lot with 100 defective items is rejected with a probability of at least 90 %?

8. *Expectation of inverse*

Suppose a parameter θ in a distribution is estimated by Y and we have $E(Y)=\theta$. Now we want to estimate $1/\theta$. It is *not* the case that $E(1/Y)=1/\theta$ even if Y cannot take the value 0. Show this by making a counter-example, e.g., for a random variable taking value 1 and 2 with probabilities p and $1-p$.

STATISTICS, ANALYSIS USED

1. *Ecology again*

In ecological investigations, one often studies the diversity of vegetation in an area by taking at random one plant after another, examining the plants and plotting successively the number of different kinds of plants in the first n examinations as a function of log n. In order to study this, we make the (quite unrealistic) assumption that there exist in a certain area N kinds of plants, and that the successive examinations can be regarded as independent trials, with a probability $1/N$ for each kind of plants to be examined.

Show that the expectation of the number of the first experiment when one has m different kinds of plants is

$$N \sum_{k=N+1-m}^{N} 1/k.$$

2. Nonparametric confidence interval

Let $X_1, X_2, \ldots, X_n$ be independent continuous random variables, with the same density f, and median m. Define $X^{(1)}, X^{(2)}, \ldots, X^{(n)}$ as random variables, whose outcomes are the smallest, the next smallest, etc. of the outcomes of $X_1, X_2, \ldots, X_n$.

(a) Determine the confidence coefficient for the confidence interval $[X^{(1)}, X^{(5)}]$ for m when $n=5$.

b) Determine the confidence coefficient for the confidence interval $[X^{(2)}, X^{(7)}]$ for m when $n=8$.

3. Traffic flow

We want to study the traffic flow between three towns A, B, and C. The number of cars going from A to B or from B to A each day is supposed to be Poisson distributed with parameter λ_{AB} and in the same way the number of cars going from B to C or from C to B each day is supposed to be Poisson distributed with parameter λ_{BC}. The road between A and C is quite bad, and thus many drivers don't go directly between A and C, they instead go via B. Suppose the number going directly and the number going via B to be Poisson distributed with parameters λ_{AC} and λ_{ABC}, respectively. All mentioned Poisson distributed random variables are supposed to be independent.

(a) Show that the sum of two independent Poisson distributed random variables (with parameters λ_1 and λ_2) is Poisson distributed (with parameter $\lambda_1 + \lambda_2$).

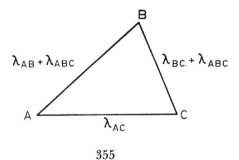

355

(b) By some automatic counter the number of cars travelling the three ways are counted each day for n days. Let the number of cars counted on the different days travelling between AB, AC, and BC be $X_1, \ldots, X_n$, $Y_1 \ldots, Y_n$ and $Z_1, \ldots, Z_n$. We now want to estimate the different parameters λ in this case. The parameter λ_{AC} is estimated by

$$\bar{Y} = \frac{1}{n} \sum_{k=1}^{n} y_k.$$

Show that $E(Y) = \lambda_{AC}$.

(c) In order to estimate λ_{ABC}, determine the expectation of the variable

$$\sum_{k=1}^{n} X_k Z_k - n \bar{X} \bar{Z}$$

and then give an estimate of λ_{ABC} with expectation λ_{ABC}.

(d) Give estimates with expectations λ_{AB} and λ_{BC}.

4. Simultaneous confidence intervals

In an investigation you have to make n confidence intervals (Y_1, Z_1), $(Y_2, Z_2), \ldots, (Y_n, Z_n)$ for parameters $\gamma_1, \gamma_2, \gamma_3, \ldots, \gamma_n$. You want the simultaneous confidence coefficient, i.e., the probability

$$P(Y_k \leqslant \gamma_k \leqslant Z_k, \quad k = 1, 2, \ldots, n)$$

to be at least q.

(a) Show that the simultaneous confidence coefficient can be made equal to q, if the intervals are independent, by choosing the confidence coefficient $q^{1/n}$ for each interval.

(b) Show that the simultaneous confidence coefficient can be made at least q by choosing the confidence coefficient $1 - \frac{1}{n}(1-q)$ for each interval even if they are dependent.

(c) In practical cases there are no great differences between the confidence coefficients for the separate intervals in (a) and (b). Compare them for example when $q = 0.95$ and $n = 5$.

5. Sequential testing in production

In the manufacturing of certain items one wants some measure assigned to items to be between two limits. In order to control this, one takes every day 20 items from the production line and checks the measure. If it is between the limits for all items one lets the production continue, but if two or more items have measures outside the limits you stop production and make adjustments. If only one item of the 20 samples have measures outside the limits one takes another 20 items from the production line. If at least one of these has a measure outside the limits you stop the production and adjust, otherwise, you let production continue. Assume that the events that different items have measures outside the limits are independent.

(a) Determine the probability of stopping production as a function of the probability that the separate items have measures outside the limits.

(b) Determine the expectation of the number of items taken from production for control as a function of the probability that the items have measures outside the limits.

(c) Graph the functions in (a) and (b).

Program of the First CSMP International Conference

March 18–27, 1969
Carbondale, Illinois, U.S.A.

Co-sponsored by Southern Illinois University and
Central Midwestern Regional Educational Laboratory

Tuesday, March 18

Welcome by H. Howard Russell, CEMREL; B. Kaufman and L. Råde, CEMREL-CSMP.
Orientation on CSMP components by R. Exner, H. Steiner and V. Haag.
Movie: *CSMP: Where Students and Mathematics Meet*
Multi-screen presentation of Southern Illinois.

Wednesday, March 19

Visit to CSMP offices.
Exhibition of books and teaching aids for probability and statistics.
Observation of CSMP students.
Lecture by A. Rényi to high school class.
Relations, Functions and Expectations. Video-taped discussion between L. Råde and three students.
Demonstration of activity packages.

Thursday, March 20

Welcome to Southern Illinois University, Robert W. MacVicar, Chancellor, Carbondale Campus.
Lecture by H. Freudenthal: *The Aims of Probability and of its Teaching.*
Lecture by A. Rényi: *Remarks on the Teaching of Probability.*
Tour of campus including visits to Decision Laboratory, Communication Building, etc.
Dinner at Holiday Inn.
Man's Function in the Universe by R. Buckminster Fuller.

Friday, March 21

Lecture by J. Neyman: *Elementary Teaching of Probability and Statistics with Indeterminism in Science as a Background.*
Lecture by W. Kruskal: *Statistical Examples for Use in High School.*
Lecture by D. V. Lindley: *A Non-Frequentist View of Probability and Statistics.*
Lecture by J. Gani: *The Use of Mathematics in Conceptual Models.*

Saturday, March 22

Lecture by A. Engel: *Teaching Probability in Intermediate Grades.*
Remarks by S. Holm: *Probability and Problem Solving.*

Lecture by J. B. Douglas: *On the Teaching of Probability and Statistics at the Pre-College Level in Australia.*
Group sessions.

Sunday, March 23

Trip to St. Louis by bus, tour of Gateway Arch and other sites.

Monday, March 24

Lecture by Hilda M. Davies: *The Role of Practical Experimentation in the Teaching of Probability and Statistics.*
Lecture by L. Råde: *The Teaching of Probability and Statistics at the Pre-college Level in Sweden.*
Lecture by S. Goldberg: *Probability and Pre-calculus Analysis.*
Lecture by E. F. Beckenbach: *Combinatorics for School Mathematics Curricula.*

Tuesday, March 25

Discussion on the teaching of probability.
Trip to Giant City State Park. Luncheon and random walk around the area.
Lecture by H. Steiner: *The Theory of Voting Bodies: An Example of Mathematization.*

Wednesday, March 26

Lecture by C. B. Bell: *Nonparametric Statistics at the Pre-College Level.*
Lecture by P. L. Hennequin: *Teaching of Probability and Statistics in the French Lycée.*
Group sessions.
Discussion on the teaching of statistics.

Thursday, March 27

Report from group sessions.
Discussion on recommendations.
Lecture by J. Gani to high school students.
Lecture by D. V. Lindley at Department of Mathematics, Southern Illinois University: *The Concept of Information in an Experiment.*

List of Participants

360

Robert Exner, Department of Mathematics, Syracuse University, Syracuse, New York, U.S.A.
Vincent Haag, Department of Mathematics, Franklin and Marshall College, Lancaster, Pennsylvania, U.S.A.
Lennart Råde, Department of Mathematics, Chalmers Institute of Technology, Gothenburg, Sweden.
Hans G. Steiner, Karlsruhe University, Karlsruhe, West Germany.

CEMREL ADMINISTRATIVE STAFF

Wade M. Robinson, Executive Director, CEMREL, St. Ann, Missouri, U.S.A.
H. Howard Russell, St. Ann, Missouri, U.S.A.

CSMP STAFF

Diane Boesch, Dale Carlson, Peter Drees, Jerry Exum, Roy Hajek, Kerstin Hallenrud, Richard Halsey, Clare Heidema, Martin Herbert, Laura Hinshaw, Marvin Hinshaw, Bob Hunter, Joseph S. Karmos, Burt Kaufman, Ernie Lewis, Fr. Larry Lorenzoni, SDB, Dave Masters, Fred Matejcek, Ann Narel.

SOUTHERN ILLINOIS UNIVERSITY, CARBONDALE

Thomas Paine, Michael Skalsky, Thomas Starks.

SOUTHERN ILLINOIS UNIVERSITY, EDWARDSVILLE

Kermit G. Clemans, Robert B. Rutledge, Eric A. Sturley.

OBSERVERS

Jack Easley, University of Illinois, Urbana, Illinois, U.S.A.
William Hale, Educational Research Council of America, Cleveland, Ohio, U.S.A.
Julius H. Hlavaty, President National Council of Teachers of Mathematics, New Rochelle, New York, U.S.A.
Chancey Jones, Mathematics Department, Educational Testing Service, Princeton, New Jersey, U.S.A.
Bob Kansky, Mathematics Education, College of Education, Florida State University, Tallahassee, Florida, U.S.A.
Roland Long, Mathematics Supervisor, Office of the Superintendent of Public Instruction, Springfield, Illinois, U.S.A.

Asher Marcus, Tel Aviv, Israel.

Eugene Tallent, State Department of Education, Frankfort, Kentucky, U.S.A.

Maurice M. Tatsuoka, Department of Educational Psychology, College of Educa-* tion, University of Illinois, Urbana, Illinois, U.S.A.

Lauren G. Woodby, Mathematics Department, Michigan State University, East Lansing, Michigan, U.S.A.

Russell E. Zwoyer, UICSM Mathematics Project, University of Illinois, Urbana, Illinois, U.S.A.

Bibliography

The following bibliography contains a selection of material (articles, textbooks, etc.) which is hoped will be useful for teachers of probability and statistics. See also the lists of references at the end of the articles in this volume. (For instance, Hennequin's article has an extensive list of references to French articles and textbooks.)

1. PROBABILITY AND STATISTICS

1.1. Articles

Blom, G. & Råde, L., Probability and statistics courses for students of engineering at the university level. Review International Statistical Institute. 34 (1966) p. 165–173.

Bernoulli, J., The law of large numbers. The World of Mathematics. New York (Simon and Schuster). 1956 p. 1452–1455.

Breny, H., Réflexions méthodologiques sur l'enseignement de la théorie des probabilités et la statistique au niveau secondaire. Nico. 3 (1969) p. 2–19.

Breny, H., Réflexions méthodologiques sur l'enseignement de la statistique au niveau secondaire. Nico. 1 (1968) p. 42–50.

Brunk, H. D. & Gref, L. G., A geometrical approach to probability. Mathematics Magazine. 37 (1964) p. 287–296.

Bunt, L. N. H., Probability and statistical inference in the secondary school. Dialectica. 21 (1967) p. 366–382.

Carnap, R., What is probability? Scientific American. Sept. 1953 p. 128–138.

Christ, L. E., A lost boy and a random walk. The Mathematics Student Journal. January 1969.

Cohen, J., Subjective probability. Scientific American. Nov. 1957 p. 128–138.

Committee on the undergraduate program in mathematics (CUPM). Report on a conference on preparation for graduate study in statistics. Mathematical Association of America.

Committee on probability and statistics in the secondary school. Report. American Statistician. 18.4 (1964) p. 17–25.

Cornfield, J., Bayes theorem. Review International Statistical Institute. 35 (1967) p. 34–49.

Donat, C. D., Empfehlungen zur methodischen Gestaltung eines Lehrgang der Anfangsgründe der Wahrscheinlichkeitsrechnung. Matematik in der Schule. 7 (1969) p. 222–230.

Engel, A., Propädeutische Wahrscheinlichkeitstheorie. Der Mathematikunterricht. 12 (1966) p. 5–20.

Engel, A., Kombinatorik und Wahrscheinlichkeitstheorie im Unterricht der Unter- und Mittelstufe der Gymnasien. Mathematischer Unterricht an deutschen Universitäten und Schulen. Göttingen 1967 p. 169–210.

Engel, A., Mathematical research and instruction in probability theory. Mathematics Teacher. 59 (1968) p. 771–782.

Engel, A., Systematic use of applications in mathematics teaching. Educational Studies in Mathematics. 1.2 (1968) p. 202–221.

Fine, N. J., Generating functions. Enrichment mathematics for high school. (28th Yearbook National Council Teachers of Mathematics, U.S.A.) p. 355–367.

Fischbein, E., Pampu, I. & Mînsat, Initiation aux probabilités à l'ecole élémentaire. Educational Studies in Mathematics. 2 (1969) p. 16–31.

Fisher, R. A., Mathematics of a lady tasting tea. The World of Mathematics. New York (Simon and Schuster) 1956 p. 1512–1521.

Gani, J., Whodunit? Or the Reverend Mr Bayes FRS helps to decide. Mathematical Spectrum. 1 (1968) p. 9–13.

Gehan, E. A., Note on the "Birthday problem". American Statistician. 22.2 (1968) p. 28.

Gardner, M., Mathematical games. The rambling random walk and its gambling equivalent. Scientific American. May 1969 p. 118–120.

Gnedenko, B. V., The teaching of probability theory and mathematical statistics. Report of the second conference on mathematical education in South Asia. Bombay. 1960 p. 115–136.

Gnedenko, B. V. & Jurbenko, I. G., Theory of probability and combinatorics. Matematika v Shkole. 2–3 (1968) p. 72–84 and p. 30–49. (In Russian.)

Gnedenko, B. V. & Shurbenko, I. G., Wahrscheinlichkeitsrechnung und Kombinatorik. Mathematik in der Schule. 7 (1969) p. 170–210 and p. 284–295. (German translation of the foregoing article.)

Gramann, R. H., A queueing simulation. Mathematics Teacher. 57 (1964).

Graunt, J., Foundations of vital statistics. The World of Mathematics. New York (Simon and Schuster) 1956 p. 1421–1434.

Halley, E., First life insurance tables. The World of Mathematics. New York (Simon and Schuster) 1956 p. 1437–1447.

Harrison, R. D., An activity approach to the teaching of statistics and probability. Mathematics Teaching. 34 (1966) p. 31–38.

Helma, G., Experimentelle Mathematik auf der Oberstufe: Monte Carlo-Methoden. Der Mathematikunterricht. 1964.4 p. 48–61.

Hersh, R. & Griego, R. J., Brownian motion and potential theory. Scientific American. March 1969 p. 67–74.

Hotelling, H., The teaching of statistics. Contributions to Probability and Statistics. Stanford (Stanford University Press) 1960 p. 11–24.

Håstad, M., Probability and statistics in school program. Regional Seminar Cairo. Unesco mathematics project for the Arab States. Unesco 1969.

Ineichen, R., Über die Behandlung der Normalverteilung. Der Mathematikunterricht. 1966.4 p. 62–75.

Jacobs, K., Rot und Schwarz. Math.-phys. Semesterberichte. Göttingen. 15.2 (1968) p. 188–212.

Jeger, M., Ein Zugang zur Wahrscheinlichkeitsrechnung im modernen Mathematikunterricht. Der Mathematikunterricht. 1966.4 p. 21–47.

Kac, M., Probability theory: its role and its impact. SIAM Review. 4 (1962) p. 1–11.

Kac, M., Probability. Scientific American. Sept. 1964 p. 92–108.

Keynes, J. M., The application of probability to conduct. The World of Mathematics. New York (Simon and Schuster) 1956 p. 1360–1373.

Kendall, M. G., On the future of statistics—a second look. Journal Royal Statistical Society A. 131 (1968) p. 182–204.

Kemeny, J. G., Random walks. Enrichment Mathematics for High School (28th yearbook of National Council Teachers of Mathematics, U.S.A.) p. 285–300.

Knowles, E. A. G., Experiment with a random selector as an aid for the teaching of statistics. Applied Statistics. 3 (1954) p. 90–103.

Kolmogorov, A. N., Introduction to probability theory and combinatorics. Matematika v Shkole. 1968.2 p. 63–72. (In Russian.)

Kolmogorov, A. N., Einführung in die Wahrscheinlichkeitsrechnung und die Kombinatorik. Mathematik in der Schule. 7 (1969) p. 296–308. (German translation of the foregoing article.)

Kruskal, W., Statistics, Moliere and Henry Adams. American Scientist. Dec. 1967 p. 416–428.

Kuller, R. G., Coin tossing, probability and the Weierstrass approximation theorem. Mathematics Magazine. 37 (1964) p. 262–265.

Leibowitz, M. A., Queues. Scientific American. Aug. 1968, p. 96–103.

Lindley, D. V., Professor Hogben's "crisis"—A survey of the foundations of statistics. Applied Statistics. 7 (1958) p. 186–198.

Mantel, N., More Light Bulb Statistics. American Statistician. 23.2 (1969) p. 21–23.

Menger, K., Random variables from the point of view of a general theory of variables. Third Berkeley Symposium on Mathematical Statistics and Probability vol. 2 (ed. J. Neyman). Berkeley and Los Angeles (University of California Press) 1956 p. 215–229.

Mosteller, F., Understanding the birthday problem. Mathematics Teacher 55 (1962) p. 322–325.

Mosteller, F., Optimal length of play for a binomial game. Mathematics Teacher. 55 (1961) p. 411–412.

Mosteller, F., Continental classroom television course in probability and statistics. Review International Statistical Institute. 31 (1963) p. 153–162.

Mosteller, F., What has happened to probability in the high school? Mathematics Teacher. 60 (1967) p. 824–831.

Nagel, E., The meaning of probability. The World of Mathematics. New York (Simon and Schuster) 1956 p. 1398–1414.

Neyman, J., Statistics, servant of all sciences. Science. 122 (1955) p. 401–406.

Noble, B., Applications of probability theory. Part V of Applications of Undergraduate Mathematics in Engineering. New York (Macmillan) 1967.

Nüesch, P., Testverfahren. Der Mathematikunterricht. 1966.4 p. 76–86.

Ore, O., Pascal and the invention of probability. American Mathematical Monthly. 67 (1960) p. 409–419.

O'Toole, A. L., Probability and statistics teaching in Western European Secondary Schools. The American Statistician. 20 (1966) p. 23–24.

Page, D. A., Probability. The Growth of Mathematical Ideas Grades K-12. (24th Yearbook National Council Teachers of Mathematics, U.S.A.) p. 229–271.

Papy, G., Statistique et vectoriels euclidiens. Nico. 2 (1968) p. 17–33.

Peirce, C. S., The red and black. The World of Mathematics. New York (Simon and Schuster) 1956 p. 1334–1340.

Peirce, C. S., The probability of induction. The World of Mathematics. New York (Simon and Schuster) 1956 p. 1341–1354.

Pieters, R. S., Statistics. The Growth of Mathematical Ideas Grades K-12. (24th Yearbook National Council Teachers of Mathematics U.S.A.) p. 272–326.

Poincaré, H., Chance. The World of Mathematics. New York (Simon and Schuster) 1956 p. 1380–1394.

Polya, G., On picture-writing. American Mathematical Monthly. 63 (1956) p. 689–697.

Reimers, B., Boolescher Verband und Wahrscheinlichkeitsrechnung. Der Mathematische und Naturwissenschaftliche Unterricht. 22 (1969) p. 86–92.

Rényi, A., Axiomatischer Aufbau der Wahrscheinlichkeitsrechnung. Bericht über die Tagung Wahrscheinlichkeitsrechnung und Mathematische Statistik in Berlin von 19. bis 22. Oktober 1954. Berlin (VEB Deutscher Verlag der Wissenschaften) 1956 p. 7–15.

Richardson, L. F., Statistics of deadly quarrels. The World of Mathematics. New York (Simon and Schuster) 1956 p. 1254–1263.

Richter, G., Wahrscheinlichkeitsrechnung in der Schule? Mathematik in der Schule. 7 (1969) p. 210–221.

Robbins, H., The theory of probability. Insights into Modern Mathematics. (23rd Yearbook National Council Teachers of Mathematics, U.S.A.) p. 336–371.

Royal Statistical Society. Interim report of the Royal Statistical Society Committee on the teaching of statistics in schools. Journal Royal Statistical Society A. 131 (1968) p. 478–499.

Råde, L., A course in probability theory for secondary schools. Mathematics Teacher. 58 (1965) p. 528–535.

Scheid, F., Clock arithmetic and nuclear energy. Mathematics Teacher 52 (1959).

Simon, J. L. & Holmes, A., A new way to teach probability and statistics. Mathematics Teacher. 62 (1969) p. 283–288.

Shaw, G. B., The vice of gambling and the virtue of insurance. The World of Mathematics. New York (Simon and Schuster) 1956, p. 1524–1531.

Spitznagel, E. L., An experimental approach in the teaching of probability. Mathematics Teacher. 61 (1968) p. 565–568.

Steiner, H. G., Elementare Logik und Wahrscheinlichkeitstheorie. Der Mathematikunterricht. 1962.1 p. 16–38.

Tippet, L. C., Sampling and standard error. The World of Mathematics. New York (Simon and Schuster) 1956 p. 1459–1486.

Varga, T., Combinatorials and probability for young children. Sherbrooke (Sherbrooke Mathematics Project, University of Sherbrooke, Canada) 1967.

Varga, T., Combinatorials and probability for young children. Journal of structural learning, 1 (1969) p. 49–99 and 139–161.

Weaver, W., Probability. Scientific American. Oct. 1950 p. 44–47.

Yates, F. & Healy, M. J. R. How should we reform the teaching of statistics? Journal Royal Statistical Society A. 127 (1964) p. 199–233.

Zastrow, W., Der radioaktive Zerfall in statistischer Behandlung. Der Mathematische und Naturwissenschaftliche Unterricht. 22 (1969) p. 92–97.

1.2. Books, elementary level

Adler, I., Probability and statistics for everyman. New York (John Day) 1963.

Bates, G. E., Probability. Reading (Addison-Wesley) 1965.

Bergendal, G., Håstad, M. & Råde, L., Statistik och sannolikhetslära. Stockholm (Biblioteksförlaget) 1968.

Borel, É., Le Hasard. Paris (Presses Universitaires de France) 1948.

Breny, H., Introduction élémentaire aux principes et méthodes de la théorie des probabilités y compris l'analyse statistique. Bruxelles (Presses Universitaires de Bruxelles) 1969.

Bross, I. D. J., Design for decision. New York (Macmillan) 1953.

Christiansen, B., Elementær kombinatorik og sandsynlighedsregning. Copenhagen (Munksgaard) 1964.

Cramér, H., The elements of probability theory and some of its applications. Stockholm and New York (Almqvist & Wiksell and John Wiley) 1954.

Diamond, S., The world of probability. New York (Basic Books) 1964.

Dwass, M., First steps in probability. New York (McGraw-Hill) 1967.

Dynkin, E. B. & Uspenskii, V. A., Random walks. Boston (Heath) 1963.

Fehr, H. F., Bunt, L. N. H. & Grossman, G., An introduction to sets, probability and hypothesis testing. Boston (Heath) 1964.

Freudenthal, H., Probability and statistics. New York (Elsevier) 1965.

Gangolli, R. A. & Ylvisaker, D., Discrete probability. New York (Harcourt, Brace & World) 1967.

Gnedenko, B. V. & Khinchin, A. Ya., An elementary introduction to the theory of probability. San Francisco (W. H. Freeman) 1961.

Goldberg, S., Probability, an introduction. Englewood Cliffs (Prentice Hall) 1960.

Gray, J. R., Probability. Edinburgh (Oliver & Boyd) 1967.

Guerber, L. & Hennequin, P. L., Initiation a la statistique. Paris (Bibliothèque d'Enseignement Mathématique. Association des Professurs de Mathematiques de l'Enseignement Public) 1967.

Guerber, L. & Hennequin, P. L., Initiation aux probabilités. Paris (Bibliothèque d'Enseignement Mathématique. Association des Professeurs de Mathematiques de l'Enseignement Public) 1968.

Hadley, G., Introduction to probability and statistical decision theory. San Francisco (Holden Day) 1967.

Hajek, J. & Dupac, V., Probability in science and engineering. New York (Academic Press) 1967.

Hodges, J. L. & Lehmann, E. L., Basic concepts of probability and statistics. San Francisco (Holden-Day) 1964.

Hodges, J. L. & Lehmann, E. L., Elements of finite probability. San Francisco (Holden-Day) 1964.

Huff, D., How to lie with statistics. London (Victor Gollancz) 1954.

Huff, D., How to take a chance. London (Victor Gollancz) 1960.

Ineichen, R., Einführung in die elementare Statistik und Wahrscheinlichkeitsrechnung. Luzern (Räber Verlag) 1962.

Johnston, J. B., Price, G. B. & van Vleck, F. S., Sets, functions and probability. Reading (Addison Wesley) 1968.

Kerrich, J. E., An experimental introduction to the theory of probability. Copenhagen (Belgisk Import) 1950.

Kemeny, J. G., Mirkil, H., Snell, J. L. & Thompson, G. L., Finite mathematical structures. Englewood Cliffs (Prentice-Hall) 1959.

Kemeny, J. G., Schleifer, J. L. & Thompson, G. L., Finite mathematics with business applications. Englewood Cliffs (Prentice-Hall) 1964.

Kemeny, J. G., Snell, J. L. & Thompson, G. L., Introduction to finite mathematics. Englewood Cliffs (Prentice Hall) 1956.

Kristensen, E. & Rindung, O., Sandsynlighedsregning. Copenhagen (C. E. C. Gad) 1965.

Lindley, D. V., The fundamentals of decision making (to be published).

Moroney, M. J., Facts from figures. London (Penguin Books) 1967.

Mosteller, F., Rourke, R. E. K. & Thomas, G. B., Probability with statistical applications. Reading (Addison-Wesley) 1961.

Nuffield Mathematics Project, Probability and Statistics. London (Chambers) 1969.

Rényi, A., Briefe über die Wahrscheinlichkeit. Berlin (VEB Deutscher Verlag der Wissenschaften) 1969 and also Basel (Birkhäuser) 1969.

School Mathematics Study Group, Probability for elementary grades. 1965.

School Mathematics Study Group, Probability for intermediate grades. 1965.

School Mathematics Study Group, Introduction to probability. 1965.

Tatsuoka, M., Games and chance. University of Illinois Committee on School Mathematics.

Thorp, E. O., Elementary Probability. New York (John Wiley) 1966.

Weaver, W., Lady Luck, the theory of probability. New York (Doubleday) 1963.

Wellnitz, K. Klassische Wahrscheinlichkeitsrechnung. Braunschweig (Fr. Vieweg und Sohn) 1962.

Wykes, A., Gambling. London (Spring Books) 1964.

Young, H. D., Statistical treatment of experimental data. New York (McGraw-Hill) 1962.

1.3. Books, intermediate level

Breiman, L., Probability. Reading (Addison-Wesley) 1968.

Feller, W., An introduction to probability theory and its applications. Volume 1, 3rd edition. New York (John Wiley) 1968.

Fisz, M., Probability theory and mathematical statistics. New York (John Wiley) 1963.

Gnedenko, B. V., The theory of probability. New York (Chelsea) 1962.

Karlin, S., A first course in stochastic processes. New York (Academic Press) 1966.

Kemeny, J. G. & Snell, J. L., Finite Markov chains. Princeton (van Nostrand) 1960.

Larson, H. J., Introduction to probability theory and statistical inference. New York (John Wiley) 1969.

Lindley, D. V., Introduction to probability and statistics. Part 1 Probability. Part 2 Inference. Cambridge (Cambridge University Press) 1965.

Meyer, P. L., Introductory probability and statistical applications. Reading (Addison-Wesley) 1965.

Morgenstern, D., Einführung in die Wahrscheinlichkeitsrechnung und mathematische Statistik. Berlin (Springer) 1968.

Neyman, J., First course in probability and statistics. New York (Henry Holt) 1950.

Parzen, E., Modern probability theory and its applications. New York (John Wiley) 1960.

Rényi, A., Wahrscheinlichkeitsrechnung. Berlin (VEB Deutscher Verlag der Wissenschaften) 1962.

van der Waerden, B. L., Mathematische Statistik. Berlin (Springer) 1965.

2. COMBINATORICS

Combinatorics can be introduced into the cur-
riculum of the earliest school years, and the
subject should recur in a spiral development
throughout the K-12 program.

E. F. Beckenbach (p. 19 this volume).

Beckenbach, E. F. (editor), Applied Combinatorical Mathematics. New York (John Wiley) 1964.

Berge, C., Principes de Combinatoire. Dunod (Paris) 1968.

Bose, R. C. & Dowling, T. A. (editors), Proceedings of the Conference on Combinatorical Mathematics and its Applications. Chapel Hill (University of North Carolina) 1968.

David, F. N. & Barton, D. E., Combinatorial chance. London (Griffin) 1962.

Golomb, S. W., Polyominoes. New York (Scribner) 1964.

Hall, M. Jr., Combinatorial analysis. Waltham (Blaisdell) 1967.

Kaufmann, A., Introduction à la combinatorique en vue des applications. Paris (Dunod) 1968.

Liu, C. L., Introduction to Combinatorial Mathematics. New York (McGraw-Hill) 1968.

MacMahon, P. A., Combinatorial Analysis, I–II. New York (Chelsea) 1960.

Netto, E., Lehrbuch der Kombinatorik. Leipzig (Teubner) 1901.

Niven, I., Mathematics of choice. New York (Random House) 1965.

Papy, G., Mathématique moderne 5. Bruxelles (Didier) 1966.

Riordan, J., An introduction to Combinatorial Analysis. New York (John Wiley) 1958.

Ryser, H. J., Combinatorial Mathematics. Carus Mathematical Monographs 14. New York (John Wiley) 1963.

Wellnitz, K., Kombinatorik, Einführung und Beispiele. Braunschweig (Fr. Vieweg und Sohn) 1961.

Whitworth, W. A., Choice and Chance. New York (Hafner) 1948.

3. INFORMATION THEORY

I would like to emphasize that I consider
entropy and information as basic concepts of
probability, and I strongly recommend that
the teacher should spend some time in the
discussion of these notions, too.

A. Rényi (p. 277 this volume).

Ash, R. B., Information theory. New York (Interscience) 1967.

Brillouin, L., Science and information theory. New York (Academic Press) 1956.

Jaglom, A. M. & Jaglom, I. M., Wahrscheinlichkeit und Information. Berlin (VEB Deutscher Verlag der Wissenschaften) 1960.

Khinchin, A. I., Mathematical foundations of information theory. New York (Dover) 1957.

McMillan, B., An elementary approach to the theory of information. SIAM Review. 3 (1961) p. 211–229.

Peters, J., Einführung in die allgemeine Informationstheorie. Berlin (Springer) 1967.

Rényi, A., Wahrscheinlichkeitsrechnung. Berlin (VEB Deutscher Verlag der Wissenschaften) 1962 p. 435–498.

Rényi, A., Information and statistics. Studies in mathematical statistics, theory and applications. Budapest (Akadémiai Kiadó) 1968.

Reza, F. M., An introduction to information theory. New York (McGraw-Hill) 1961.

Shannon, C. E., A mathematical theory of communication. Bell System Tech. J. 27 (1948) p. 379–423, 623–656.

Ville, J. A., Leôons sur quelques aspects noveaux de la théorie des probabilités. Ann. Inst. Henri Poincaré. 14 (1954) p. 61–143.

Weaver, W., The mathematics of communication. Scientific American. July 1949.

Åslund, N., Informationsteoriens fundamentalsatser. Nordisk Matematisk Tidskrift 9 (1961) p. 5–25, 97–108.

4. SIMULATION

The student should be encouraged to learn the art of simulation because it is important in its own right and ... it is the best means to develop the intuitive background of probability and to learn to think in statistical terms.

A. Engel (p. 92 this volume).

Berkeley, E. C., Probability and Statistics Lab. New York (Science Materials Center, 59 Fourth Avenue, New York) 1961.

Hammersley, J. M. & Maudscomb, A. C., Monte Carlo methods. London (Methuen) 1964.

Hamaker, H. C., Cylindrical die of 10 sides. A simple technique for producing random sampling numbers. Nederl. Acad. Proc. 52 (1949) p. 145–150.

Hull, T. E. & Dobell, A. R., Random number generators. SIAM Review. 4 (1962) p. 230–254.

Jansson, R., Random number generators. Stockholm (Victor Pettersons Bokindustri AB) 1966.

Schreider, Y. A., Method of statistical testing. New York (Elsevier) 1964.

Tocher, K. D., The art of simulation. London (English University Press) 1963.

Rand Corporation, A million random digits with 100,000 normal deviates. New York (The Free Press) 1955.

5. COLLECTIONS OF PROBLEMS

Our first aim, of course, should be to present problems which cause students to think about important and central topics in probability.

S. Goldberg (p. 192 this volume).

Günther, N. M. & Kusmin, R. O., Aufgabensammlung zur höheren Mathematik vol II. Berlin (VEB Deutscher Verlag der Wissenschaften) 1957 p. 188–221.

Kendall, M. G., Exercises in theoretical statistics with answers and hints on solutions. London (Griffin) 1954.

Mosteller, F., Fifty challenging problems in probability. Reading (Addison-Wesley) 1965.

Rahman, N. A., Exercises in probability and statistics for mathematics undergraduates. London (Griffin) 1967.

Sveshnikov, A. A., Problems in probability theory, mathematical statistics and theory of random functions. Philadelphia (Saunders) 1968.

Yaglom, A. M. & Yaglom, I. M., Challenging mathematical problems with elementary solutions. Vol. 1. Combinatorial analysis and probability theory. San Francisco (Holden-Day) 1964.

Whitworth, W. A., DCC exercises in choice and chance. New York (Hafner) 1959.

6. HISTORY

I think that, while the inclusion of some historical material is useful and desirable in the teaching of any subject, this is particularly helpful in teaching probability.

A. Rényi (p. 277 this volume).

Bayes, T., An essay towards solving a problem on the doctrine of chances (with a biographical note by G. A. Barnard). Biometrika. 45 (1958) p. 283–315.

Bernoulli, D., The most probable choice between several discrepant observations and the formation therefrom of the most likely induction (with a comment by L. Euler). Biometrika. 48 (1961) p. 3–19.

David, F. N., Dicing and gaming. Biometrika. 42 (1955) p. 1–15.

David, F. N., Games, gods and gambling. London (Griffin) 1962.

David, F. N., Some notes on Laplace. Bernoulli – Bayes – Laplace. Proceedings of an international research seminar. Berlin (Springer) 1965, p. 30–44.

Freudenthal, H. & Steiner, H. G., Aus der Geschichte der Wahrscheinlichkeitsrechnung und der mathematischen Statistik. Grundzüge der Mathematik IV. Göttingen (Vandenhoeck & Ruprecht) 1966.

Gnedenko, B. V., The development of probability theory in Russia. Trudy Inst. Esteet., 2 (1948), p. 390–425. (In Russian.)

Haldane, J. B. S., Karl Pearson, 1857–1957. Biometrika. 44 (1957) p. 303–313.

Hasofer, A. M., Random mechanisms in Talmudic literature. Biometrika. 54 (1967) p. 316–321.

Kendall, M. G., The beginnings of a probability calculus. Biometrika. 43 (1956) p. 1–14.

Kendall, M. G., A note on playing cards. Biometrika. 44 (1957) p. 260–262.

Kendall, M. G., When shall the history of statistics begin? Biometrika. 47 (1960) p. 447–449.

Kendall, M. G., Daniel Bernoulli on maximum likelihood. Biometrika. 48 (1961) p. 1–2.

Kendall, M. G., The book of fate. Biometrika. 48 (1961) p. 220–222.

Kendall, M. G., Isaac Todhunter's history of the mathematical theory of probability. Biometrika. 50 (1963) p. 204–205.

Kendall, M. G., Thomas Young on coincidences. Biometrika. 55 (1968) p. 249–250.

Kendall, M. G., Francis Ysidro Edgeworth 1845–1926. Biometrika. 55 (1968) p. 269–275.

Kendall, M. G., The early history of index numbers. Review International Statistical Institute. 37 (1969) p. 1–12.

Lord, R. D., de Morgan and the statistical study of literary style. Biometrika. 45 (1958) p. 282.

Maystrow, L. E., Teoria veroiatnostei isotoricheski ocherk. (Probability—a historical sketch). Moscow (Nauka) 1967.

Ore, O., Cardano, the gambling scholar. Princeton (Princeton University Press) 1953.

Pearson, E. S., Some incidents in the early history of biometry and statistics. Biometrika. 52 (1965) p. 3–18.

Pearson, E. S., The Neyman-Pearson story: 1926–1934. Research papers in statistics. New York (John Wiley) 1966 p. 1–23.

Pearson, E. S., Some reflections on continuity in the development of mathematical statistics 1885–1920. Biometrika. 54 (1967) p. 341–355.

Pearson, E. S., Some early correspondence between W. S. Gosset, R. A. Fisher and Karl Pearson, with notes and comments. Biometrika. 55 (1968) p. 445–467.

Plackett, R. L., The principle of the arithmetic mean. Biometrika. 45 (1958) p. 130–135.

Rabinovitch, N. L., Probability in the Talmud. Biometrika. 56 (1969) p. 437–441.

Royston, E., A note on the history of the graphical presentation of data. Biometrika. 43 (1956) p. 241–247.

Seal, H. L., The historical development of the Gauss linear model. Biometrika. 54 (1967) p. 1–24.

Sheynin, O. B., On the early history of the law of large numbers. Biometrika. 55 (1968) p. 459–467.

Shu, S. S., Brief history of probability in physics and engineering. Proceedings of the first symposium on engineering applications of random function theory and probability. New York (John Wiley) 1963 p. 3–30.

Thatcher, A. R., A note on the early solution of the duration of play. Biometrika. 44 (1957) p. 515–518.

Todhunter, I., A history of the mathematical theory of probability from the time of Pascal to that of Laplace. New York (Chelsea) 1949.

Williams, C. B., A note on the early statistical study of literary style. Biometrika. 43 (1956) p. 248–257.

7. SOME JOURNALS DEVOTED TO ELEMENTARY MATHEMATICS OR DIDACTICS OF MATHEMATICS

Arithmetic Teacher. National Council of Teachers of Mathematics. U.S.A.

Bulletin de l'association des professeurs de mathématiques de l'enseignement public. France.

Educational Studies in Mathematics. Dordrecht (Reidel Publishing Company). Netherland.

Elementa. Tidskrift för matematik, fysik och kemi. Uppsala. Sweden.

Elemente der Mathematik. Basel (Birkhäuser Verlag). Switzerland.

L'Enseignement Mathématique. Organe officiel de la commission de l'enseignement mathématique. Geneve (Kundig). Switzerland.

Euclides. Maanblad voor de Didactiek van de Wiskunde. Groningen (Wollters-Noordhoff). Netherland.

Mathematica & Paedagogia. Revue trimestrielle publiée par la Société Belge de Professeur de Mathematiques. Belgium.

Mathematical Gazette. Journal of the Mathematical Association. England.

Mathematical Spectrum. A magazine of contemporary mathematics. Oxford University Press. England.

Mathematics Magazine. Mathematical Association of America. U.S.A.

Mathematics Teacher. National Council of Teachers of Mathematics. U.S.A.

Mathematics Teaching. Bulletin of the Association of Teachers of Mathematics. England.

Mathematik in der Schule. Berlin (Volk und Wissen Volkseigener Verlag). East Germany.

Der Mathematikunterricht. Stuttgart (Ernst Klett Verlag). West Germany.

Der Mathematische und Naturwissenschaftliche Unterricht. Bonn (F. Dümmler Verlag). West Germany.

Nico. Centre Belge de Pédagogie de la Mathématique. Bruxelles. Belgium.

Nordisk Matematisk Tidskrift. Matematisk Institutt. Blindern. Oslo. Scandinavia.

Praxis der Mathematik. Köln (Aulis Verlag). West Germany.

Zentralblatt für Didaktik der Mathematik. Stuttgart (Ernst Klett Verlag). West Germany.